Teacher's Edition

Inside Earth

PRENTICE HALL **Science** Explorer

PEARSON

Boston, Massachusetts • Chandler, Arizona • Glenview, Illinois • Upper Saddle River, New Jersey

Copyright © 2009 by Pearson Education, Inc., or its affiliates. All Rights Reserved. Printed in the United States of America. This publication is protected by copyright, and permission should be obtained from the publisher prior to any prohibited reproduction, storage in a retrieval system, or transmission in any form or by any means, electronic, mechanical, photocopying, recording, or likewise. For information regarding permission(s), write to Pearson School Rights & Permissions, One Lake Street, Upper Saddle River, New Jersey 07458.

Lab zone™ is a trademark of Pearson Education, Inc.

Planet Diary® is a registered trademark of Addison Wesley Longman, Inc.

Discovery Channel School® is a registered trademark of Discovery Communications, LLC., used under license. The Discovery Channel School logo is a trademark of Discovery Communications, LLC.

Prentice Hall® and **Pearson Prentice Hall™** are trademarks, in the U.S. and/or in other countries, of Pearson Education, Inc., or its affiliate(s).

SciLinks® is a trademark of the National Science Teachers Association. The SciLinks® service includes copyrighted materials and is owned and provided by the National Science Teachers Association. All rights reserved.

Science News® is a registered trademark of Science Services, Inc.

13-digit ISBN   978-0-13-366846-9
10-digit ISBN   0-13-366846-0

3 4 5 6 7 8 9 10   12 11 10 09

Pacing Options

PRENTICE HALL
TeacherEXPRESS™
Plan · Teach · Assess

Lab zone™

SCIENCE EXPLORER offers many aids to help you plan your instruction time, whether regular class periods or block scheduling. Section-by-section lesson plans for each chapter include suggested times for Student Edition activities. TeacherExpress™ and the Lab zone™ Easy Planner CD-ROM will help you manage your time electronically.

Pacing Chart

	PERIODS	BLOCKS		PERIODS	BLOCKS
Chapter 1 Plate Tectonics			**Chapter 4 Minerals**		
Chapter 1 Project *Make a Model of Earth*	Ongoing	Ongoing	Chapter 4 Project *Growing a Crystal Garden*	Ongoing	Ongoing
1 Earth's Interior	2	1	**1** Properties of Minerals	2	1
2 Integrating Physics: Convection and the Mantle	1	$^1/_2$	**2** How Minerals Form	2	1
			3 Tech & Design: Using Mineral Resources	2	1
3 Drifting Continents	2	1	Chapter 4 Review and Assessment	1	$^1/_2$
4 Sea-Floor Spreading	3	$1^1/_2$	**Chapter 5 Rocks**		
5 The Theory of Plate Tectonics	2	1	Chapter 5 Project *Collecting Rocks*	Ongoing	Ongoing
Chapter 1 Review and Assessment	1	$^1/_2$	**1** Classifying Rocks	1	$^1/_2$
Chapter 2 Earthquakes			**2** Igneous Rocks	1	$^1/_2$
Chapter 2 Project *Design and Build an Earthquake-Safe House*	Ongoing	Ongoing	**3** Sedimentary Rocks	1	$^1/_2$
			4 Integrating Life Science: Rocks From Reefs	1	$^1/_2$
1 Forces in Earth's Crust	3	$1^1/_2$	**5** Metamorphic Rocks	2	1
2 Earthquakes and Seismic Waves	3	$1^1/_2$	**6** The Rock Cycle	2	1
3 Tech & Design: Monitoring Earthquakes	2	1	Chapter 5 Review and Assessment	1	$^1/_2$
4 Earthquake Safety	1	$^1/_2$			
Chapter 2 Review and Assessment	1	$^1/_2$			
Chapter 3 Volcanoes					
Chapter 3 Project *Volcanoes and People*	Ongoing	Ongoing			
1 Volcanoes and Plate Tectonics	2	1			
2 Integrating Chemistry: Properties of Magma	1	$^1/_2$			
3 Volcanic Eruptions	3	$1^1/_2$			
4 Volcanic Landforms	1	$^1/_2$			
Chapter 3 Review and Assessment	1	$^1/_2$			

Research-Based and Proven to Work

As the originator of the small book concept in middle school science, and as the nation's number one science publisher, Prentice Hall takes pride in the fact that we've always listened closely to teachers. In doing so, we've developed programs that effectively meet the needs of your classroom.

As we continue to listen, we realize that raising the achievement level of all students is the number one challenge facing teachers today. To assist you in meeting this latest challenge, Prentice Hall has combined the very best author team with solid research to create a program that meets your high standards and will ensure that no child is left behind.

With Prentice Hall, you can be confident that your students will not only be motivated, inspired, and excited to learn science, but that they will also achieve the success needed in today's environment of the No Child Left Behind (NCLB) legislation and testing reform.

On the following pages, you will read about the key elements found throughout *Science Explorer* that truly set this program apart and ensure success for you and your students.

As we continue to listen, we realize that raising the achievement level of all students is the number one challenge facing teachers today.

A Science Program Backed by Research

In developing Prentice Hall *Science Explorer*, we used research studies as a central, guiding element. Research on *Science Explorer* indicated key elements of a textbook program that ensure students' success: support for reading and mathematics in science, consistent opportunities for inquiry, and an ongoing assessment strand. This research was conducted in phases and continues today.

1. Exploratory: Needs Assessment

Along with periodic surveys concerning state and national standards as well as curriculum issues and challenges, we conducted specific product development research, which included discussions with teachers and advisory panels, focus groups, and quantitative surveys. We explored the specific needs of teachers, students, and other educators regarding each book we developed in Prentice Hall *Science Explorer*.

2. Formative: Prototype Development and Field-Testing

During this phase of research, we worked to develop prototype materials. Then we tested the materials by field-testing with students and teachers and by performing qualitative and quantitative surveys. In our early prototype testing, we received feedback about our lesson structure. Results were channeled back into the program development for improvement.

3. Summative: Validation Research

Finally, we conducted and continue to conduct long-term research based on scientific, experimental designs under actual classroom conditions. This research identifies what works and what can be improved in the next revision of Prentice Hall *Science Explorer*. We also continue to monitor the program in the market. We talk to our users about what works, and then we begin the cycle over again. The next section contains highlights of this research.

A Science Program With Proven Results

In a year-long study in 2000–2001, students in six states using Prentice Hall *Science Explorer* outscored students using other science programs on a nationally normed standardized test.

The study investigated the effects of science textbook programs at the eighth-grade level. Twelve eighth-grade science classes with a total of 223 students participated in the study. The selected classes were of similar student ability levels.

Each class was tested at the beginning of the school year using the TerraNova CTBS Basic Battery Plus, and then retested at the end of the school year. The final results, shown in the graph, show a significant improvement in test scores from the pre-test to the post-test evaluation.

• All tests were scored by CTB/McGraw-Hill, the publisher of the TerraNova exam. Statistical analyses and conclusions were performed by an independent firm, Pulse Analytics, Inc.

In Japan, Lesson Study Research has been employed for a number of years as a tool for teachers to improve their curriculum. In April 2003, Prentice Hall adapted this methodology to focus on a lesson from this edition. Our goal was to test the effectiveness of lesson pedagogy and improve it while in the program development stage. In all three classrooms tested, student learning increased an average of 10 points from the pre- to the post-assessment.

• Detailed results of these studies can be obtained at **www.PHSchool.com/research.**

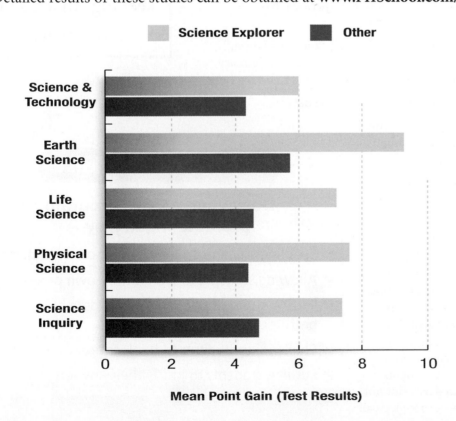

Mean Point Gain (Test Results)

Foundational Research: Inquiry in the Science Classroom

"How do I know if my students are inquiring?" "If students are busy doing lots of hands-on activities, are they using inquiry?" "What is inquiry, anyway?" If you're confused, you are not alone. Inquiry is the heart and soul of science education, with most of us in continuous pursuit of achieving it with our students!

Defining Science Inquiry

What is it? Simply put, inquiry is the intellectual side of science. It is thinking like a scientist—being inquisitive, asking why, and searching for answers. The National Science Education Content Standards define inquiry as the process in which students begin with a question, design an investigation, gather evidence, formulate an answer to the original question, and communicate the investigative process and results. Since it is often difficult to accomplish all this in one class period, the standards also acknowledge that at times students need to practice only one or two inquiry components.

Understanding Inquiry

The National Research Council in Inquiry and the National Science Education Standards (2000) identified several "essential features" of classroom inquiry. We have modified these essential features into questions to guide you in your quest for enhanced and more thoughtful student inquiry.

1. *Who asks the question?* In most curricula, these focusing questions are an element given in the materials. As a teacher you can look for labs that, at least on a periodic basis, allow students to pursue their own questions.

2. *Who designs the procedures?* To gain experience with the logic underlying experimentation, students need continuous practice with designing procedures. Some labs in which the primary target is content acquisition designate procedures. But others should ask students to do so.

3. *Who decides what data to collect?* Students need practice in determining the data to collect.

4. *Who formulates explanations based upon the data?* Students should be challenged to think—to analyze and draw conclusions based on their data, not just copy answers from the text materials.

5. *Who communicates and justifies the results?* Activities should push students not only to communicate but also to justify their answers. Activities also should be thoughtfully designed and interesting so that students want to share their results and argue about conclusions.

Making Time for Inquiry

One last question—Must each and every activity have students do all of this? The answer is an obvious and emphatic "No." You will find a great variety of activities in *Science Explorer*. Some activities focus on content acquisition, and thus they specify the question and most of the procedures. But many others stress in-depth inquiry from start to finish. Because inquiry is an intellectual pursuit, it cannot merely be characterized by keeping students busy and active. Too many students have a knack for being physically but not intellectually engaged in science. It is our job to help them engage intellectually.

Michael J. Padilla, Ph.D.
Program Author of *Science Explorer*
Associate Dean and Director
Eugene T. Moore
School of Education
Clemson University
Clemson, South Carolina

"Because inquiry is an intellectual pursuit, it cannot merely be characterized by keeping students busy and active."

Evaluator's Checklist

Does your science program promote inquiry by—

✔ Enabling students to pursue their own questions

✔ Allowing students to design their own procedures

✔ Letting students determine what data are best to collect

✔ Challenging students to think critically

✔ Pushing students to justify their answers

Inquiry in *Science Explorer*

Science Explorer offers the most opportunities to get students to think like a scientist. By providing inquiry opportunities throughout the program, *Science Explorer* enables students to enhance their understanding by participating in the discovery.

Student Edition Inquiry

Six lab and activity options are included in every chapter, structured from directed to open-ended—providing you the flexibility to address all types of learners and accommodate your class time and equipment requirements. As Michael Padilla notes, some activities focus on content acquisition, and thus the question and most of the procedures are specified. But many others stress in-depth inquiry from start to finish. The graph below shows how, in general, inquiry levels are addressed in the Student Edition.

Science Explorer encourages students to develop inquiry skills across the spectrum from teacher-guided to open-ended. Even more opportunities for real-life applications of inquiry are included in Science & Society, Technology & Society, Careers in Science, and Interdisciplinary Exploration features.

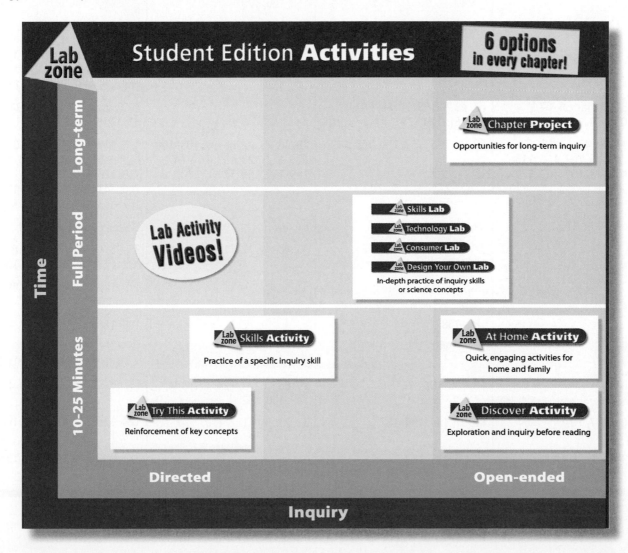

Inquiry Skills Chart

SCIENCE EXPLORER provides comprehensive teaching, practice, and assessment of science skills, with an emphasis on the process skills necessary for inquiry. This chart lists the skills covered in the program and cites the page numbers where each skill is covered.

Basic Process SKILLS

	Student Text: Projects and Labs	Student Text: Activities	Student Text: Caption and Review Questions	Teacher's Edition: Extensions
Observing	37, 66, 106–107, 113, 136, 140, 163	14, 23, 27, 51, 60, 85, 91, 94, 99, 114, 124–125, 144, 148, 152, 154, 157, 160–162, 164, 178	19, 83, 117, 131, 140, 145, 170	8, 11, 19, 23, 30, 37, 51, 53, 55, 60, 92, 112, 114, 125, 127, 130, 134, 136–137, 140, 142, 144, 148, 152–154, 161–164, 170, 178
Inferring	37, 59, 86, 107, 163	6, 14, 60, 148, 160, 178	13, 20, 40, 46, 60, 64–65, 85, 90, 98, 110, 134–135, 140, 156, 158–159, 170	6, 14, 30, 37, 55, 60, 76, 96, 112, 117–118, 125, 131, 135, 140, 148, 156, 159–160, 163, 170, 178
Predicting	37, 123, 136, 167	33, 44, 68, 119, 152, 154, 178	17, 29, 34, 36, 39–41, 48, 65, 72, 78, 85, 88–90, 98, 105, 110, 118, 122, 127, 140, 150, 156, 159, 166, 170	33, 36–37, 40–42, 44, 68, 70, 79, 115, 122–123, 127, 146, 150, 156, 159, 166, 170, 178
Classifying	80–81, 136, 143, 163, 170	48, 55, 120, 163, 164, 179	13, 78, 90, 100, 110, 120, 122, 140, 147, 155, 162, 170–171	13, 45, 48, 50, 55, 63, 65, 71, 79, 115–116, 118–120, 122, 127, 131–132, 136–137, 140, 142–143, 146–147, 149, 151, 154, 156, 162–163 166, 170–171, 179
Making Models	5, 30–31, 37, 43, 66–67, 106–107, 113, 140	27, 48, 50, 68, 70, 85, 90, 94, 99, 161, 179		4, 13, 20, 27, 30–31, 33, 36–37, 40, 42, 48, 49–50, 63, 71, 101, 159, 179
Communicating	5, 31, 37, 40, 43, 59, 65, 67, 78–81, 81, 86, 107, 110, 113, 137, 140, 143, 163, 167, 170	50, 90, 135, 151, 159, 162. 179	29, 36, 75, 77, 85, 97, 105, 109, 111, 127, 129, 139, 141, 147, 156, 166, 169, 171	4–5, 11, 19, 21, 35, 37, 40, 42, 44, 45, 50–51, 61, 67, 71, 74, 78, 112, 118, 126, 129, 131, 133, 135, 137, 140, 142–143, 147, 151, 158–159, 162–163, 165–168, 170, 179
Measuring	58–59, 86, 113, 123	64, 124, 154, 180	57, 140	57–59, 64, 112, 118, 123, 154, 180
Calculating	58, 86, 123	35, 56, 118, 119, 150, 181, 189–193	36, 40–41, 122, 150	35–36, 40–41, 58–59, 118, 122–123, 140, 150, 181, 189–193
Creating Data Tables	58, 113, 123, 136, 137, 163	11, 186–188		11, 112, 137, 163, 186–188
Graphing		186–188		186–188

Advanced Process SKILLS

	Student Text: Projects and Labs	Student Text: Activities	Student Text: Caption and Review Questions	Teacher's Edition: Extensions
Posing Questions		18, 130, 182	36, 68, 70, 73, 124, 127, 144, 147, 160, 162	18, 68, 71, 124, 130, 144, 160, 182
Developing Hypothesis	106–107, 137, 167	82, 91, 124, 164, 182	22, 73, 110, 127, 170	124–125, 127, 137, 149, 164, 170, 182
Designing Experiments	123, 137, 167	22, 90, 135, 183		22, 66, 123, 135, 137, 167, 183

	Student Text: Projects and Labs	Student Text: Activities	Student Text: Caption and Review Questions	Teacher's Edition: Extensions
Advanced Process SKILLS (continued)				
Controlling Variables	136–137, 167			136–137, 167
Forming Operational Definitions		87	17, 32, 36, 44, 50, 65	32, 76, 115, 119
Interpreting Data	58–59, 86, 123, 136, 167	12, 87, 183	120, 140	4, 58, 79, 121, 123, 131, 136–137, 140, 167, 183
Drawing Conclusions	37, 58–59, 78, 80–81, 123, 136–137, 140, 163, 167, 170	32, 119, 154, 157, 183	28, 118, 140	19, 32, 37, 58, 60, 112, 119, 121, 123, 136–137, 140, 142, 154, 157, 163, 167,183
Critical Thinking SKILLS				
Comparing and Contrasting	31, 66, 113, 136	91, 114, 119, 124, 130, 154, 160	9, 13, 40, 63, 73, 103, 105, 109–110, 118, 122, 140, 146–147, 151, 170	11, 20, 24, 40, 45, 49, 54–55, 62–63, 69, 72, 112, 116, 119–122, 125, 127, 140, 144, 147, 150–151, 153–154, 170
Applying Concepts	5, 31, 43, 167	17, 73	13, 17, 25, 29, 55, 57, 75, 90, 121, 129	4, 8, 11–12, 15–16, 25, 35, 37, 42, 45, 53–55, 61, 63, 69–73,120–121, 126, 134, 146, 151, 162, 167
Interpreting Diagrams, Graphs, Photographs, and Maps		12, 18, 56, 82, 89, 119, 150	10, 26, 33, 40, 52, 56–57, 61, 69, 78–79, 89, 93, 110–111, 117–118, 127, 140–141, 150, 165, 170–171	12, 21, 35, 41, 46–47, 56–59, 69, 72, 79, 112, 117–119, 126, 133, 140–141, 150, 170–171
Relating Cause and Effect	43	70	13, 17, 29, 36, 40, 45, 50, 73, 77, 85, 98, 105, 110, 127, 140, 149, 153, 156, 162, 166, 170	27, 32, 36, 40, 42, 77, 127, 140, 156, 162, 166, 170
Making Generalizations			65, 78, 110	79
Making Judgments	67		22, 40, 151, 162	40, 151, 162
Problem Solving	5, 31, 37, 59, 67, 78, 86, 107, 163		129, 135	31, 74, 135, 149
Informational Organizational SKILLS				
Concept Maps		197	109, 169	9, 22, 29, 122, 127, 131–132, 149, 169, 197
Compare/Contrast Tables		196	39	13, 36, 39, 156, 196
Venn Diagrams		196	139	15, 139, 196
Flowcharts			23, 29, 60, 65	60, 135, 142, 153
Cycle Diagrams			164, 166	142, 163, 165

The *Science Explorer* program provides additional teaching, reinforcement, and assessment of skills in the *Inquiry Skills Activities Book* and the *Integrated Science Laboratory Manual*.

A National Look at Science Education

Project 2061 was established by the American Association for the Advancement of Science (AAAS) as a long-term project to improve science education nationwide. A primary goal of Project 2061 is to define a "common core of learning"—the knowledge and skills we want all students to achieve. Project 2061 published *Science for All Americans* in 1989 and followed this with *Benchmarks for Science Literacy* in 1993. *Benchmarks* recommends what students should know and be able to do by the end of grades 2, 5, 8, and 12. Project 2061 clearly states that *Benchmarks* is not a curriculum but a tool for designing successful curricula.

The National Research Council (NRC) used *Science for All Americans* and *Benchmarks* to develop the National Science Education Standards (NSES), which were published in 1996. The NSES are organized into six categories (Content, Teaching, Assessment, Professional Development, Program, and System) to help schools establish the conditions necessary to achieve scientific literacy for all students.

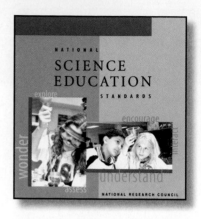

Michael Padilla, the program author of *Science Explorer*, guided one of six teams of teachers whose work led to the publication of *Benchmarks*. He also was a contributing writer of the National Science Education Standards. Under his guidance, *Science Explorer* has implemented these standards through its inquiry approach, a focus on student learning of important concepts and skills, and teacher support aligned with the NSES teaching standards.

Neither *Benchmarks* nor the NSES requires a single, uniform national curriculum, and in fact there is a great diversity nationwide in science curricula. The correlations that follow are designed to help you use the *Science Explorer* program to meet your particular curriculum needs.

Meeting the National Science Education Standards

PLATE TECTONICS

Science as Inquiry (Content Standard A)

● **Develop descriptions, explanation, predictions, and models using evidence** Students build a model that shows Earth's surface and interior. Students model sea-floor spreading and mantle convection currents. *(Chapter Project; Skills Labs)*

Physical Science (Content Standard B)

● **Transfer of energy** The three types of heat transfer are radiation, conduction, and convention. Students observe a model of convection currents in Earth's mantle. *(Convection and the Mantle; Skills Lab—Modeling Mantle Convection Currents)*

Earth and Space Science (Content Standard D)

● **Structure of the Earth system** The crust, mantle, and core are the three main layers of Earth's interior. Molten material from the mantle rises at mid-ocean ridges and old crust sinks back into the mantle at deep-ocean trenches. Students model sea-floor spreading. Plate tectonics explains the formation, movement, and subduction of Earth's crust. *(Earth's Interior, Sea-Floor Spreading, The Theory of Plate Tectonics; Skills Lab—Modeling Sea-Floor Spreading)*

● **Earth's history** Wegener used evidence from land features, fossils, and climate to support his hypothesis of continental drift. About 300 million years ago, the continents were joined together. *(Drifting Continents, The Theory of Plate Tectonics)*

EARTHQUAKES

Science as Inquiry (Content Standard A)

● **Use appropriate tools and techniques to gather, analyze, and interpret data** Students locate an epicenter. *(Skills Lab)*

Physical Science (Content Standard B)

● **Transfer of energy** Stress is a force that acts on rock. Seismic waves carry energy from an earthquake through Earth. *(Forces in Earth's Crust, Earthquakes and Seismic Waves)*

Earth and Space Science (Content Standard D)

● **Structure of the Earth system** Earthquakes result from the movement of rock beneath Earth's surface. Movement of rock along a fault causes changes in the land surface. *(Forces in Earth's Crust, Earthquakes and Seismic Waves)*

A National Look at Science Education (continued)

EARTHQUAKES (continued)

Science and Technology (Content Standard E)
● **Design a solution or product** Students design a model earthquake-resistant structure and a seismograph. (*Chapter Project; Technology Lab*)

Science in Personal and Social Perspectives (Content Standard F)
● **Natural hazards** Earthquakes can cause great damage. (*Earthquake Safety*)
● **Science and technology in society** Structures can be designed to reduce earthquake damage. Geologists have invented instruments to monitor faults. Students analyze the risk of an earthquake and design a seismograph. (*Chapter Project; Monitoring Earthquakes, Earthquake Safety; Skills Lab, Technology Lab*)

VOLCANOES

Science as Inquiry (Content Standard A)
● **Develop descriptions, explanations, predictions, and models using evidence** Students interpret data to find a pattern in the location of earthquakes and volcanoes. Students model the flow of magma inside a volcano. (*Skills Labs*)
● **Communicate scientific procedures and explanations** Students make a documentary about life in a volcanic region. (*Chapter Project*)

Earth and Space Science (Content Standard D)
● **Structure of the Earth system** Most volcanoes occur along diverging plate boundaries or in subduction zones. A volcano erupts when magma breaks through Earth's crust and lava flows over the surface. Students model the flow of magma inside a volcano. Volcanoes create a variety of landforms. (*Volcanoes and Plate Tectonics, Properties of Magma, Volcanic Eruptions, Volcanic Landforms; Skills Lab—Gelatin Volcanoes*)

Science in Personal and Social Perspectives (Content Standard F)
● **Natural hazards** A volcanic eruption can cause great damage. Volcanic eruptions have affected the land and people around them. (*Volcanic Eruptions; Science & History*)
● **Risks and benefits** Students research how volcanoes have affected people in volcanic regions. (*Chapter Project; Volcanic Landforms*)

MINERALS

Science as Inquiry (Content Standard A)
● **Use appropriate tools and techniques to gather, analyze, and interpret data** Students create a crystal garden. Students measure and compare the density of different minerals. Students test minerals in toothpaste on their ability to clean. (*Chapter Project; Skills Lab, Consumer Lab*)

Physical Science (Content Standard B)
● **Properties and changes of properties in matter** A mineral is a naturally occurring, inorganic solid that has a crystal structure and a definite chemical composition. Students measure and compare the density of different minerals. (*Properties of Minerals, How Minerals Form; Skills Lab*)

Earth and Space Science (Content Standard D)
● **Structure of the Earth system** Some minerals form as magma cools inside Earth's crust or as lava hardens on the surface. (*How Minerals Form*)

Science and Technology (Content Standard E)
● **Understandings about science and technology** After miners remove ore from a mine, smelting is necessary to remove the metal from the ore. Toothpaste contains minerals that clean, whiten, and strengthen teeth. (*Using Mineral Resources; Consumer Lab*)

Science in Personal and Social Perspectives (Content Standard F)
● **Science and technology in society** Students examine the issue of who owns the ocean's minerals. (*Science and Society*)

ROCKS

Science as Inquiry (Content Standard A)
● **Design and conduct a scientific investigation** Students investigate what kind of stone makes the best flooring. (*Design Your Own Lab*)
● **Use appropriate tools and techniques to gather, analyze, and interpret data** Students collect, classify, and display rocks. (*Chapter Project; Skills Lab*)

Life Science (Content Standard C)
● **Populations and ecosystems** Coral animals produce skeletons that build after the animals have died to form a coral reef. (*Rocks From Reefs*)

Earth and Space Science (Content Standard D)
● **Structure of the Earth system** There are three major groups of rocks: igneous, sedimentary, and metamorphic. Students classify rocks. Igneous rocks form from magma or lava. Sedimentary rocks generally form from particles deposited by water and wind. Coral buried by sediments can turn into limestone. Heat and pressure can change any rock into metamorphic rock. Forces inside Earth and at the surface produce a rock cycle that builds, destroys, and changes the rocks in the crust. (*Classifying Rocks, Igneous Rocks, Sedimentary Rocks, Rocks From Reefs, Metamorphic Rocks, The Rock Cycle; Skills Lab*)

Science and Technology (Content Standard E)
● **Understandings about science and technology** Humans use rocks in different ways. (*Igneous Rocks, Sedimentary Rocks, Metamorphic Rocks; Design Your Own Lab*)

Note: To see how the benchmarks are supported by *SCIENCE EXPLORER,* go to PHSchool.com.

Reading Comprehension in the Science Classroom

Q&A

Q: Why are science texts often difficult for students to read and comprehend?

A: In general, science texts make complex literacy and knowledge demands on learners. They have a more technical vocabulary and a more demanding syntax, and place a greater emphasis on inferential reasoning.

Q: What does research say about facilitating comprehension?

A: Studies comparing novices and experts show that the conceptual organization of experts' knowledge is very different from that of novices. For example, experts emphasize core concepts when organizing knowledge, while novices focus on superficial details. To facilitate comprehension, effective teaching strategies should support and scaffold students as they build an understanding of the key concepts and concept relationships within a text unit.

Q: What strategies can teachers use to facilitate comprehension?

A: Three complementary strategies are very important in facilitating student comprehension of science texts. First, guide student interaction with the text using the built-in strategies. Second, organize the curriculum in terms of core concepts (e.g., the **Key Concepts** in each section). Third, develop visual representations of the relationships among the key concepts and vocabulary that can be referred to during instruction.

Nancy Romance, Ph.D.
Professor of Science Education
Florida Atlantic University
Fort Lauderdale, Florida

"Effective teaching strategies should support and scaffold students as they build an understanding of the key concepts and concept relationships within a text unit."

Reading Support in *Science Explorer*

The latest research emphasizes the importance of activating learners' prior knowledge and teaching them to distinguish core concepts from less important information. These skills are now more important than ever, because success in science requires students to read, understand, and connect complex terms and concepts.

Before students read—
Reading Preview introduces students to the key concepts and key terms they'll find in each section. The **Target Reading Skill** is identified and applied with a graphic organizer.

During the section—
Boldface Sentences identify each key concept and encourage students to focus on the big ideas of science.

Reading Checkpoints reinforce students' understanding by slowing them down to review after every concept is discussed.

Caption Questions draw students into the art and photos, helping them connect the content to the images.

After students read—
Section Assessment revisits the **Target Reading Skill** and encourages students to use the graphic organizer.

Each review question is scaffolded and models the way students think, by first easing them into a review and then challenging them with increasingly more difficult questions.

Evaluator's Checklist

Does your science program promote reading comprehension with—

✔ Text structured in an outline format and key concepts highlighted in boldface type

✔ Real-world applications to activate prior knowledge

✔ Key concepts, critical vocabulary, and a reading skill for every section

✔ Sample graphic organizers for each section

✔ Relevant photos and carefully constructed graphics with questions

✔ Reading checkpoints that appear in each section

✔ Scaffolded questions in section assessments

Math in the Science Classroom

Why should students concern themselves with mathematics in your science class?

Good science requires good data from which to draw conclusions. Technology enhances the ability to measure in a variety of ways. Often the scientist must measure large amounts of data, and thus an aim of analysis is to reduce the data to a summary that makes sense and is consistent with established norms of communication—i.e., mathematics.

Calculating measures of central tendency (e.g., mean, median, or mode), variability (e.g., range), and shape (graphic representations) can effectively reduce 500 data points to 3 without losing the essential characteristics of the data. Scientists understand that a trade-off exists between precision and richness as data are folded into categories, and so margins of error can be quantified in mathematical terms and factored into all scientific findings.

Mathematics is the language used by scientists to model change in the world. Understanding change is a vital part of the inquiry process. Mathematics serves as a common language to communicate across the sciences. Fields of scientific research that originated as separate disciplines are now integrated, such as happened with bioengineering. What do the sciences have in common? Each uses the language of mathematics to communicate about data and the process of data analysis. Recognizing this need, *Science Explorer* integrates mathematics practice throughout the program and gives students ample opportunity to hone their math skills.

Clearly, mathematics plays an important role in your science classroom!

William Tate, Ph.D.
Professor of Education and
Applied Statistics and
Computation
Washington University
St. Louis, Missouri

> "Mathematics is the language used by scientists to model change in the world."

Integrated Math Support

In the Student Edition
The math instruction is based on principles derived from Prentice Hall's research-based mathematics program.

Sample Problems, Math Practice, Analyzing Data, and a Math Skills Handbook all help to provide practice at point of use, encouraging students to Read and Understand, Plan and Solve, and then Look Back and Check.

Color-coded variables aid student navigation and help reinforce their comprehension.

In the Teacher's Edition
Math teaching notes enable the science teacher to support math instruction and math objectives on high-stakes tests.

In the Guided Reading and Study Workbook
These unique worksheets help students master reading and enhance their study and math skills. Students can create a record of their work for study and review.

Evaluator's Checklist

Does your science program promote math skills by—

✔ Giving students opportunities to collect data

✔ Providing students opportunities to analyze data

✔ Enabling students to practice math skills

✔ Helping students solve equations by using color-coded variables

✔ Using sample problems to apply science concepts

Technology and Design

Technology and Design in the Science Classroom

Much of the world we live in is designed and made by humans. The buildings in which we live, the cars we drive, the medicines we take, and often the food we eat are products of technology. The knowledge and skills needed to understand the processes used to create these products should be a component of every student's basic literacy.

Some schools offer hands-on instruction on how technology development works through industrial arts curricula. Even then, there is a disconnect among science (understanding how nature works), mathematics (understanding data-driven models), and technology (understanding the human-made world). The link among these fields of study is the engineering design process—that process by which one identifies a human need and uses science knowledge and human ingenuity to create a technology to satisfy the need. Engineering gives students the problem-solving and design skills they will need to succeed in our sophisticated, three-dimensional, technological world.

As a complement to "science as inquiry," the National Science Education Standards (NRC, 1996) call for students at all age levels to develop the abilities related to "technology as design," including the ability to identify and frame a problem and then to design, implement, and evaluate a solution. At the 5–8 grade level, the standards call for students to be engaged in complex problem-solving and to learn more about how science and technology complement each other. It's also important for students to understand that there are often constraints involved in design as well as trade-offs and unintended consequences of technological solutions to problems.

As the *Standards for Technological Literacy* (ITEA, 2000) state, "Science and technology are like conjoined twins. While they have separate identities they must remain inextricably connected." Both sets of standards emphasize how progress in science leads to new developments in technology, while technological innovation in turn drives advances in science.

Ioannis Miaoulis, Ph.D.
President
Museum of Science
Boston, Massachusetts

"Engineering gives students the problem-solving and design skills they will need to succeed in our sophisticated, three-dimensional, technological world."

Evaluator's Checklist

Does your science program promote technology and design by—

✔ Incorporating technology and design concepts and skills into the science curriculum

✔ Giving students opportunities to identify and solve technological design problems

✔ Providing students opportunities to analyze the impact of technology on society

✔ Enabling students to practice technology and design skills

Technology and Design

Technology and Design in *Science Explorer*

How often do you hear your students ask: "Why do I need to learn this?" Connecting them to the world of technology and design in their everyday life is one way to help answer this question. It is also why so many state science curricula are now emphasizing technology and design concepts and skills.

Science Explorer makes a special effort to include a technology and design strand that encourages students to not only identify a need but to take what they learned in science and apply it to design a possible solution, build a prototype, test and evaluate the design, and/or troubleshoot the design. This strand also provides definitions of technology and engineering and discusses the similarities and differences between these endeavors and science. Students will learn to analyze the risks and benefits of a new technology and to consider the tradeoffs, such as safety, costs, efficiency, and appearance.

In the Student Edition

Integrated Technology & Design Sections

Sections throughout *Science Explorer* specifically integrate technology and design with the content of the text. For example, students not only learn how seismographs work but also learn what role seismographs play in society and how people use the data that are gathered.

Technology Labs

These labs help students gain experience in designing and building a device or product that meets a particular need or solves a problem. Students follow a design process of Research and Investigate, Design and Build, and Evaluate and Redesign.

Chapter Projects

Chapter Projects work hand-in-hand with the chapter content. Students design, build, and test based on real-world situations. They have the opportunity to apply the knowledge and skills learned to building a product.

Special Features

This technology and design strand is also reflected in Technology & Society and Science & Society features as well as Science & History timelines and Tech & Design in History timelines. These highly visual features introduce a technology and its impact on society. For example, students learn how a hybrid car differs from a traditional car.

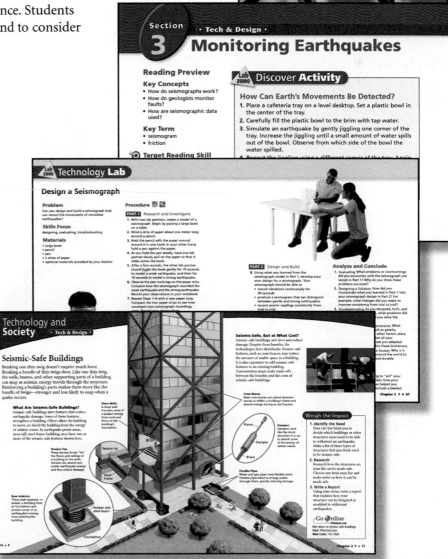

Assessment in the Science Curriculum

No Child Left Behind clearly challenges school districts across the nation to raise expectations for all students with testing of student achievement in science beginning in 2007–2008.

A primary goal of NCLB is to provide classroom teachers with better data from scientifically valid assessments in order to inform instructional planning and to identify students who are at risk and require intervention. It has been a common practice to teach a science lesson, administer a test, grade it, and move on. This practice is a thing of the past. With the spotlight now on improving student performance, it is essential to use assessment results as a way to identify student strengths and challenges. Providing student feedback and obtaining student input is a valuable, essential part of the assessment process.

Assessment is a never-ending cycle, as is shown in the following diagram. Although you may begin at any point in the assessment cycle, the basic process is the same.

An important assessment strategy is to ensure that students have ample opportunities to check their understanding of skills and concepts before moving on to the next topic. Checking for understanding also includes asking appropriate, probing questions with each example presented. This enables students and teachers to know whether the skills or concepts being introduced are actually understood.

Eileen Depka
Supervisor of Standards
and Assessment
Waukesha, Wisconsin

"Meeting the NCLB challenge will necessitate an integrated approach to assessment with a variety of assessment tools."

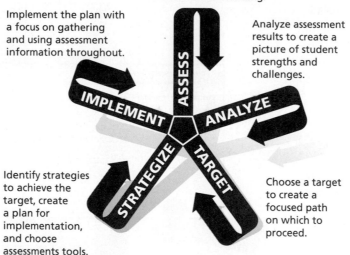

Use a variety of assessment tools to gain information and strengthen student understanding.

Implement the plan with a focus on gathering and using assessment information throughout.

Analyze assessment results to create a picture of student strengths and challenges.

Identify strategies to achieve the target, create a plan for implementation, and choose assessments tools.

Choose a target to create a focused path on which to proceed.

IMPLEMENT · ASSESS · ANALYZE · TARGET · STRATEGIZE

Evaluator's Checklist

Does your science program include assessments that—

✔ Are embedded before, during, and after lesson instruction
✔ Align to standards and to the instructional program
✔ Assess both skill acquisition and understanding
✔ Include meaningful rubrics to guide students
✔ Mirror the various formats of standardized tests

Assessment in *Science Explorer*

Science Explorer's remarkable range of strategies for checking progress will help teachers find the right opportunity for reaching all their students.

The assessment strategies in *Science Explorer* will help both students and teachers alike ensure student success in content mastery as well as high-stakes test performance. A wealth of opportunities built into the Student Edition helps students monitor their own progress. Teachers are supported with ongoing assessment opportunities in the Teacher's Edition and an easy-to-use, editable test generator linked to content objectives. These integrated, ongoing assessment tools assure success.

Especially to support state and national testing objectives, Prentice Hall has developed test preparation materials that model the NCLB approach.

- **Diagnostic Assessment** tools provide in-depth analysis of strengths and weaknesses, areas of difficulty, and probable underlying causes that can help teachers make instructional decisions and plan intervention strategies.

- **Progress Monitoring** tools aligned with content objectives and state tests provide ongoing, longitudinal records of student achievement detailing individual student progress toward meeting end-of-year and end-of-schooling grade level, district, or state standards.

- **Outcomes** tools that mimic state and national tests show whether individual students have met the expected standards and can help a school system judge whether it has made adequate progress in improving its performance year by year.

Caption Questions enhance critical thinking skills.

Reading Checkpoints reinforce students' understanding.

Scaffolded Section Assessment Questions model the way students think.

Comprehensive Chapter Reviews and Assessments provide opportunities for students to check their own understanding and practice valuable high-stakes test-taking skills.

ExamView® **Computer Test Bank CD-ROM** provides teachers access to thousands of modifiable test questions in English and Spanish.

Test Preparation Blackline Masters and Student Workbook include diagnostic and prescription tools, progress-monitoring aids, and practice tests that help teachers focus on improving test scores.

Section 3 Assessment

Target Reading Skill Sequencing Refer to your flowchart about seismographs as you answer Question 1.

Reviewing Key Concepts

1. a. **Defining** What is a seismogram?
   b. **Explaining** How can geologists tell apart the different types of seismic waves on a seismogram?
   c. **Comparing and Contrasting** Two identical seismographs are located 1,000 km and 1,200 km from an earthquake's epicenter. How would the two seismograms for the earthquake compare?

2. a. **Reviewing** What changes are measured by the instruments used to monitor faults?
   b. **Describing** How are satellites used to measure movements along a fault?
   c. **Inferring** A satellite that monitors a fault detects an increasing tilt in the land surface along the fault. What could this change in the land surface indicate?

3. a. **Listing** What are three ways in which geologists use seismographic data?
   b. **Explaining** How do geologists use seismographic data to make maps of faults?
   c. **Making Generalizations** Why is it difficult to predict earthquakes?

Writing in Science

Dialogue Geologists in Alaska have just detected an earthquake and located the earthquake's epicenter. Write a dialogue in which the geologists notify a disaster response team that will help people in the earthquake area.

Chapter 2 F ◆ 65

Standardized Test Prep

Test-Taking Tip
When answering questions about diagrams, read all parts of the diagram carefully, including title, captions, and labels. Make sure that you understand the meaning of arrows and other symbols. Determine exactly what the question asks. Then eliminate those answer choices that are not supported by the diagram.

Practice answering this question.
The diagram shows how stress affects a mass of rock in a process called
   A compression.
   B tension.
   C squeezing.
   D shearing.
The correct answer is D because the arrows show rock being pulled in opposite directions.

Choose the letter that best answers the question or completes the statement.

1. In a strike-slip fault, rock masses along the fault move
   A in the same direction.
   B down only.
   C together.
   D sideways past each other.

2. Stress will build until an earthquake occurs if friction along a fault is
   F decreasing.   G high.
   H low.   J changed to heat.

Use the information below and your knowledge of science to answer Questions 3 and 4.

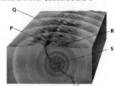

Seismic waves

3. When an earthquake occurs, seismic waves travel
   A from P in all directions.
   B from R to S.
   C from S in all directions.
   D from Q to P.

4. At point R, seismic waves from an earthquake would be
   F weaker than at P.
   G likely to cause little damage.
   H weaker than at Q.
   J likely to cause the most damage.

5. To estimate the total energy released by an earthquake, a geologist should use the
   A Mercalli scale.   B Richter scale.
   C epicenter scale.   D moment magnitude scale.

Constructed Response

6. A geologist discovers a large fault beneath a major city. Why would this information be helpful in determining earthquake risk in the area? What three safety steps should the geologist recommend?

Chapter 2 F ◆ 79

Master Materials List

SCIENCE EXPLORER offers an abundance of activity options in the Student Edition so you can pick and choose those that suit your needs. Prentice Hall has worked with Science Kit to develop Consumable Kits and Nonconsumable Kits that precisely match the needs of the SCIENCE EXPLORER labs. Use this Master Materials List or contact your local Prentice Hall sales representative or Science Kit at 1-800-828-7777 or www.sciencekit.com/scienceexplorer.

SK Science Kit & Boreal Laboratories
Helping Teachers Make a World of Difference

Consumable Materials

Description	Textbook Section(s)	Quantity per class	Description	Textbook Section(s)	Quantity per class
Aluminum foil, roll	1-5 (Lab)	1	Paint, tempera, 8 oz	5-6 (Lab)	1
Audiotape, blank	1-4 (TT)	1	* Paper, construction, black, pkg. of 6	4-2 (TT)	5
Baking soda, 454 g	3-3 (TT)	1	* Paper, tracing, sheet	1-5 (DIS)	10
Balloons, round, pkg. of 20	3-4 (DIS)	1	* Paper towel, roll	4-1 (DIS)	1
* Bread, slice	5-3 (DIS)	5	* Paper, unlined sheets	1-4 (Lab), 1-5 (DIS), 1-5 (Lab), 2-3 (Lab), 3-4 (Lab), 5-3 (DIS)	25
* Butter, stick	5-6 (Lab)	1	* Pen, felt tip	2-3 (Lab), 4-3 (Lab)	5
Candles	4-2 (DIS)	5	* Pencil	2-3 (DIS), 2-3 (Lab), 4-3 (DIS)	5
Cards, Index 3" x 5", pkg. of 100	5-6 (DIS)	1	* Pencils, colored, pkg. of 4	3-1 (Lab), 5-6 (DIS)	5
Clay, modeling, (four colors), 1 lb	5-5 (TT)	2	Pipettes, disposable, 150 x 5 mm	1-2 (DIS), 5-4 (DIS), 5-6 (Lab)	1
* Crayons	5-6 (Lab)	5	* Plastic putty	2-1 (TT)	5
Cup, plastic, 300 mL, pkg. of 50	1-2 (DIS), 3-2 (DIS), 3-4 (Lab)	1	Popsicle sticks, pkg. of 50	2-1 (DIS)	1
Epsom salts, 500 g	4-1 (CP), 4-2 (TT)	1	* Raisins, box	3-3 (TT)	1
Food coloring, 30 mL	1-2 (DIS), 1-5 (Lab), 3-1 (TT), 3-4 (Lab)	1	Salol (phenyl salicylate), 100 g	4-2 (DIS)	1
Gelatin, box of 4 pack	2-3 (DIS), 3-4 (Lab)	2	Salt (sodium chloride), 737 g	4-1 (CP), 4-2 (TT)	1
* Honey, 3 oz	3-2 (DIS)	5	Sand, bag, fine, 5.5 lbs	3-4 (DIS)	1
Hydrochloric acid, 1%, 500 mL	5-4 (DIS)	1	Sandpaper, 8" x 11"	2-3 (SA)	5
* Ice cube	4-2 (DIS)	5	* Sequins, pkg. of 25	5-5 (TT)	5
* Ink, 30 mL	5-6 (Lab)	1	Spoons, plastic, pkg. of 24	4-2 (DIS)	1
Knife, plastic	3-4 (Lab), 5-3 (DIS)	10	Stirrers, plastic, pkg. of 20	2-3 (DIS)	1
Labels, 1 sheet	1-1 (DIS)	1	Straws, plastic (wrapped), pkg. of 50	2-4 (DIS), 3-4 (DIS)	1
* Map, outline of the United States, 8" x 11"	2-2 (Lab)	5	String, spool	5-5 (TT)	1
Map, world outline, 8" x 11"	1-5 (DIS), 3-1 (Lab)	5	* Tape, cellophane	1-4 (TT), 2-3 (SA), 2-4 (DIS), 3-4 (DIS)	1
* Marker, colored	1-4 (Lab), 4-3 (Lab)	5	* Tape, masking, roll	1-1 (DIS), 2-3 (SA)	1
* Marker, permanent	1-1 (DIS)	5	* Toothpaste samples, 3 types	4-3 (Lab)	5
* Matches, box	4-2 (DIS)	1	Vinegar, 473 mL	3-3 (TT)	1
Microscope slides, box of 72	4-2 (DIS)	1			
* Oil, 3 oz	3-2 (DIS)	5			

KEY: CP: Chapter Project; **DIS:** Discover; **SA:** Skills Activity; **TT:** Try This; **Lab:** Skills, Consumer, Design Your Own, & Technology and * items are school supplied.

Quantities based on five groups of six students per class.

Master Materials List

Nonconsumable Materials

Description	Textbook Section(s)	Quantity per class	Description	Textbook Section(s)	Quantity per class
* Aluminum can	4-3 (DIS)	5	Magnet, bar, with marked poles	1-4 (TT)	5
* Apron, laboratory	5-4 (DIS)	30	Magnetite, mineral sample	4-1 (DIS)	5
* Balance, triple-beam, single-pan	4-1 (Lab), 5-3 (TT)	5	Marble, rock sample	5-1 (DIS)	5
Basalt, rock sample	5-5 (Lab), 5-6 (Lab)	5	Nails, steel, pkg. of 15	5-6 (Lab)	1
Bauxite, mineral sample	4-3 (DIS)	5	Obsidian, rock sample	3-3 (DIS), 5-2 (DIS)	5
Beaker, polypropylene, 250 mL	1-5 (Lab)	5	Pan, aluminum, large	3-4 (Lab)	5
* Bottle, flint glass	1-5 (Lab), 3-3 (TT)	5	Pan, shallow, 22.5 cm, diameter	1-2 (DIS), 2-3 (DIS), 1-4 (DIS), 3-4 (Lab), 4-2 (TT), 5-3 (TT)	5
Bottle, 60 mL, narrow mouth	3-1 (TT)	5			
Brick, veneer	5-5 (Lab), 5-6 (Lab)	5	* Penny	4-1 (SA), 5-1 (DIS)	5
* Brush, wire	5-6 (Lab)	5	Plastic foam, small piece	3-1 (TT)	5
Calcite, mineral sample	4-1 (SA)	5	* Plastic container, small	3-1 (TT), 3-4 (DIS)	5
* Cardboard, oatmeal boxes	3-4 (Lab)	15	Pumice, rock sample	3-3 (DIS)	5
Conglomerate, rock sample, pkg. of 16	5-1 (DIS), 5-5 (Lab), 5-6 (Lab)	1	Pyrite, mineral sample	4-1 (Lab)	5
Coquina, rock sample, pkg. of 6	5-4 (DIS)	1	Quartz, mineral sample	4-1 (SA), 4-1 (Lab)	5
Cylinder, graduated polypropylene, 100 mL	4-1 (Lab)	5	Rubber bands, pkg. of 50	1-5 (DIS)	1
			Ruler, metric, 12"	1-4 (TT), 1-4 (Lab), 5-5 (TT)	5
Drawing compass with pencil	2-2 (Lab)	5	Sandstone, rock sample	5-3 (TT), 5-5 (Lab), 5-6 (Lab)	5
* Film canisters	1-1 (DIS)	15			
Galena, mineral sample, pkg. of 6	4-1 (Lab)	1	* Scissors	1-4 (TT), 1-4 (Lab), 1-5 (DIS), 2-3 (DIS)	5
* Globe	1-3 (DIS)	5			
* Gloves, laboratory	3-4 (Lab)	30	Shale, rock sample	5-3 (TT)	5
Gneiss, rock sample	5-5 (DIS), 5-5 (Lab), 5-6 (Lab)	5	Slate, rock sample	5-5 (Lab), 5-6 (Lab)	5
			Slide holder	4-2 (DIS)	5
* Goggles, chemical splash	2-1 (DIS), 4-2 (DIS), 4-2 (TT), 5-4 (DIS)	30	Spring scale	2-3 (SA)	5
			Spring toy	2-2 (DIS)	5
Granite, rock sample	5-2 (DIS), 5-5 (DIS), 5-5 (Lab), 5-6 (Lab)	5	* Stopwatch	3-2 (DIS)	5
			Streak plate, pkg. of 8	4-1 (DIS), 4-3 (Lab)	1
Graphite, mineral sample	4-3 (DIS)	5	Syringe, 10 cc	3-4 (Lab)	5
Hand lens, 3x and 6x, pkg. of 6	3-3 (DIS), 4-2 (DIS), 5-1 (DIS), 5-2 (DIS), 5-3 (TT), 5-4 (DIS), 5-5 (DIS), 5-5 (Lab), 5-6 (Lab)	1	Talc, mineral sample	4-1 (SA)	5
			* Toothbrushes	4-3 (Lab)	15
			* Towels, hand	2-4 (TT)	10
Hematite, black mineral sample, pkg. of 6	4-1 (DIS)	1	* Tray, shallow	3-4 (Lab)	5
			* Washcloth	1-4 (DIS)	5
Limestone, rock sample	5-4 (DIS)	5	Weight, small	2-3 (SA)	5
			Wood block, 3.5" x 3.5"	5-5 (TT)	10

KEY: CP: Chapter Project; **DIS**: Discover; **SA**: Skills Activity; **TT**: Try This; **Lab**: Skills, Consumer, Design Your Own, & Technology and * items are school supplied.

Quantities based on five groups of six students per class.

Inside Earth

Book-Specific Resources

Student Edition
StudentExpress™ CD-ROM
Interactive Textbook Online
Teacher's Edition
All-in-One Teaching Resources
Color Transparencies
Guided Reading and Study Workbook
Student Edition in MP3 Audio
Discovery Channel School® Video
Consumable and Nonconsumable Materials Kits

Program Print Resources

Integrated Science Laboratory Manual
Computer Microscope Lab Manual
Inquiry Skills Activity Books
Progress Monitoring Assessments
Test Preparation Workbook
Test-Taking Tips With Transparencies
Teacher's ELL Handbook
Reading Strategies for Science Content

Differentiated Instruction Resources

Adapted Reading and Study Workbook
Adapted Tests
Differentiated Instruction Guide for Labs and Activities

Program Technology Resources

TeacherExpress™ CD-ROM
Interactive Textbooks Online
PresentationExpress™ CD-ROM
ExamView®, Test Generator CD-ROM
Lab zone™ Easy Planner CD-ROM
Probeware Lab Manual With CD-ROM
Computer Microscope and Lab Manual
Materials Ordering CD-ROM
Discovery Channel School® DVD Library
Lab Activity Video Library—DVD and VHS
Web Site at PearsonSchool.com

Spanish Print Resources

Spanish Student Edition
Spanish Guided Reading and Study Workbook
Spanish Teaching Guide With Tests

Acknowledgments appear on p. 214, which constitutes an extension of this copyright page.

Cover
Lava flows down Mount Etna on the island of Sicily.

13-digit ISBN 978-0-13-365105-8
10-digit ISBN 0-13-365105-3
4 5 6 7 8 9 10   13 12 11 10 09

Program Authors

Michael J. Padilla, Ph.D.
Associate Dean and Director
Eugene T. Moore School of Education
Clemson University
Clemson, South Carolina

Michael Padilla is a leader in middle school science education. He has served as an author and elected officer for the National Science Teachers Association and as a writer of the National Science Education Standards. As lead author of Science Explorer, Mike has inspired the team in developing a program that meets the needs of middle grades students, promotes science inquiry, and is aligned with the National Science Education Standards.

Ioannis Miaoulis, Ph.D.
President
Museum of Science
Boston, Massachusetts

Originally trained as a mechanical engineer, Ioannis Miaoulis is in the forefront of the national movement to increase technological literacy. As dean of the Tufts University School of Engineering, Dr. Miaoulis spearheaded the introduction of engineering into the Massachusetts curriculum. Currently he is working with school systems across the country to engage students in engineering activities and to foster discussions on the impact of science and technology on society.

Martha Cyr, Ph.D.
Director of K–12 Outreach
Worcester Polytechnic Institute
Worcester, Massachusetts

Martha Cyr is a noted expert in engineering outreach. She has over nine years of experience with programs and activities that emphasize the use of engineering principles, through hands-on projects, to excite and motivate students and teachers of mathematics and science in grades K–12. Her goal is to stimulate a continued interest in science and mathematics through engineering.

Book Authors

Carole Garbuny Vogel
Science Writer
Lexington, Massachusetts

Michael Wysession, Ph.D.
Associate Professsor of
     Earth and Planetary Sciences
Washington University
St. Louis, Missouri

Contributing Writers

Sharon M. Stroud
Science Instructor
Widefield High School
Colorado Springs, Colorado

Thomas R. Wellnitz
Science Instructor
The Paideia School
Atlanta, Georgia

Consultants

Reading Consultant

Nancy Romance, Ph.D.
Professor of Science
     Education
Florida Atlantic University
Fort Lauderdale, Florida

Mathematics Consultant

William Tate, Ph.D.
Professor of Education and
     Applied Statistics and
     Computation
Washington University
St. Louis, Missouri

Reviewers

Tufts University Content Reviewers

Faculty from Tufts University in Medford, Massachusetts, developed *Science Explorer* chapter projects and reviewed the student books.

Astier M. Almedom, Ph.D.
Department of Biology

Wayne Chudyk, Ph.D.
Department of Civil and Environmental
   Engineering

John L. Durant, Ph.D.
Department of Civil and Environmental
   Engineering

George S. Ellmore, Ph.D.
Department of Biology

David Kaplan, Ph.D.
Department of Biomedical Engineering

Samuel Kounaves, Ph.D.
Department of Chemistry

David H. Lee, Ph.D.
Department of Chemistry

Douglas Matson, Ph.D.
Department of Mechanical Engineering

Karen Panetta, Ph.D.
Department of Electrical Engineering and
   Computer Science

Jan A. Pechenik, Ph.D.
Department of Biology

John C. Ridge, Ph.D.
Department of Geology

William Waller, Ph.D.
Department of Astronomy

Content Reviewers

Paul Beale, Ph.D.
Department of Physics
University of Colorado
Boulder, Colorado

Jeff Bodart, Ph.D.
Chipola Junior College
Marianna, Florida

Michael Castellani, Ph.D.
Department of Chemistry
Marshall University
Huntington, West Virginia

Eugene Chiang, Ph.D.
Department of Astronomy
University of California – Berkeley
Berkeley, California

Charles C. Curtis, Ph.D.
Department of Physics
University of Arizona
Tucson, Arizona

Daniel Kirk-Davidoff, Ph.D.
Department of Meteorology
University of Maryland
College Park, Maryland

Diane T. Doser, Ph.D.
Department of Geological Sciences
University of Texas at El Paso
El Paso, Texas

R. E. Duhrkopf, Ph.D.
Department of Biology
Baylor University
Waco, Texas

Michael Hacker
Co-director, Center for
   Technological Literacy
Hofstra University
Hempstead, New York

Michael W. Hamburger, Ph.D.
Department of Geological Sciences
Indiana University
Bloomington, Indiana

Alice K. Hankla, Ph.D.
The Galloway School
Atlanta, Georgia

Donald C. Jackson, Ph.D.
Department of Molecular Pharmacology,
   Physiology, & Biotechnology
Brown University
Providence, Rhode Island

Jeremiah N. Jarrett, Ph.D.
Department of Biological Sciences
Central Connecticut State University
New Britain, Connecticut

David Lederman, Ph.D.
Department of Physics
West Virginia University
Morgantown, West Virginia

Becky Mansfield, Ph.D.
Department of Geography
Ohio State University
Columbus, Ohio

Elizabeth M. Martin, M.S.
Department of Chemistry and Biochemistry
College of Charleston
Charleston, South Carolina

Joe McCullough, Ph.D.
Department of Natural and
   Applied Sciences
Cabrillo College
Aptos, California

Robert J. Mellors, Ph.D.
Department of Geological Sciences
San Diego State University
San Diego, California

Joseph M. Moran, Ph.D.
American Meteorological Society
Washington, D.C.

David J. Morrissey, Ph.D.
Department of Chemistry
Michigan State University
East Lansing, Michigan

Philip A. Reed, Ph.D.
Department of Occupational & Technical
   Studies
Old Dominion University
Norfolk, Virginia

Scott M. Rochette, Ph.D.
Department of the Earth Sciences
State University of New York, College at
   Brockport
Brockport, New York

Laurence D. Rosenhein, Ph.D.
Department of Chemistry
Indiana State University
Terre Haute, Indiana

Ronald Sass, Ph.D.
Department of Biology and Chemistry
Rice University
Houston, Texas

George Schatz, Ph.D.
Department of Chemistry
Northwestern University
Evanston, Illinois

Sara Seager, Ph.D.
Carnegie Institution of Washington
Washington, D.C.

Robert M. Thornton, Ph.D.
Section of Plant Biology
University of California
Davis, California

John R. Villarreal, Ph.D.
College of Science and Engineering
The University of Texas – Pan American
Edinburg, Texas

Kenneth Welty, Ph.D.
School of Education
University of Wisconsin–Stout
Menomonie, Wisconsin

Edward J. Zalisko, Ph.D.
Department of Biology
Blackburn College
Carlinville, Illinois

Teacher Reviewers

David R. Blakely
Arlington High School
Arlington, Massachusetts

Jane E. Callery
Two Rivers Magnet Middle
    School
East Hartford, Connecticut

Melissa Lynn Cook
Oakland Mills High School
Columbia, Maryland

James Fattic
Southside Middle School
Anderson, Indiana

Dan Gabel
Hoover Middle School
Rockville, Maryland

Wayne Goates
Eisenhower Middle School
Goddard, Kansas

Katherine Bobay Graser
Mint Hill Middle School
Charlotte, North Carolina

Darcy Hampton
Deal Junior High School
Washington, D.C.

Karen Kelly
Pierce Middle School
Waterford, Michigan

David Kelso
Manchester High School Central
Manchester, New Hampshire

Benigno Lopez, Jr.
Sleepy Hill Middle School
Lakeland, Florida

Angie L. Matamoros, Ph.D.
ALM Consulting, INC.
Weston, Florida

Tim McCollum
Charleston Middle School
Charleston, Illinois

Bruce A. Mellin
Brooks School
North Andover, Massachusetts

Ella Jay Parfitt
Southeast Middle School
Baltimore, Maryland

Evelyn A. Pizzarello
Louis M. Klein Middle School
Harrison, New York

Kathleen M. Poe
Fletcher Middle School
Jacksonville, Florida

Shirley Rose
Lewis and Clark Middle School
Tulsa, Oklahoma

Linda Sandersen
Greenfield Middle School
Greenfield, Wisconsin

Mary E. Solan
Southwest Middle School
Charlotte, North Carolina

Mary Stewart
University of Tulsa
Tulsa, Oklahoma

Paul Swenson
Billings West High School
Billings, Montana

Thomas Vaughn
Arlington High School
Arlington, Massachusetts

Susan C. Zibell
Central Elementary
Simsbury, Connecticut

Safety Reviewers

W. H. Breazeale, Ph.D.
Department of Chemistry
College of Charleston
Charleston, South Carolina

Ruth Hathaway, Ph.D.
Hathaway Consulting
Cape Girardeau, Missouri

Douglas Mandt, M.S.
Science Education Consultant
Edgewood, Washington

Activity Field Testers

Nicki Bibbo
Witchcraft Heights School
Salem, Massachusetts

Rose-Marie Botting
Broward County Schools
Fort Lauderdale, Florida

Colleen Campos
Laredo Middle School
Aurora, Colorado

Elizabeth Chait
W. L. Chenery Middle School
Belmont, Massachusetts

Holly Estes
Hale Middle School
Stow, Massachusetts

Laura Hapgood
Plymouth Community
    Intermediate School
Plymouth, Massachusetts

Mary F. Lavin
Plymouth Community
    Intermediate School
Plymouth, Massachusetts

James MacNeil, Ph.D.
Cambridge, Massachusetts

Lauren Magruder
St. Michael's Country
    Day School
Newport, Rhode Island

Jeanne Maurand
Austin Preparatory School
Reading, Massachusetts

Joanne Jackson-Pelletier
Winman Junior High School
Warwick, Rhode Island

Warren Phillips
Plymouth Public Schools
Plymouth, Massachusetts

Carol Pirtle
Hale Middle School
Stow, Massachusetts

Kathleen M. Poe
Fletcher Middle School
Jacksonville, Florida

Cynthia B. Pope
Norfolk Public Schools
Norfolk, Virginia

Anne Scammell
Geneva Middle School
Geneva, New York

Karen Riley Sievers
Callanan Middle School
Des Moines, Iowa

David M. Smith
Eyer Middle School
Allentown, Pennsylvania

Gene Vitale
Parkland School
McHenry, Illinois

Contents

Inside Earth

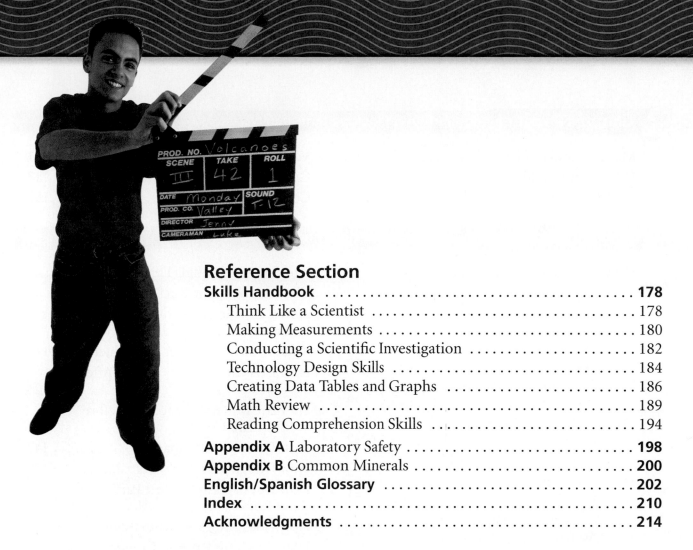

Reference Section

Enhance understanding through dynamic video.

Preview Get motivated with this introduction to the chapter content.

Field Trip Explore a real-world story related to the chapter content.

Assessment Review content and take an assessment.

Get connected to exciting Web resources in every lesson.

SciLINKS Find Web links on topics relating to every section.

Active Art Interact with selected visuals from every chapter online.

Planet Diary® Explore news and natural phenomena through weekly reports.

Science News® Keep up to date with the latest science discoveries.

Experience the complete textbook online and on CD-ROM.

Activities Practice skills and learn content.

Videos Explore content and learn important lab skills.

Audio Support Hear key terms spoken and defined.

Self-Assessment Use instant feedback to help you track your progress.

F ● vii

Activities

Dancing with Volcanoes

Inquiry and Volcanology

Volcanologist Margaret Mangan conducts research about volcanic processes. By reading about her work, students will gain insights about how research is done. They will read about how Dr. Mangan plans and conducts her research. They also will learn about fieldwork, sampling, and laboratory work. The skills that Dr. Mangan uses every day are the same inquiry skills that students need to become successful young scientists.

Build Background Knowledge

Knowledge About Kilauea Remind students about film clips that they have seen of Kilauea erupting. Ask: **Which types of lava features did you notice in the clips?** *(Many will have seen lava flowing smoothly from a vent. Some might have seen footage of the spectacular lava fountains that sometimes occur.)* Make students aware that Dr. Mangan studies why these different types of eruptions occur.

Introduce the Career

Before students read the feature, let them read the title, examine the pictures, and read the captions on their own. Then ask: **What questions came into your mind as you looked at these pictures?** *(Students might suggest questions about why lava fountains occur, the nature of lava, or how lava could form thick layers of flood basalt.)* Point out to students that just as they had questions about what they are seeing, scientists also have questions about what they observe.

Careers in Science

Dancing With Volcanoes

A helicopter moves toward the top of an erupting volcano. With care and speed, a team of scientists gets out to do their work.

"I've been out there sometimes when lava is shooting out of the ground 100 meters high," says volcanologist Margaret Mangan. "The main thing you're struck with is the sound. It's like the roaring of many jet engines. Then there's the smell of sulfur, which is choking. The wind can blow particles from the lava fountain over you, little bits of congealed lava. It feels like a hot sandstorm."

Other times, the eruption is gentler. Lava flows out of the ground in a single channel. "You can walk right up to the channel, just like you'd walk up to a river's edge. We wear what's like a ski mask to keep our faces from getting burnt by the radiant heat. We wear fire-retardant cloth and thick shoes and gloves, to keep our clothes from catching fire. It's hot and sweaty, but you're too excited about what you're doing to think about it."

As a helicopter hovers nearby, lava oozes down Mount Kilauea, a volcano on the island of Hawaii.

x ◆ F

Background

Facts and Figure Kilauea is located on the big island of Hawaii. The volcano currently is at the Hawaiian hot spot, where a plume of hot mantle material rises toward Earth's surface. As this plume rises, pressure is reduced and melting occurs.

Kilauea has been active since about 1790. The current Puù Òò eruption began from the East Rift in 1983. This eruption has produced about 2.0 km³ of mostly basaltic lava. More than 200 hectares of new land have been added to the island as a result of the eruption.

Margaret Mangan grew up in Washington, D.C., and received a Ph.D. from Johns Hopkins University in Baltimore, Maryland. She is a geologist with the Volcano Hazards Team of the U.S. Geological Survey in Menlo Park, California. Formerly, she was the scientist-in-charge of the Hawaiian Volcano Observatory. Maggie has two daughters. She enjoys giving talks and hands-on workshops for middle school science students.

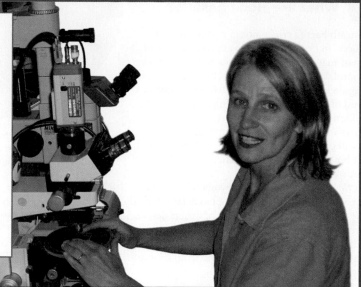

Dr. Margaret Mangan studies lava samples.

Talking With
Dr. Margaret Mangan

? How did you get interested in science?

When I was little, I had no interest in science. I wanted to be a dancer. But I did have a good teacher in high school who taught earth science. He was amazingly interesting and funny. In the back of my mind, that stuck with me. After high school, I worked and studied dance. Then I decided to go to college. Because of that earth science course, I took geology and really liked it. But I had to catch up. I had never taken chemistry, physics, or precalculus in high school. So I did some "quick study" work and got up to speed.

? How did you choose volcanology?

When I became a graduate student in geology, I studied crystals and mineral science. It appealed to the artist in me because the study of crystals has a lot to do with symmetry and structure—how things are put together. When I needed to support myself, I got a job with the U.S. Geological Survey. I worked as an assistant to a volcanologist in an area of Oregon and Washington called the Columbia River flood basalts.

F ◆ 1

Explore the Career

Choose from among the teaching strategies on these pages as you help your students explore the practical application of inquiry skills.

Use Maps Use a map to review with students the location of Kilauea volcano. Tell them that the Big Island currently is over a spot on Earth's surface where volcanism occurs. Ask: **How did the Big Island of Hawaii form?** *(It formed as layer after layer of volcanic eruptions built up from the seafloor.)*

Connect Culture Tell students that according to Hawaiian tradition, Pele, goddess of the volcano, resides at the summit of Kilauea. When Pele is active, the volcano erupts.

Research Interested students might want to research the various ways that volcanologists at the United States Geological Survey study and monitor Kilauea. *(Lava and gases are analyzed, seismometers record minor earthquakes associated with the movement of magma, tiltmeters record changes in the volcano's flank, satellites provide thermal data and data about changes in the volcano's surface)*

Build Inquiry Skills Point out in the photo the microscope that Dr. Mangan is using. Ask: **Why might it be helpful to examine rocks under a microscope?** *(Mineral crystals that are too small to be seen with the unaided eye can be observed with a microscope.)* Tell students that thin slices of rock are glued to glass slides and then viewed under the microscope. A trained observer can recognize minerals and rock textures. Ask: **What do you think is mounted on top of the microscope?** *(a camera for photographing what is seen through the microscope)*

Discuss Ask: **What do you think of when you hear about a river flood?** *(a flow of water much higher than normal)* Tell students that flood basalt eruptions put forth much more lava than comes from normal volcanic eruptions. The flood basalts that erupted in the northwest United States have a volume of about 195,000 km³ and an average thickness of about 900 m.

Use Visuals Ask: **Why would layers of basalt occur in flood basalt deposits?** *(The different layers represent different volcanic eruptions. Through time, the layers pile up to great thickness.)*

Demonstrate Pile books one atop another. Point out to students that the individual books are similar to individual layers of basalt in flood basalt deposits. Ask: **Which book was placed first?** *(the one on the bottom)* **Which layer of basalt in a flood basalt deposit erupted first?** *(the one on the bottom)*

Show Examples Show students photographs of a variety of eruptions from Kilauea. Some photos should show more explosive eruptions, and others should show quiet eruptions. An excellent selection of photos is available from the United States Geological Survey. Ask students to speculate about gas release in each photo.

What are flood basalts?

Beneath Earth's crust, molten rock, or magma, collects in pockets called magma chambers. On top of magma chambers, cracks can open in the ground. We call them fissures. The underground magma is so hot and so fluid that it runs out as a flood of lava, eventually forming a flood basalt. Millions of years ago in the part of Washington where I was working, fissures opened up and lava began to flow west. Our research was to find out how big the lava flows were and how far they traveled.

We hiked into beautiful canyons, which look like birthday cakes with layers of basalt lava stacked one on top of another, hundreds of meters deep. I loved being outside in the middle of canyons and rolling hills. In the midst of that amazing outpouring of volcanism, I learned I wanted to do science outdoors and to study volcanoes.

I kept working for the U.S. Geological Survey, but also started my Ph.D. thesis research on magma chambers. After completing my degree, I hopped on a plane with my husband and daughters to live and work in Hawaii.

Layers of lava formed these flood basalts in Columbia Gorge, Washington.

What was your work like in Hawaii?

I had two main jobs. One was to keep track of the eruption that's gone on at Kilauea volcano since 1983. We wanted to make sure that people coming to the volcano and living near the volcano were safe. We observed the volcano closely and then passed information to the local government and the National Park Service.

I also started a research project related to the Kilauea eruption. I wanted to know why some explosions are bigger than others. You start with the same volcano, the same type of magma underneath. But sometimes it'll come oozing out of the ground and other times it'll erupt in big explosions. My research, which I'm still doing here in California, takes me back and forth between the real volcanoes and the laboratory. I try to simulate or model a volcanic eruption by making a very small magma chamber right in the lab.

Background

Facts and Figures The flood basalts that Dr. Mangan studied are part of the Columbia River Flood Basalt province. These flood basalts cover large portions of Washington, Oregon, and Idaho. They were erupted through a period of about 10 million years during the Miocene Epoch of geologic time. Much of this lava probably erupted from long fissures that were fed by dikes. Huge dike swarms can be observed in the deposits.

In the laboratory, I put a small piece of lava and some water inside a capsule about as big as my index finger. Then I subject it to the temperature and pressures that would be underneath a volcano. After a few days, I lower the temperature and pressure. This simulates the way the pressure lessens and the magma starts to cool as it rises to the surface of a volcano. Finally, I put the capsule in contact with ice. This stops the process in its tracks, and simulates how magma suddenly cools when it comes out of a vent into the atmosphere.

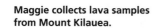

What are you learning from your research?

I'm looking for what affects how explosive an eruption is. Right now, the research is very much focused on the "soda can model." You take a soda can, shake it a tad, open it, and the soda kind of wells over your hand. But if you shake it a lot, then open it, it flies up to the ceiling. There's no difference in the carbonation. The percentage of CO_2 gas is the same in both cans. What is different is the rate of degassing—the rate at which the bubbles of gas form. That's what makes the "eruption" strong or gentle.

Maggie collects lava samples from Mount Kilauea.

Isn't studying volcanoes dangerous?

Well, the danger is a drawback. There's always a concern for safety, even in the lab work. When I do field work, I ask myself: What are the conditions I'm approaching? There's a level of danger, but I'm very careful to think it through and act in ways that keep me safe. Once you make a decision to do something, you move in, you do it. You can't let the fear affect your actions, because then you get clumsy. You have to be controlled and organized.

Writing in Science

Career Link Maggie says her training as a dancer gave her a sense of discipline. She feels that learning about practice, self-control, and organization have helped her be a better scientist. What interests, experiences, or parts of your personality might make you a good scientist? Why do you think so?

Go Online
PHSchool.com
For: More on this career
Visit: PHSchool.com
Web Code: cfb-1000

F ♦ 3

Go Online
PHSchool.com
For: More on this career
Visit: PHSchool.com
Web Code: cfb-1000

Students can do further research on this career and others that are related to the study of earth science.

Help Students Read

Know-Want to Know-Learned Have students make a KWL chart about being a volcanologist. This will help students to recall prior knowledge, will guide their reading, and will encourage review.

Use Math Skills To help students understand the volume of the Columbia River Basalts, have them calculate the size of a cube that has the same volume, 195,000 km³: $\sqrt[3]{195,000 \text{ km}^3} \approx 58$ km. The cube would be about 58 km on each side.

Research Have student groups research the risks faced by volcanologists. Each group then can prepare a poster-board display illustrating the hazards. Groups also should include safety precautions taken by volcanologists to minimize the risk.

Writing in Science

Writing Skill Description
Scoring Rubric
4 Student writing thoroughly addresses the required task and thoughtfully links the trait, interest, or experience with useful science skills or abilities.
3 Student writing identifies the trait, interest, or experience that would be helpful and explains how it would be helpful.
2 Student writing identifies a trait, interest, or experience but does not make a logical connection with science skills or abilities.
1 Student writing includes some self-description only.

Chapter at a Glance

Chapter Project *Make a Model of Earth*

Technology

Local Standards

 Video Preview

All in One Teaching Resources
- Chapter Project Teacher Notes, pp. 38–39
- Chapter Project Student Overview, pp. 40–41
- Chapter Project Student Worksheets, pp. 42–43
- Chapter Project Scoring Rubric, p. 44

 Section 1

Earth's Interior
2 periods
1 block

F.1.1.1 Explain how geologists learn about Earth's inner structures.

F.1.1.2 Identify the characteristics of Earth's crust, mantle, and core.

 Go Online SCLINKS NSTA

 Section 2

Convection and the Mantle
1 period
1/2 block

F.1.2.1 Explain how heat is transferred.

F.1.2.2 Identify what causes convection currents.

F.1.2.3 Describe convection currents in Earth's mantle.

 Go Online PHSchool.com

 Section 3

Drifting Continents
2 periods
1 block

F.1.3.1 Explain Alfred Wegener's hypothesis about the continents.

F.1.3.2 List the evidence used by Wegener to support his hypothesis.

F.1.3.3 Explain why other scientists of Wegener's day rejected his hypothesis.

 Go Online SCLINKS NSTA

 **Section 4**

Sea-Floor Spreading
3 periods
1 1/2 blocks

F.1.4.1 List the evidence for sea-floor spreading.

F.1.4.2 Explain the process of sea-floor spreading.

F.1.4.3 Describe the process of subduction.

 Go Online PHSchool.com

 Video Field Trip

 Section 5

The Theory of Plate Tectonics
2 periods
1 block

F.1.5.1 Explain the theory of plate tectonics.

F.1.5.2 Describe the three types of plate boundaries.

 Go Online *active art*

 Go Online PHSchool.com

Review and Assessment

Test Preparation

All in One Teaching Resources
- Key Terms Review, p. 86
- Transparency F13
- Performance Assessment Teacher Notes, p. 95
- Performance Assessment Scoring Rubric, p. 96
- Performance Assessment Student Worksheet, p. 97
- Chapter Test, pp. 98–101

 Go Online PHSchool.com

  Video Assessment

Test Preparation Blackline Masters

Lab zone Chapter Activities Planner

For more activities

LAB ZONE
Easy Planner
CD-ROM

Student Edition	Inquiry	Time	Materials	Skills	Resources
Chapter Project, p. 5	Open-Ended	Ongoing (2–3 weeks)	**All in One Teaching Resources,** p. 38	Applying concepts, interpreting data	**Lab zone Easy Planner**
Section 1					
Discover Activity, p. 6	Open-Ended	10 minutes	3 film canisters with tops, 3 different materials, masking tape, permanent marker, labels	Inferring	**Lab zone Easy Planner**
Skills Activity, p. 11	Directed	15 minutes	Pencil and paper	Creating data tables	**Lab zone Easy Planner**
Section 2					
Discover Activity, p. 14	Guided	10 minutes	Shallow pan, clear plastic cup, hot water, cold water, plastic dropper, food coloring	Inferring	**Lab zone Easy Planner**
Section 3					
Discover Activity, p. 18	Guided	15 minutes	Globe that shows physical features	Posing questions	**Lab zone Easy Planner**
Section 4					
Discover Activity, p. 23	Guided	10 minutes	Sink or large dishpan, water, washcloth	Observing	**Lab zone Easy Planner**
Try This, p. 27	Directed	15 minutes	Audiotape, scissors, metric ruler, plastic tape, bar magnet	Making models	**Lab zone Easy Planner**
Skills Lab, pp. 30–31	Directed	Prep: 15 minutes Class: 30 minutes	Scissors, metric ruler, 2 sheets of unlined paper, colored marker	Making models	**All in One Teaching Resources** Skills Lab: *Modeling Sea-Floor Spreading, pp. 73–76*
Section 5					
Discover Activity, p. 32	Guided	20 minutes	World map in an atlas, tracing paper, scissors, sheet of paper, tape	Drawing conclusions	**Lab zone Easy Planner**
Skills Lab, p. 37	Guided	Prep: 20 minutes Class: 40 minutes	Large plastic bottle, food coloring, small glass jar, aluminum foil, rubber band, several small pieces of paper about 0.5 cm square, tap water	Making models, observing	**All in One Teaching Resources** Skills Lab: *Modeling Mantle Convection Currents, pp. 84–85*

Section 1 Earth's Interior

 *2 periods, 1 block*

Objectives

F.1.1.1 Explain how geologists learn about Earth's inner structures.
F.1.1.2 Identify the characteristics of Earth's crust, mantle, and core.

Local Standards

Key Terms

- seismic waves • pressure • crust • basalt • granite • mantle • lithosphere
- asthenosphere • outer core • inner core

Preteach

Build Background Knowledge

Students share their experiences digging holes in the ground and discussing what is below Earth's surface.

Lab zone Discover Activity *How Do Scientists Find Out What's Inside Earth?* **L1**

Targeted Print and Technology Resources

All in One Teaching Resources

L2 Reading Strategy Transparency F1: Using Prior Knowledge

 PresentationExpress™ CD-ROM

Instruct

Exploring Inside Earth Use visuals and leading questions to open discussion of how activity in Earth's interior affects the surface.

A Journey to the Center of Earth Explain why changes in pressure and temperature increase with depth.

The Crust Help students compare and contrast oceanic and continental crust.

The Mantle Use hard candy and taffy to open discussion of characteristics of the lithosphere and asthenosphere.

The Core Use an apple to help students compare and contrast Earth's inner core and outer core.

Targeted Print and Technology Resources

All in One Teaching Resources

L2 Guided Reading, pp. 47–50
L2 Transparency F2

www.SciLinks.org Web Code: scn-1011

 Student Edition on Audio CD

Assess

Section Assessment Questions

Have students use their completed graphic organizers, with their paragraphs using prior knowledge to answer the questions.

Reteach

Students discuss characteristics of continental crust and oceanic crust.

Targeted Print and Technology Resources

All in One Teaching Resources

- Section Summary, p. 46
L1 Review and Reinforce, p. 53
L3 Enrich, p. 51

Section 2 Convection and the Mantle

1 period, 1/2 block

Objectives

F.1.2.1 Explain how heat is transferred.

F.1.2.2 Identify what causes convection currents.

F.1.2.3 Describe convection currents in Earth's mantle.

Local Standards

Key Terms

- radiation • conduction • convection • density • convection current

Preteach

Build Background Knowledge

Students recall experiences about convection currents in a room.

 **Discover Activity** *How Can Heat Cause Motion in a Liquid?* **L1**

Targeted Print and Technology Resources

 Teaching Resources

L2 Reading Strategy Transparency F3: Outlining

⊙ **PresentationExpress™ CD-ROM**

Instruct

Types of Heat Transfer Use everyday examples to describe and explain the three mechanisms of heat transfer: radiation, conduction, and convection.

Convection Currents Review the concepts of density and gravity to explain why convection occurs.

Convection Currents in Earth Use a diagram to explain how temperature differences in Earth's mantle create convection currents in solid rock.

Targeted Print and Technology Resources

Teaching Resources

L2 Guided Reading, pp. 55–57

L2 Transparency F4

PHSchool.com Web Code: cfd-1012

⊙ **Student Edition on Audio CD**

Assess

Section Assessment Questions

Have students use their completed outlines to answer the questions.

Reteach

Students consider heat transfer in a glass containing water and ice cubes.

Targeted Print and Technology Resources

Teaching Resources

- Section Summary, p. 54

L1 Review and Reinforce, p. 58

L3 Enrich, p. 59

Section 3 Drifting Continents

 *2 periods, 1 block*

Objectives

F.1.3.1 Explain Alfred Wegener's hypothesis about the continents.

F.1.3.2 List the evidence used by Wegener to support his hypothesis.

F.1.3.3 Explain why other scientists of Wegener's time rejected his hypothesis.

Key Terms

• continental drift • Pangaea • fossil

Local Standards

Preteach

Build Background Knowledge

Students recall knowledge about continents and consider whether continents change.

Discover Activity *How Are Earth's Continents Linked Together?* **L2**

Targeted Print and Technology Resources

All in One Teaching Resources

L2 Reading Strategy Transparency F5: Identifying Supporting Evidence

◉ **PresentationExpress™ CD-ROM**

Instruct

Continental Drift Use a jigsaw puzzle and a world map to demonstrate Wegener's hypothesis of continental drift and consider evidence that can be used to reassemble Pangaea.

Wegener's Hypothesis Rejected Consider historic arguments against continental drift and explain why the hypothesis was not accepted by most of Wegener's contemporaries.

Targeted Print and Technology Resources

All in One Teaching Resources

L2 Guided Reading, pp. 62–63

L2 Transparency F6

www.SciLinks.org Web Code: scn-1013

◉ **Student Edition on Audio CD**

Assess

Section Assessment Questions

Have students use their graphic organizers showing the evidence they have identified to answer the questions.

Reteach

Students work together to create a concept map about continental drift.

Targeted Print and Technology Resources

All in One Teaching Resources

• Section Summary, p. 61

L1 Review and Reinforce, p. 64

L3 Enrich, p. 65

Section 4 Sea-Floor Spreading

 3 periods, 1 1/2 blocks

Objectives

F.1.4.1 List the evidence for sea-floor spreading.
F.1.4.2 Explain the process of sea-floor spreading.
F.1.4.3 Describe the process of subduction.

Local Standards

Key Terms

• mid-ocean ridge • sonar • sea-floor spreading • deep-ocean trench
• subduction

Preteach

Build Background Knowledge

Students recall prior knowledge about lava. They speculate about constructive and destructive processes affecting the sea floor.

 **Discover Activity** *What Is the Effect of a Change in Density?* L1

Targeted Print and Technology Resources

 Teaching Resources

L2 Reading Strategy Transparency F7: Identifying Sequence

 PresentationExpress™ CD-ROM

Instruct

Mid-Ocean Ridges Use visuals and maps to show that mountains exist on the sea floor, and explain how sonar is used to map underwater features.

What Is Sea-Floor Spreading? Work together with the class to summarize the processes of sea-floor spreading. Develop understanding that these processes occur slowly through long periods of time.

Evidence for Sea-Floor Spreading Use the leading questions to review the evidence that led to the theory of sea-floor spreading.

Subduction at Trenches Compare the sea-floor to a giant conveyor belt in order to show how it forms at mid-ocean ridges and returns to the mantle at deep-ocean trenches.

 Skills Lab *Modeling Sea-Floor Spreading* L2

Targeted Print and Technology Resources

 Teaching Resources

L2 Guided Reading, pp. 68–70
L2 Transparency F8, F9
L2 Skills Lab: *Modeling Sea-Floor Spreading,* pp. 73–76

Lab Activity Video/DVD
Skills Lab: *Modeling Sea-Floor Spreading*

PHSchool.com Web Code: cfd-1014

Student Edition on Audio CD

Assess

Section Assessment Questions

Have students use their completed graphic organizers with the sequence of events to answer the questions.

Reteach

The class creates a concept map about sea-floor spreading.

Targeted Print and Technology Resources

Teaching Resources
• Section Summary, p. 67
L1 Review and Reinforce, p. 71
L3 Enrich, p. 72

Section 5 The Theory of Plate Tectonics

 2 periods, 1 block

ABILITY LEVELS
L1 Basic to Average
L2 For All Students
L3 Average to Advanced

Objectives

F.1.5.1 Explain the theory of plate tectonics.
F.1.5.2 Describe the three types of plate boundaries.

Key Terms

• plate • scientific theory • plate tectonics • fault • divergent boundary
• rift valley • convergent boundary • transform boundary

Local Standards

Preteach

Build Background Knowledge

Students create a general definition of the word *plate*.

 **Discover Activity** *How Well Do the Continents Fit Together?* **L1**

Targeted Print and Technology Resources

All in One Teaching Resources

L2 Reading Strategy: Building Vocabulary

 PresentationExpress™ CD-ROM

Instruct

How Plates Move Demostrate how tectonic plates move over the asthenosphere below.

Plate Boundaries Show students how to use their hands to model motion along the three types of plate boundaries. Then connect these motions to different types of real-world boundaries.

 Skills Lab *Modeling Mantle Convection Currents* **L2**

Targeted Print and Technology Resources

All in One Teaching Resources

L2 Guided Reading, pp. 79–81
L2 Transparencies F10, F11, F12
L2 Laboratory Investigation: *Modeling Mantle Convection Currents,* pp. 84–85

Lab Activity Video/DVD
Skills Lab: *Modeling Mantle Convection Currents*

PHSchool.com Web Code: cfp-1015

 Student Edition on Audio CD

Assess

Section Assessment Questions

Have students use their definitions of key terms to answer the questions.

Reteach

Students make a compare and contrast table about plate boundaries.

Targeted Print and Technology Resources

All in One Teaching Resources

• Section Summary, p. 78
L1 Review and Reinforce, p. 82
L3 Enrich, p. 83

Chapter 1 **Content Refresher**

Section 1 **Earth's Interior**

Composition of Earth's Interior Most of the evidence for Earth's internal structure and composition is indirect. It comes from seismic waves. Scientists use seismic waves generated by earthquakes to study Earth's interior. The seismic waves travel through different types of rock at different speeds. When the waves encounter a layer with properties that are different from those of the one they are traveling through, the waves will be reflected or refracted. Scientists use the deflection to infer the physical properties of the two layers.

Seismic wave speeds for different rock types have been determined in the laboratory. These lab studies are then used to infer what rock type the seismic waves from earthquakes encounter deep within Earth. But there are many variables to consider, including temperature, pressure, and Earth's complex underground structure. In addition, there is rock composition to consider. Earth's crust does not form simple, flat-lying layers like those of an onion. There are many faults and folds. There-fore, determining the composition of Earth's interior from seismic waves is difficult.

Address Misconceptions

Many students may think that Earth's interior is molten; however, Earth's mantle is solid. For a strategy for overcoming this misconception, see **Address Misconceptions** in the section *Earth's Interior*.

Section 2 **Convection and the Mantle**

Yellowstone Hot Spot Convection currents in the mantle move like giant conveyor belts flowing through the plastic asthenosphere. But in some areas hot mantle plumes remain stationary for long periods of time. These stationary mantle plumes are called hot spots. Hot spots are important because they allow scientists to study relatively closely the mechanism that drives plate tectonics—the heat flow within the mantle convection currents. One famous hot spot is the Hawaiian Island chain.

Hot spots can also be found under the continents. One particularly well-studied continental hot spot is found under Yellowstone National Park. This hot spot provides heat for the geysers and hot springs in the park. This hot spot has been active for 16.5 million years. Geologists have plotted the track

of the hot spot from northern Nevada through Idaho to its current location under Yellowstone. This track is marked by volcanic eruptions. More than 142 separate eruptions have been identified so far. The hot spot itself has remained stationary while the North American continent has moved slowly west-southwest at 1 to 2 centimeters per year. The volcanic activity in the Yellowstone area began about 2 million years ago. Because of the hot spot, Yellowstone National Park has been and will continue to be an active volcanic area.

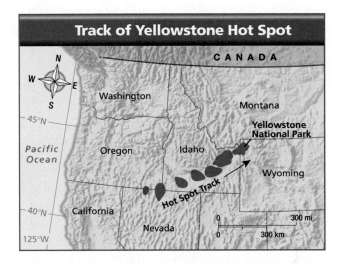

Track of Yellowstone Hot Spot

Section 3 **Drifting Continents**

Explaining the Fossil Evidence In the early 1900s, most scientists considered Alfred Wegener's idea of drifting continents to be ridiculous. However, the evidence Wegener cited was not disputed. Fossils of the reptiles *Mesosaurus* and *Lystrosaurus* had been found in Africa and South America. The fossil seed fern *Glossopteris* was found in Africa, South America, Australia, and Antarctica.

If the theory of moving continents was so unbelievable, how did scientists explain the fossil evidence? No one thought that the freshwater reptile *Mesosaurus* or the bulky semi-aquatic *Lystrosaurus* could have swum great distances across salt water, so how did these organisms get across oceans? Three theories were considered: rafting, island stepping stones, and land bridges. According to the rafting theory, individuals could have been carried across the oceans on logs or mats of vegetation. This scenario seems possible for a very small animal, but not likely for larger animals such as the *Mesosaurus*. These reptiles were about 1 meter in length. And it would seem even more unlikely for the *Lystrosaurus*, which was the size of a large dog.

According to the island stepping-stones theory, animals used islands like stepping stones to move across large expanses of ocean. How a land, semi-aquatic, or freshwater reptile moved from island to island was a problem with this theory. Also, there was no evidence for a series of islands extending across the south Atlantic Ocean from Africa to South America.

The land bridge theory was the most widely accepted. The Bering land bridge, between Asia and Alaska, was used extensively as evidence for this theory. But no evidence of land bridges could be found across the south Atlantic Ocean. It also appeared difficult for a freshwater reptile, such as *Mesosaurus*, or a plant, such as *Glossopteris*, to travel along a narrow strip of land. When maps of the ocean floor were made, they indicated no evidence of submerged land bridges. The theory was rejected.

Section 4 Sea-Floor Spreading

Submarines and Sea Floor Maps Until the nineteenth century, the ocean floors were considered to be flat, featureless plains. Early attempts to map the ocean floors used soundings taken with weighted lines from ships. This method was slow and inaccurate. In 1855, U.S. Navy Lieutenant Matthew Maury published a bathymetric chart, which indicated that an underwater mountain existed in the middle of the Atlantic Ocean. Soon after that, in the 1860s, narrow strips of the sea floor were surveyed, during the laying of the first trans-Atlantic telegraph cables.

Mapping the ocean floor accelerated after World War I. The German Navy began to use early sonar systems to make maps that their U-boats (submarines) could use to navigate. These echo-sounding devices measured ocean depth by recording the time it took an electronically generated "ping" to travel from a ship to the sea floor and then to bounce back to the ship. After World War II, both the United States and the Soviet Union expanded and improved maps of the sea floor. These maps were needed to provide accurate information for submarine navigation. In the 1950s, scientists began to use magnetic instruments to map magnetic anomalies across the sea floor. These magnetometers were adapted from World War II instruments that had been used to detect submarines from airplanes.

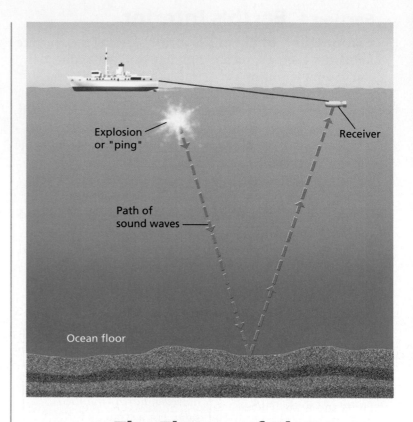

Explosion or "ping"

Receiver

Path of sound waves

Ocean floor

Section 5 The Theory of Plate Tectonics

Ancestral Rocky Mountains The place where two plates converge is called a convergent boundary. When two continental plates come together at a convergent boundary, huge mountain ranges, such as the Himalayas, are formed. About 300 million years ago, a similar mountain range was formed in the middle of North America—the Ancestral Rocky Mountains. The Ancestral Rockies were located in what are now the states of Colorado, Utah, Arizona, and New Mexico. Tall mountain ranges and narrow, deep basins formed from the collision of Africa and South America with North America. The collision occurred during the formation of the supercontinent Pangaea. Other mountain belts formed along the margins of North America as the collisions continued, including the Ouachita Mountains in Oklahoma, Texas, and Arkansas, and the Appalachian Mountains along the East Coast.

The Ancestral Rockies were unusual because they formed far from the margins of the continent where the collisions occurred. Like the Himalayas, these mountains formed as the continental crust broke into huge blocks, pushed by the converging continents. The deformation extends hundreds of kilometers into the continent. Imagine an icebreaking ship plowing slowly into a thick sheet of ice. Cracks extend in front of the ship and large blocks of ice are pushed up, pushed down, and pushed away from the direction in which the ship is moving. In a similar way, huge blocks of continental crust deep within North America were pushed up to form the Ancestral Rockies and down to form the nearby basins. In the case of the Himalayas, the continent of India pushes into and under Asia to form the mountains.

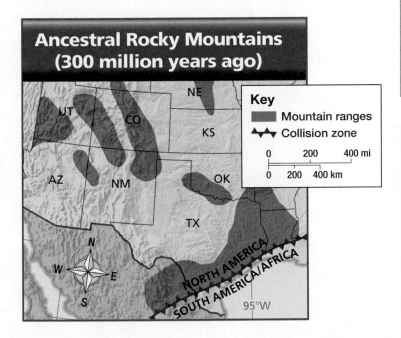

Ancestral Rocky Mountains (300 million years ago)

Key
- Mountain ranges
- Collision zone

0   200   400 mi

0   200   400 km

Help Students Read

Previewing Visuals

Setting a Purpose Before Reading

Strategy Help students set a purpose for reading and determine an idea of how the text is organized. Point out that previewing visuals is like looking at a travel brochure before you begin a trip. It lets you see what main attractions lie before you. Before students begin to read, direct their attention to Figure 5 and Figure 6.

Example

1. Have students look closely at the visual of Earth and its layers. Ask: **What does this picture tell you to expect as you begin to read the section?** *(Text will be about the interior of Earth.)*

2. Next, tell students to look for connections to what they already know. Are there any familiar concepts in this visual? Are there new concepts?

3. Have students look at other visuals in the chapter and ask themselves the same questions. They may wish to create a graphic organizer in the form of a table. Column headings might be "Visual," "Purpose Set by Visual," "New Concept," and "Familiar Concept."

The BIG Idea

The Big Idea is the major scientific concept of the chapter. It is followed by the Essential Question. Read aloud the question to students. As students study the chapter, tell them to think about the Essential Question. Explain that they will discover the answer to the question as they read. The chapter Study Guide provides a sample answer.

Chapter Project   L3

Objectives

This project will enhance students' understanding of Earth's interior, plates, and plate boundaries. After this Chapter Project, students will be able to

- apply the concepts learned in the chapter to a model of Earth's interior
- interpret data to make a model to scale
- design and make a model of Earth's interior and features of the surface
- communicate the features of the model in a presentation to the class

Skills Focus

Applying concepts, interpreting data, designing, making models, communicating

Project Time Line   2 to 3 weeks

All in One Teaching Resources

- Chapter Project Teacher Notes
- Chapter Project Overview
- Chapter Project Worksheet 1
- Chapter Project Worksheet 2
- Chapter Project Scoring Rubric

Developing a Plan

Each student should make a preliminary sketch of a model and discuss the design and possible materials with classmates. Groups can experiment with different materials to see which might work best. A second set of sketches can demonstrate how the model could incorporate the concept of sea-floor spreading. Students can begin to construct the base of the model and incorporate plate boundaries into the design as they progress.

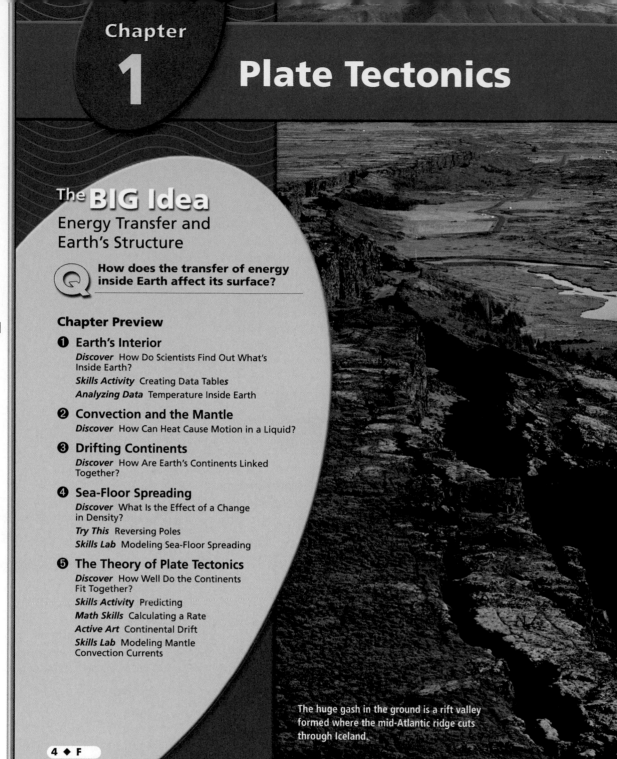

Chapter

1

Plate Tectonics

The BIG Idea
Energy Transfer and Earth's Structure

Q **How does the transfer of energy inside Earth affect its surface?**

Chapter Preview

❶ **Earth's Interior**
Discover How Do Scientists Find Out What's Inside Earth?
Skills Activity Creating Data Tables
Analyzing Data Temperature Inside Earth

❷ **Convection and the Mantle**
Discover How Can Heat Cause Motion in a Liquid?

❸ **Drifting Continents**
Discover How Are Earth's Continents Linked Together?

❹ **Sea-Floor Spreading**
Discover What Is the Effect of a Change in Density?
Try This Reversing Poles
Skills Lab Modeling Sea-Floor Spreading

❺ **The Theory of Plate Tectonics**
Discover How Well Do the Continents Fit Together?
Skills Activity Predicting
Math Skills Calculating a Rate
Active Art Continental Drift
Skills Lab Modeling Mantle Convection Currents

The huge gash in the ground is a rift valley formed where the mid-Atlantic ridge cuts through Iceland.

Possible Materials

- A variety of materials could be used for the base of the model, including papier-mâché, modeling clay, chicken wire, cardboard, plywood, and wood blocks. Groups may also suggest other materials.
- To help students make models more realistic, have available paints, paint brushes, and permanent markers.

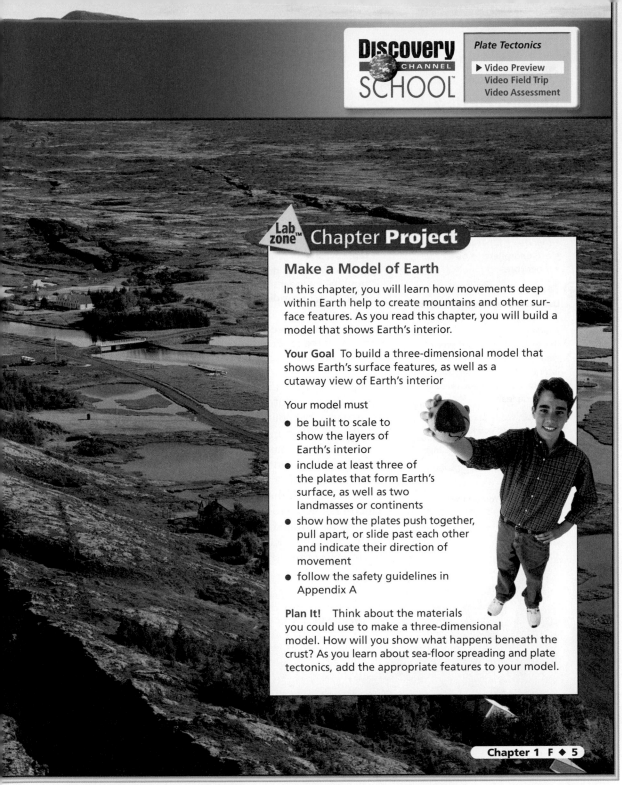

Chapter **Project**

Make a Model of Earth

In this chapter, you will learn how movements deep within Earth help to create mountains and other surface features. As you read this chapter, you will build a model that shows Earth's interior.

Your Goal To build a three-dimensional model that shows Earth's surface features, as well as a cutaway view of Earth's interior

Your model must

● be built to scale to show the layers of Earth's interior

● include at least three of the plates that form Earth's surface, as well as two landmasses or continents

● show how the plates push together, pull apart, or slide past each other and indicate their direction of movement

● follow the safety guidelines in Appendix A

Plan It! Think about the materials you could use to make a three-dimensional model. How will you show what happens beneath the crust? As you learn about sea-floor spreading and plate tectonics, add the appropriate features to your model.

Chapter 1 F ◆ 5

Launching the Project

To introduce this project, show students a large world globe and ask: **If the inside of this globe reflected Earth's interior as well as it reflects Earth's surface, what would it show when cut in half?** *(Students might mention dirt, water, and rock.)* Explain that in this chapter, students will learn that Earth's interior has several layers, each with different characteristics. Also point out that movements within the interior affect processes on the surface of the planet.

Video Preview

Plate Tectonics

Show the Video Preview to introduce the Chapter Project and overview the chapter content. Discussion Questions: **On which two continents were fossil bones of Brachiosaurus found?** *(Africa and North America)* **Why do you think that bones of the same type of dinosaur were found in two distant parts of the world?** *(The two continents were once part of one larger continent.)*

Performance Assessment

The Chapter Project Scoring Rubric will help you evaluate how well students complete the Chapter Project. You might want to share the rubric with your students so that they know what is expected. Students will be assessed on

● how well they make their sketches and plan their models

● how well they incorporate the required features and create an attractive model of Earth's interior

● how effectively they present the model and explain its features to the class

● how well they work in the group and how much they contribute to the group's effort

Portfolio

F ● 5

Objectives

After completing this lesson, students will be able to

F1.1.1 explain how geologists learn about Earth's inner structures

F1.1.2 identify the characteristics of Earth's crust, mantle, and core

Target Reading Skill

Using Prior Knowledge Explain that using prior knowledge helps students connect what they already know to what they are about to read.

Answers

This is one possible way to complete the graphic organizer. Accept all logical answers.

What You Know

1. Earth's crust is made of rock.
2. Earth is very hot near the center.
3. Dry land is part of the crust.
4. The mantle is very hot.
5. The core contains iron.

What You Learned

1. Geologists use seismic waves to study Earth's interior.
2. Radioactive substances heat the interior of Earth.
3. The crust is thickest under high mountains.
4. The mantle is solid.
5. Movements in the outer core create Earth's magnetic field.

All in One Teaching Resources

- Transparency F1

Preteach

Build Background Knowledge `L2`

Knowledge About Earth's Interior

Begin by having students recall times when they've dug holes in the ground. Ask: **If you dig down far enough through the dirt, what does your shovel hit?** (*Most students will suggest that below the dirt is rock.*) **Other than rock, what else do you think is below the surface of Earth?** (*Students might mention oil and water.*)

Reading Preview

Key Concepts

- How have geologists learned about Earth's inner structure?
- What are the characteristics of Earth's crust, mantle, and core?

Key Terms

- seismic waves • pressure
- crust • basalt • granite
- mantle • lithosphere
- asthenosphere • outer core
- inner core

Target Reading Skill

Using Prior Knowledge Before you read, look at the section headings and visuals to see what this section is about. Then write what you know about Earth's interior in a graphic organizer like the one below. As you read, write what you learn.

What You Know
1. Earth's crust is made of rock.
2.

What You Learned
1.
2.

Lab zone Discover **Activity**

How Do Scientists Find Out What's Inside Earth?

1. Your teacher will provide you with three closed film canisters. Each canister contains a different material. Your goal is to determine what is inside each canister—even though you can't directly observe what it contains.
2. Tape a paper label on each canister.
3. To gather evidence about what is in the canisters, you may tap, roll, shake, or weigh them. Record your observations.
4. What differences do you notice between the canisters? Apart from their appearance on the outside, are the canisters similar in any way? How did you obtain this evidence?

Think It Over

Inferring From your observations, what can you infer about the contents of the canisters? How is a canister like Earth?

Imagine watching an island grow! That's exactly what you can do on the island of Hawaii. On the south side of the island, molten material pours out of cracks in Mount Kilauea (kee loo AY uh) and flows into the ocean. As this lava flows over the land, it cools and hardens into rock.

The most recent eruptions of Mount Kilauea began in 1983. An area of cracks 7 kilometers long opened in Earth's surface. Through the cracks spurted "curtains of fire"—fountains of hot liquid rock from deep inside Earth. Since that time, the lava has covered more than 100 square kilometers of land with a layer of rock. When the lava reaches the sea, it extends the borders of the island into the Pacific Ocean.

FIGURE 1
Lava Flows in Hawaii
These people are watching lava from vents in Kilauea flow into the Pacific Ocean.

Lab zone Discover **Activity**

Skills Focus Inferring `L1`

Materials 3 film canisters with tops, 3 different materials, masking tape, permanent marker, labels

Time 10 minutes

Tips The different materials can include practically anything that will fit in the canisters. Include both liquids and solids, and vary them in viscosity, density, size, and other physical characteristics.

Think It Over Answers will vary, depending on the materials used. Accept any reasonable explanation about how scientists gather evidence about Earth's interior.

FIGURE 2
Getting Beneath the Surface
Geologists (left) examine rocks for clues about what's inside Earth. Even though caves like this one in Georgia (below) may seem deep, they reach only a relatively short distance beneath the surface.

Exploring Inside Earth

Earth's surface is constantly changing. Throughout our planet's long history, its surface has been lifted up, pushed down, bent, and broken. Thus Earth looks different today from the way it did millions of years ago.

Volcanic eruptions like those at Mount Kilauea make people wonder, What's inside Earth? Yet this question is very difficult to answer. Much as geologists would like to, they cannot dig a hole to the center of Earth. The extreme conditions in Earth's interior prevent exploration far below the surface.

The deepest mine in the world, a gold mine in South Africa, reaches a depth of 3.8 kilometers. But that mine only scratches the surface. You would have to travel more than 1,600 times that distance—over 6,000 kilometers—to reach Earth's center. **Geologists have used two main types of evidence to learn about Earth's interior: direct evidence from rock samples and indirect evidence from seismic waves.** The geologists in Figure 2 are observing rock on Earth's surface.

F ◆ 7

Differentiated Instruction

Gifted and Talented [L3]
Preparing a Display Ask students to research the words *xenolith* and *xenocryst*. Students then should prepare a display that shows how these rocks and crystals reach Earth's surface and what can be learned from them. (*Xenoliths are pieces of rock that are captured by ascending magma and carried to the surface. Xenocrysts are mineral crystals that are captured and carried to the surface. Some xenoliths and xenocrysts come from the mantle, and so provide geologists with actual samples of mantle rock. Diamonds, which form in Earth's mantle, are xenocrysts that provide information about the pressure, temperature, and composition of the mantle.*)
learning modality: visual

Teach Key Concepts
Earth's Changing Surface

Focus Remind students that Earth's surface has changed over time by processes such as lifting, pushing, bending, and breaking.

Teach Ask: **What are some other ways that Earth's surface has changed over time?** (*A typical answer might mention earthquakes, erosion, flooding, and glaciers.*)

Apply Ask: **Does the interior of Earth change over time? How do you know?** (*Possible answer: Yes, the interior of Earth changes over time because the surface changes; what occurs in the interior affects the surface.*)
learning modality: logical/mathematical

Use Visuals [L2]
Caves

Focus Ask: **Who has ever visited a cave?** (*Some students may have visited caverns or national parks with caves.*) Encourage students to relate their experiences to the class.

Teach Ask: **Why would a geologist study the interior of a cave?** (*To examine the materials below ground and to determine the processes that formed the caves*)

Apply Ask: **What is a limitation of studying a cave to learn about the interior of Earth?** (*Possible answer: Even the deepest caves extend only a short distance into Earth's crust.*)
learning modality: logical/mathematical

Independent Practice [L2]

All in One Teaching Resources
• Guided Reading and Study Worksheet: *Earth's Interior*

 Student Edition on Audio CD

Monitor Progress [L2]

Writing Have each student write a short paragraph that explains in his or her own words what a geologist does. Students can save their paragraphs in their portfolios.

Portfolio

Predicting Movement of Waves

Materials 2-L bowl, small glass jar or
bottle, pencil, water

Time 15 minutes

Focus Tell students to put on their geologist
"hats" and find out how geologists use
seismic waves to investigate Earth's interior.

Teach Encourage students to use an object
to create waves in a bowl of water and
observe the movement of the waves. Then
students could place a small jar or bottle in
the middle of the bowl of water and predict
how that jar or bottle will affect waves in
the bowl.

Apply Students sketch what they observe
and write a description of how the changes
in the waves show the location of the jar or
bottle. **learning modality: kinesthetic**

Address Misconceptions [L2]

Nature of Earth's Interior

Focus Because temperature increases with
depth and lava comes from below, many
students believe that Earth's interior is
molten beneath a thin crust. The concept of
convection in Earth's mantle adds to this
confusion because most students have a
difficult time visualizing convection in solid
materials.

Teach Tell students that high pressure can
keep rock from melting even if the rock's
temperature is above the surface melting
point. This is why Earth's mantle can remain
solid at such high temperature. Ask: **Is it
possible for solid rock to flow?** (Yes, at high
temperature and pressure, rock can flow.)

Apply Tell students that slowly flowing, but
solid, rock in Earth's mantle is responsible
for mountains, volcanoes, and earthquakes,
and that they will learn how in this chapter.
learning modality: logical/mathematical

Evidence From Rock Samples Rocks from inside Earth
give geologists clues about Earth's structure. Geologists have
drilled holes as much as 12 kilometers into Earth. The drills
bring up samples of rock. From these samples, geologists can
make inferences about conditions deep inside Earth, where
these rocks formed. In addition, forces inside Earth sometimes
blast rock to the surface from depths of more than 100 kilometers. These rocks provide more information about the interior.

Evidence From Seismic Waves Geologists cannot look
inside Earth. Instead, they must rely on indirect methods of
observation. Have you ever hung a heavy picture on a wall? If
you have, you know that you can knock on the wall to locate
the wooden beam underneath the plaster that will support the
picture. When you knock on the wall, you listen carefully for a
change in the sound.

To study Earth's interior, geologists also use an indirect
method. But instead of knocking on walls, they use seismic
waves. When earthquakes occur, they produce **seismic waves**
(SYZ mik). Geologists record the seismic waves and study how
they travel through Earth. The speed of seismic waves and the
paths they take reveal the structure of the planet.

Using data from seismic waves, geologists have learned that
Earth's interior is made up of several layers. Each layer surrounds the layers beneath it, much like the layers of an onion.
In Figure 3, you can see how seismic waves travel through the
layers that make up Earth.

✓ **Reading Checkpoint** What causes seismic waves?

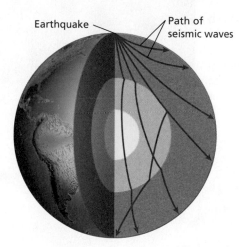

Earthquake   Path of
seismic waves

FIGURE 3
Seismic Waves
Scientists infer Earth's inner structure by
recording and studying how seismic waves
travel through Earth.

Depth
0
0.5 m
1 m
Pressure Increases
1.5 m
2 m

A Journey to the Center of Earth

The three main layers of Earth are the crust, the mantle, and the core. These layers vary greatly in size, composition, temperature, and pressure. If you could travel through these layers to the center of Earth, what would your trip be like? To begin, you will need a vehicle that can travel through solid rock. The vehicle will carry scientific instruments to record changes in temperature and pressure as you descend.

Temperature As you start to tunnel beneath the surface, the surrounding rock is cool. Then at about 20 meters down, your instruments report that the rock is getting warmer. For every 40 meters that you descend from that point, the temperature rises 1 Celsius degree. This rapid rise in temperature continues for several tens of kilometers. After that, the temperature increases more slowly, but steadily. The high temperatures inside Earth are the result of heat left over from the formation of the planet. In addition, radioactive substances inside Earth release energy. This further heats the interior.

Pressure During your journey to the center of Earth, your instruments record an increase in pressure in the surrounding rock. **Pressure** results from a force pressing on an area. Because of the weight of the rock above, pressure inside Earth increases as you go deeper. The deeper you go, the greater the pressure. Pressure inside Earth increases much as it does in the swimming pool in Figure 4.

FIGURE 4
Pressure and Depth
The deeper this swimmer goes, the greater the pressure from the surrounding water.
Comparing and Contrasting How is the water in the swimming pool similar to Earth's interior? How is it different?

A Journey to the Center of Earth

Teach Key Concepts L2
Earth's Main Layers

Focus Review with students the processes that geologists use to study Earth's interior.

Teach Explain that the layers that make up Earth vary in size, composition, temperature, and pressure. As the various layers go deeper, temperature and pressure increase. Ask: **What general statement can you make about the change in temperature through Earth's interior?** (*Temperature increases as depth increases.*) **What about pressure?** (*Pressure also increases as depth increases.*)

Apply Ask: **Why does pressure increase with depth?** (*Pressure increases toward Earth's center because more rock lies above the center.*) **Why does temperature increase?** (*Earth became very hot when it formed. Some of this heat remains. The decay of radioactive elements also contributes heat to Earth's interior.*) **learning modality: visual**

Monitor Progress _____ L2

Drawing Have each student draw a diagram that shows a cross section of Earth with an indication of how pressure and temperature change with depth.

Answers
Figure 4 The weight of the overlying water causes pressure to increase with depth, just as overlying rock causes pressure to increase with depth in Earth. The pressures and temperatures inside Earth are much greater than at the bottom of the pool.

✓ **Reading Checkpoint** Earthquakes produce seismic waves.

Differentiated Instruction

English Learners / Beginning L1
Comprehension: Key Concept Write the boldface sentences from this page on the board. Help students understand these sentences by incorporating the important information into a concept map. The center of the map might be *Earth's Layers*. Branches could be labeled *are* and *vary in*. Model setting up the map, and fill in the blanks together. **learning modality: logical/mathematical**

English Learners / Intermediate L2
Comprehension: Key Concept Provide students with the same sentences and concept map, and model by filling in one blank. Have students fill in the rest of the answers. **learning modality: logical/mathematical**

The Crust

Teach Key Concepts L2

Earth's Outer Layer

Focus The crust is Earth's outer layer and is very thin. Tell students that the crust is the skin of Earth.

Teach Help students understand the differences between continental and oceanic crust. Ask: **Which type of crust, continental or oceanic, is thickest?** *(Continental crust)* **What is the composition of continental crust?** *(Mostly granite)* **Oceanic crust?** *(Mostly basalt)*

Apply Tell students that oceanic crust is denser than continental crust. This will be important later in the chapter, when students learn about how oceanic plates can sink into Earth's mantle. **learning modality: visual**

Observing Window Glazing L1

Materials 2 cans of window glazing, small pan, water, hot plate, refrigerator

Time 10 minutes

Focus Remind students that substances can be rigid or can change shape.

Teach Keep a can of window glazing—a putty-like material used to hold glass in place—in a refrigerator overnight. Invite students to touch the glazing to observe that it does not flow. Ask: **Is this substance a solid or a liquid?** *(Most students will say that it is a solid.)* Provide another can of glazing that you have heated beforehand in a pan of water on a hot plate. Invite students to observe how much more pliable the heated glazing is than the cold glazing.

Apply Ask: **How is the heated glazing like the material that makes up the asthenosphere?** *(The heated glazing still has characteristics of a solid but can be shaped like plastic.)* **learning modality: kinesthetic**

Help Students Read

Previewing Visuals L1

Refer to the Content Refresher, which provides the guidelines for previewing visuals. Have students preview the visuals on these two pages to set the purpose for reading. Ask: **What does this visual tell you about the thickness of Earth's crust?** *(Answers may include that oceanic crust is thinner than continental crust.)*

The Crust

Your journey to the center of Earth begins in the crust. The **crust** is the layer of rock that forms Earth's outer skin. **The crust is a layer of solid rock that includes both dry land and the ocean floor.** On the crust you find rocks and mountains. The crust also includes the soil and water that cover large parts of Earth's surface.

This outer rind of rock is much thinner than the layer that lies beneath it. In fact, you can think of Earth's crust as being similar to the paper-thin skin of an onion. The crust is thickest under high mountains and thinnest beneath the ocean. In most places, the crust is between 5 and 40 kilometers thick. But it can be up to 70 kilometers thick beneath mountains.

The crust beneath the ocean is called oceanic crust. Oceanic crust consists mostly of rocks such as basalt. **Basalt** (buh SAWLT) is dark rock with a fine texture. Continental crust, the crust that forms the continents, consists mainly of rocks such as granite. **Granite** is a rock that usually is a light color and has a coarse texture.

Reading Checkpoint What is the main type of rock in oceanic crust?

FIGURE 5
Earth's Interior
Earth's interior is divided into layers: the crust, mantle, outer core, and inner core.
Interpreting Diagrams *Which of Earth's layers is the thickest?*

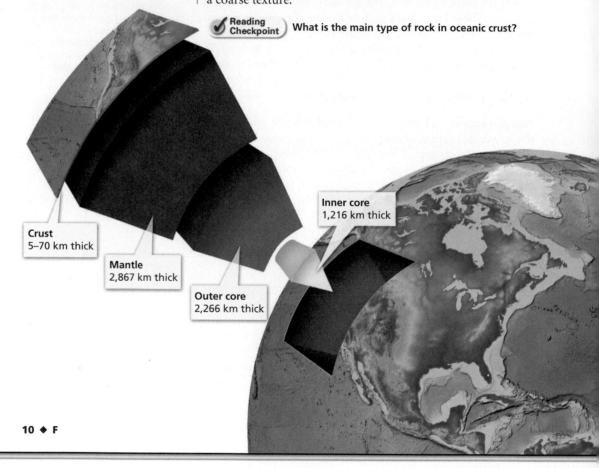

Crust
5–70 km thick

Mantle
2,867 km thick

Outer core
2,266 km thick

Inner core
1,216 km thick

The Mantle

Your journey downward continues. About 40 kilometers beneath the surface, you cross a boundary. Below the boundary is the solid material of the **mantle,** a layer of hot rock. **Earth's mantle is made up of rock that is very hot, but solid. Scientists divide the mantle into layers based on the physical characteristics of those layers.** Overall, the mantle is nearly 3,000 kilometers thick.

The Lithosphere The uppermost part of the mantle is very similar to the crust. The uppermost part of the mantle and the crust together form a rigid layer called the **lithosphere** (lith UH sphere). In Greek, *lithos* means "stone." As you can see in Figure 6, the lithosphere averages about 100 kilometers thick.

The Asthenosphere Below the lithosphere, your vehicle encounters material that is hotter and under increasing pressure. As a result, the part of the mantle just beneath the lithosphere is less rigid than the rock above. Like road tar softened by the heat of the sun, this part of the mantle is somewhat soft—it can bend like plastic. This soft layer is called the **asthenosphere** (as THEN uh sfeer). In Greek, *asthenes* means "weak." Although the asthenosphere is softer than the rest of the mantle, it's still solid. If you kicked it, you would stub your toe.

The Lower Mantle Beneath the asthenosphere, the mantle is solid. This solid material extends all the way to Earth's core.

✔ **Reading Checkpoint** What is the asthenosphere?

Lab zone Skills Activity

Creating Data Tables

Imagine that you are in a super-strong vehicle that is tunneling deep into Earth's interior. You stop several times on your trip to collect data. Copy the data table. For each depth, identify the layer and what that layer is made of. Then complete the table.

Data Table		
Depth	Name of Layer	What Layer Is Made Of
20 km		
150 km		
2,000 km		
4,000 km		
6,000 km		

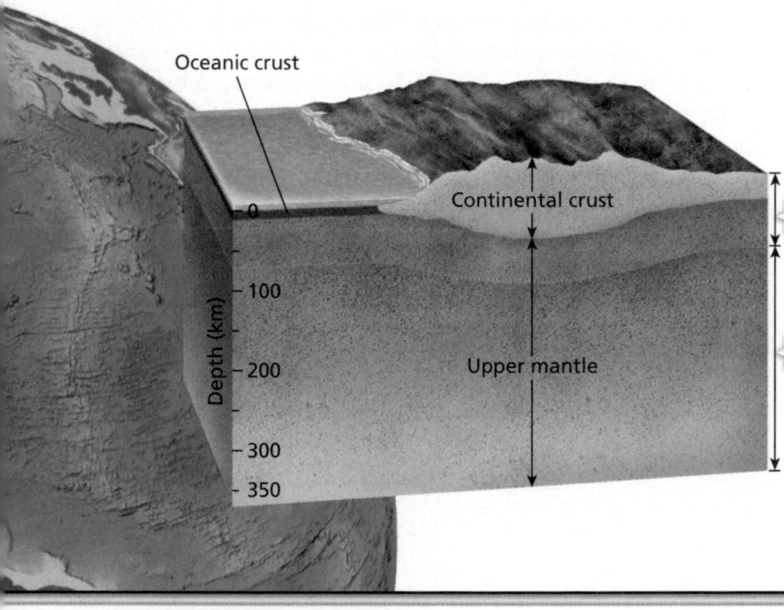

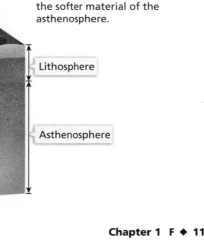

FIGURE 6
Lithosphere and Asthenosphere
The rigid lithosphere, which includes the crust, rests on the softer material of the asthenosphere.

Oceanic crust

Continental crust

Lithosphere

Upper mantle

Asthenosphere

Depth (km)
0
100
200
300
350

Chapter 1 F ◆ 11

Lab zone Skills Activity

Skills Focus Creating data tables　L2

Time 15 minutes

Expected Outcome A typical completed table may include the following information. At a depth of 20 km, the layer is the crust, which is made of solid rock, mostly granite and basalt. At 150 km, the layer is the asthenosphere, made of soft material that can flow slowly. At 2,000 km,

the layer is the mantle, which at this depth is hot, but solid, material. At 4,000 km, the layer is the outer core, which is molten iron and nickel. At 6,000 km, the layer is the inner core, which is solid iron and nickel.

Extend Pairs of students could quiz each other, using such depths as 5 km, 30 km, 1,000 km, and 5,000 km. **learning modality: logical/mathematical**

The Mantle

Teach Key Concepts　L2

Earth's Mantle

Focus Have students contrast hard candy and taffy. (*Hard candy is brittle. It breaks readily. Taffy is capable of changing shape without breaking—it can flow.*) Point out that rock also can behave in either of these two ways.

Teach Ask: **What characteristics does the lithosphere have?** (*The lithosphere is rigid. It behaves more like a brittle solid than does the asthenosphere below.*) **What characteristics does the asthenosphere have?** (*The asthenosphere is capable of flow.*) **Why does rock in the asthenosphere behave differently from the rock above?** (*Because it is hotter*)

Apply Ask: **How much time does it take for a piece of taffy to flow when you pull on it?** (*Not very long*) **How much time does it take for rock in Earth's asthenosphere to flow?** (*A long time; rates are measured in centimeters per year.*) **learning modality: logical/ mathematical**

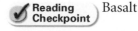 **Teaching Resources**
• Transparency F2

Monitor Progress　L2

Oral Presentation Ask students to prepare short oral presentations on the physical characteristics of the crust, mantle, inner core, and outer core. Then invite individual students to give a description of one of the layers.

Answers
Figure 5 The mantle

✔ **Reading Checkpoint** Basalt

✔ **Reading Checkpoint** A soft layer of the mantle that lies just beneath the lithosphere

Math Skill Making and Interpreting Graphs

Focus A line graph shows how temperature changes between Earth's surface and the bottom of the mantle.

Teach Have students familiarize themselves with the line graph. The *x*-axis shows the depth inside Earth as you approach the core-mantle boundary. The *y*-axis shows the temperature inside Earth. Have students assume that the temperature at Earth's surface is 0°C.

Answers
1. The depth increases.
2. About 1,200°C
3. About 3,800°C
4. It generally increases with depth.

The Core

Teach Key Concepts L2

Earth's Core

Focus Review with students the first two layers of Earth.

Teach Ask: **How does the inner core differ from the outer core?** (*The inner core is solid; the outer core is liquid.*) **Why do geologists consider the inner core and the outer core as part of the same layer instead of as two separate layers?** (*Both cores consist of the same materials, iron and nickel.*)

Apply Show students an apple and ask: **How is this apple like Earth?** (*Both are round.*) Then cut the apple in half and repeat the question. Students will be able to see the similarities. Both have layers, with a thin crust, a large middle layer, and a core.
learning modality: visual

Temperature Inside Earth

The graph shows how temperatures change between Earth's surface and the bottom of the mantle. On this graph, the temperature at Earth's surface is 0°C. Study the graph carefully and then answer the questions.

1. **Reading Graphs** As you move from left to right on the *x*-axis, how does depth inside Earth change?
2. **Estimating** What is the temperature at the boundary between the lithosphere and the asthenosphere?
3. **Estimating** What is the temperature at the boundary between the lower mantle and the core?
4. **Interpreting Data** How does temperature change with depth in Earth's interior?

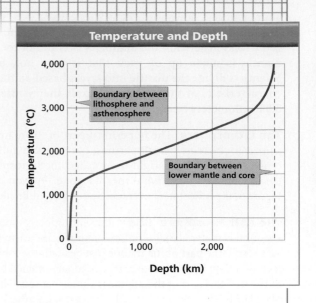

Temperature and Depth

The Core

After traveling through the mantle, you reach Earth's core. **The core is made mostly of the metals iron and nickel. It consists of two parts—a liquid outer core and a solid inner core.** Together, the inner and outer core are 3,486 kilometers thick.

Outer Core and Inner Core The **outer core** is a layer of molten metal that surrounds the inner core. Despite enormous pressure, the outer core is liquid. The **inner core** is a dense ball of solid metal. In the inner core, extreme pressure squeezes the atoms of iron and nickel so much that they cannot spread out and become liquid.

Most of the current evidence suggests that both parts of the core are made of iron and nickel. But scientists have found data suggesting that the core also contains substances such as oxygen, sulfur, and silicon. Scientists must seek more data before they decide which of these other substances is most important.

 Reading Checkpoint What is the main difference between the outer core and the inner core?

⌐ Differentiated Instruction

Special Needs L1
Interpreting Diagrams To help students who are having trouble understanding the boundaries between the various layers, draw three circles on the board to represent the crust, mantle, and core. Invite a volunteer to label Earth's three main layers. Call on another volunteer to use white chalk to shade the area that represents the lithosphere. (*The student should shade in the crust and the uppermost part of the mantle.*) Then invite another volunteer to use a different color of chalk to shade the area that represents the asthenosphere. (*The student should make a shaded circle just inside the lithosphere, wider than the lithosphere but leaving most of the mantle unshaded.*) **learning modality: visual**

Bar Magnet's Magnetic Field
The pattern of iron filings was made by sprinkling them on paper placed under a bar magnet.

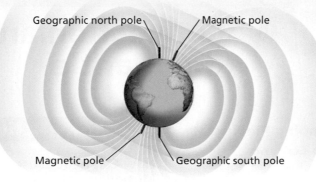

Geographic north pole   Magnetic pole

Magnetic pole   Geographic south pole

Earth's Magnetic Field
Like a magnet, Earth's magnetic field has north and south poles.

The Core and Earth's Magnetic Field Scientists think that movements in the liquid outer core create Earth's magnetic field. Because Earth has a magnetic field, the planet acts like a giant bar magnet. As you can see in Figure 7, the magnetic field affects the whole Earth.

Consider an ordinary bar magnet. If you place it on a piece of paper and sprinkle iron filings on the paper, the iron filings line up with the bar's magnetic field. If you could cover the entire planet with iron filings, they would form a similar pattern. When you use a compass, the compass needle aligns with the lines of force in Earth's magnetic field.

FIGURE 7
Earth's Magnetic Field
Just as a bar magnet is surrounded by its own magnetic field, Earth's magnetic field surrounds the planet.
Relating Cause and Effect *If you shifted the magnet beneath the paper, what would happen to the iron filings?*

Section 1 Assessment

Target Reading Skill **Using Prior Knowledge** Review your graphic organizer and revise it based on what you just learned in the section.

Reviewing Key Concepts

1. a. Explaining Why is it difficult to determine Earth's inner structure?
  b. Inferring How are seismic waves used to provide evidence about Earth's interior?
2. a. Listing List Earth's three main layers.
  b. Comparing and Contrasting What is the difference between the lithosphere and the asthenosphere? In which layer is each located?

c. Classifying Classify each of the following layers as liquid, solid, or solid but able to flow slowly: lithosphere, asthenosphere, lower mantle, outer core, inner core.

Writing in Science

Narrative Write a narrative of your own imaginary journey to the center of Earth. Your narrative should describe the layers of Earth through which you travel and how temperature and pressure change beneath the surface.

Chapter 1 F ◆ 13

Lab zone Chapter Project

Keep Students on Track Have students begin by drawing sketches of their three-dimensional models. They should consider how they will show the thicknesses of Earth's different layers to scale. They also should think about the types of materials that they might want to use to build their models. Encourage each group to begin collecting materials and experimenting with a design.

Writing in Science

Writing Skill Explanation
Scoring Rubric
4 Includes descriptions of the crust, mantle, core, and how temperature and pressure change; narrative is lively and fun to read
3 Includes all criteria
2 Includes two or three criteria or only brief descriptions
1 Includes one or two criteria or inaccurate descriptions

Convection and the Mantle

Convection and the Mantle

Objectives

After completing this lesson, students will be able to

F1.2.1 explain how heat is transferred
F1.2.2 identify what causes convection currents
F1.2.3 describe convection currents in Earth's mantle

Target Reading Skill

Outlining Explain that using an outline format helps students organize information by main topic, subtopic, and details.

Answers

Convection and the Mantle

I. Types of Heat Transfer
   A. Radiation
   B. Conduction
   C. Convection
II. Convection Currents
III. Convection in Earth's Mantle

All in One Teaching Resources

• Transparency F3

Preteach

Build Background Knowledge   L2

Movement of Air

Ask students: **In a room in a drafty house, why is it colder near the floor than near the ceiling?** (*Cold air sinks, while hot air rises.*) Be sure students understand that the air in such a room circulates as drafts of cold air move over the floor and warmer air from the furnace rises. Point out that differences in temperature cause this redistribution.

Reading Preview

Key Concepts

• How is heat transferred?
• What causes convection currents?
• What causes convection currents in Earth's mantle?

Key Terms

• radiation • conduction
• convection • density
• convection current

Target Reading Skill

Outlining An outline shows the relationship between major ideas and supporting ideas. As you read, make an outline about heat transfer. Use the red headings for the main topics and the blue headings for the subtopics.

Convection and the Mantle

I. Types of Heat Transfer
  A. Radiation
  B.
  C.
II. Convection Currents

Lab zone Discover Activity

How Can Heat Cause Motion in a Liquid?

1. Carefully pour some hot water into a small, shallow pan. Fill a clear, plastic cup about half full with cold water. Place the cup in the pan.
2. Allow the water to stand for two minutes until all motion stops.
3. Fill a plastic dropper with some food coloring. Then, holding the dropper under the water's surface and slightly away from the edge of the cup, gently squeeze a small droplet of the food coloring into the water.
4. Observe the water for one minute.
5. Add another droplet at the water's surface in the middle of the cup and observe again.

Think It Over
Inferring How do you explain what happened to the droplets of food coloring? Why do you think the second droplet moved in a way that was different from the way the first droplet moved?

Earth's molten outer core is nearly as hot as the surface of the sun. What makes an object hot? Whether the object is Earth's core or a cooking pot, the cause is the same. When an object is heated, the particles that make up the object move faster. The faster-moving particles have more energy.

If you have ever touched a hot pot accidentally, you have discovered for yourself (in a painful way) that heat moves. In this case, it moved from the hot pot to your hand. The movement of energy from a warmer object to a cooler object is called heat transfer. To explain how heat moves from Earth's core through the mantle, you need to know how heat is transferred.

Lab zone Discover Activity

Skills Focus Inferring   L1

Materials shallow pan, clear plastic cup, hot water, cold water, plastic dropper, food coloring

Time 10 minutes

Expected Outcome When students add the first droplet, food coloring should move toward the center, down to the bottom, and then upward along the edges of the cup toward the surface. When students add the second droplet, the coloring should move quickly to the bottom, spread out toward the edges of the cup, and then upward.

Think It Over Heat is transferred from the hot water in the pan to the cold water in the

cup. As the water in the bottom of the cup warms, it becomes less dense and rises. The colder water at the top of the cup sinks, setting currents in the water in motion. The two droplets moved differently because they entered the currents at different places.

Types of Heat Transfer

Heat always moves from a warmer substance to a cooler substance. For example, holding an ice cube will make your hand begin to feel cold in a few seconds. But is the coldness in the ice cube moving to your hand? No! Since cold is the absence of heat, it's the heat in your hand that moves to the ice cube. This is one of the ways that heat is transferred. **There are three types of heat transfer: radiation, conduction, and convection.**

Radiation The transfer of energy through space is called **radiation.** Heat transfer by radiation takes place with no direct contact between a heat source and an object. Sunlight is radiation that warms Earth's surface. Other familiar forms of radiation include the heat you feel around a flame or open fire.

Conduction Heat transfer within a material or between materials that are touching is called **conduction.** For example, a spoon in a pot of soup heats up by conduction, as shown in Figure 8. Heat moves from the hot soup and the pot to the particles that make up the spoon. The particles near the bottom of the spoon vibrate faster as they are heated, so they bump into other particles and heat them, too. Gradually the entire spoon heats up. When your hand touches the spoon, conduction transfers heat from the spoon directly to your skin. Then you feel the heat. Conduction is responsible for some of the heat transfer inside Earth.

 Reading Checkpoint What is conduction?

FIGURE 8
Conduction
In conduction, the heated particles of a substance transfer heat through contact with other particles in the substance. Conduction heats the spoon and the pot itself. That's why you need a mitt to protect your hand from the hot handle.

F ◆ 15

Instruct

Convection Currents

Teach Key Concepts `L2`

Density, Gravity, and Convection

Focus Review the concepts of density and gravity with students. These are essential for understanding convection currents.

Teach Ask: **How does the density of most substances change when the substance is heated?** *(In most cases, the density decreases because the molecules in the substance move farther apart. This is true for air and rock. It also is true for freshwater above the temperature of 4°C.)* **Why do less dense substances rise?** *(Gravity pulls everything toward Earth's center. Denser material is pulled harder (F = mg), forcing less dense material upward.)*

Apply Provide students with this problem: Oil is less dense than water. What will happen if a drop of oil is released at the bottom of a glass of water? *(The oil drop will rise to the surface.)* **learning modality: logical/mathematical**

Convection Currents in Earth

Teach Key Concepts `L2`

Mantle Flow

Focus Tell students that convection in Earth's mantle is very slow. A particle of rock in Earth's mantle might move only a few centimeters each year.

Teach Ask: **What could cause some rock to rise through Earth's mantle?** *(It is hotter and less dense than surrounding rock.)* **Why might rock sink into Earth's mantle?** *(It is cooler and more dense than surrounding rock.)* **How can solid rock flow?** *(Under sufficient heat and pressure, solid rock can flow like putty.)*

Apply Have students examine Figure 10. Explain that the circular cells shown in the figure are called convection currents. Ask: **Where is the hottest rock in each cell?** *(The rising arrow)* **The coolest?** *(The sinking arrow)* **learning modality: visual**

All in One Teaching Resources

• Transparency F4

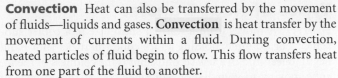
Go Online
PHSchool.com

For: More on convection currents in the mantle
Visit: PHSchool.com
Web Code: cfd-1012

FIGURE 9
Convection Currents
Differences in temperature and density cause convection currents. In the pot, convection currents arise because the soup close to the heat source is hotter and less dense than the soup near the surface.

16 ◆ F

Convection Heat can also be transferred by the movement of fluids—liquids and gases. **Convection** is heat transfer by the movement of currents within a fluid. During convection, heated particles of fluid begin to flow. This flow transfers heat from one part of the fluid to another.

Heat transfer by convection is caused by differences of temperature and density within a fluid. **Density** is a measure of how much mass there is in a volume of a substance. For example, rock is more dense than water because a given volume of rock has more mass than the same volume of water.

When a liquid or gas is heated, the particles move faster and spread apart. As a result, the particles of the heated fluid occupy more space. The fluid's density decreases. But when a fluid cools, its particles move more slowly and settle together more closely. As the fluid becomes cooler, its density increases.

Convection Currents

When you heat soup on a stove, convection occurs in the soup, as shown in Figure 9. As the soup at the bottom of the pot gets hot, it expands and therefore becomes less dense. The warm, less dense soup moves upward and floats over the cooler, denser soup. At the surface, the warm soup cools, becoming denser. Then gravity pulls this cooler, denser soup back down to the bottom of the pot, where it is heated again.

A constant flow begins as the cooler, denser soup sinks to the bottom of the pot and the warmer, less dense soup rises. A **convection current** is the flow that transfers heat within a fluid. **Heating and cooling of the fluid, changes in the fluid's density, and the force of gravity combine to set convection currents in motion.** Convection currents continue as long as heat is added. Without heat, convection currents eventually stop.

Reading Checkpoint What is the role of gravity in creating convection currents?

16 • F

Convection Currents in Earth

In Earth's mantle, large amounts of heat are transferred by convection currents, as shown in Figure 10. **Heat from the core and the mantle itself causes convection currents in the mantle.**

How is it possible for mantle rock to flow? Over millions of years, the great heat and pressure in the mantle cause solid mantle rock to flow very slowly. Many geologists think that plumes of mantle rock rise slowly from the bottom of the mantle toward the top. The hot rock eventually cools and sinks back through the mantle. Over and over, the cycle of rising and sinking takes place. Convection currents like these have been moving inside Earth for more than four billion years!

There are also convection currents in the outer core. These convection currents cause Earth's magnetic field.

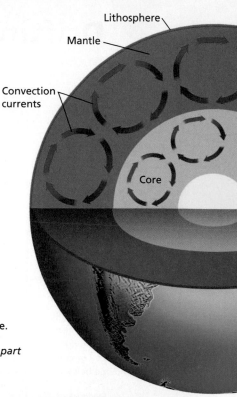

Lithosphere

Mantle

Convection currents

Core

FIGURE 10
Mantle Convection
Most geologists think that convection currents rise and sink through the mantle.
Applying Concepts *What part of Earth's interior is like the soup in the pot? What part is like the burner on the stove?*

For: More on convection currents in the mantle
Visit: PHSchool.com
Web Code: cfd-1012

Students can review convection currents in an online activity.

Monitor Progress _____ L2

Figure 10 Earth's mantle is like the soup in a pot. Earth's core is the heat source.

✓ Reading Checkpoint Gravity pulls denser (cooler) material toward Earth's center more strongly than it pulls less dense (hotter) material.

Assess

Reviewing Key Concepts
1. a. radiation, conduction, and convection. **b.** radiation.
2. a. the flow that transfers heat within a fluid. **b.** As a fluid is heated, its density decreases. **c.** Using soup as an example, soup near the bottom of the pot is heated. It becomes less dense and rises. Cooler, more dense soup sinks to the bottom of the pot, where it is heated and then rises. The cycle continues.
3. a. the outer core and the mantle. **b.** Cooler rock near the top of the mantle sinks as hotter rock near the bottom of the mantle rises. **c.** Eventually, convection in Earth's mantle will stop. When sufficient heat no longer is supplied to the mantle, the rock will no longer be able to flow in currents.

Reteach L1
To help students understand the nature of heat transfer, discuss why ice cubes make a glass of drinking water colder. *(Heat from the warmer water is transferred to the colder ice, causing some of the ice to melt.)*

Performance Assessment L2
Drawing Have student groups create labeled diagrams that illustrate radiation, conduction, and convection.

All in One Teaching Resources
- Section Summary: *Convection and the Mantle*
- Review and Reinforce: *Convection and the Mantle*
- Enrich: *Convection and the Mantle*

Section 2 Assessment

Target Reading Skill Outlining Use the information in your outline about heat transfer to help you answer the questions below.

Reviewing Key Concepts
1. a. Listing What are the three types of heat transfer?
  b. Explaining How is heat transferred through space?
2. a. Defining What is a convection current?
  b. Relating Cause and Effect In general, what happens to the density of a fluid as it becomes hotter?
  c. Summarizing Describe how convection currents form.
3. a. Identifying Name two layers of Earth in which convection currents take place.
  b. Relating Cause and Effect What causes convection currents in the mantle?
  c. Predicting What will happen to the convection currents in the mantle if Earth's interior eventually cools down? Explain.

Lab zone At-Home Activity

Tracing Heat Flow Convection currents may keep the air inside your home at a comfortable temperature. Air is made up of gases, so it is a fluid. Regardless of the type of home heating system, heated air circulates through a room by convection. You may have tried to adjust the flow of air in a stuffy room by opening a window. When you did so, you were making use of convection currents. With an adult family member, study how your home is heated. Look for evidence of convection currents.

Lab zone At-Home Activity

Tracing Heat Flow L2 Outcomes will vary, depending on the type of heating system in a student's home. Be sure that students understand that convection plays a part in all heating systems, though fans may also help circulate the air. Students also may conclude that heating units or vents are best located near the floor, so that heat rises throughout the room.

Section 3 Drifting Continents

Objectives

After completing this lesson, students will be able to

F1.3.1 explain Alfred Wegener's hypothesis about the continents

F1.3.2 list the evidence used by Wegener to support his hypothesis

F1.3.3 explain why other scientists of Wegener's time rejected his hypothesis

Target Reading Skill

Identifying Supporting Evidence

Explain that identifying supporting evidence helps students understand the relationship between the facts and the hypothesis.

Answers

One way students might complete the graphic organizer is by using the following words or phrases to fill the empty ovals: *fossils, climate change.*

All in One Teaching Resources

• Transparency F5

Preteach

Build Background Knowledge ▪ L2

The Continents

Ask students: **What is a continent?** (*A continent is one of Earth's seven large landmasses.*) **Can you name the continents?** (*Asia, Africa, North America, South America, Europe, Australia, Antarctica*) Then have students speculate about whether the continents have always had the same shapes and whether they have always been in the same places that they occupy today.

Reading Preview

Key Concepts

• What was Alfred Wegener's hypothesis about the continents?

• What evidence supported Wegener's hypothesis?

• Why was Wegener's hypothesis rejected by most scientists of his day?

Key Terms

• continental drift • Pangaea
• fossil

Target Reading Skill

Identifying Supporting Evidence As you read, identify the evidence that supports the hypothesis of continental drift. Write the evidence in a graphic organizer like the one below.

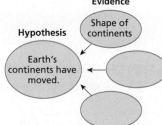

Lab zone Discover Activity

How Are Earth's Continents Linked Together?

1. Find the oceans and the seven continents on a globe showing Earth's physical features.

2. How much of the globe is occupied by the Pacific Ocean? Does most of Earth's dry land lie in the Northern or Southern Hemisphere?

3. Find the points or areas where most of the continents are connected. Find the points at which several of the continents almost touch, but are not connected.

4. Examine the globe more closely. Find the great belt of mountains running from north to south along the western side of North and South America. Can you find another great belt of mountains on the globe?

Think It Over
Posing Questions What questions can you pose about how oceans, continents, and mountains are distributed on Earth's surface?

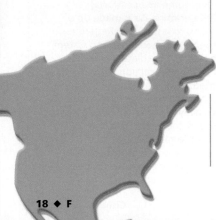

Five hundred years ago, the sea voyages of Columbus and other explorers changed the map of the world. The continents of Europe, Asia, and Africa were already known to mapmakers. Soon mapmakers were also showing the outlines of the continents of North and South America. Looking at these world maps, many people wondered why the coasts of several continents matched so neatly. For example, the coasts of Africa and South America look as if they could fit together like jigsaw-puzzle pieces. In the 1700s, geologists thought that the continents had always remained in the same place. But early in the 1900s, one scientist began to think that the continents could have once been joined in a single landmass.

Lab zone Discover Activity

Skills Focus Posing questions   L2

Materials globes that show physical features

Time 15 minutes

Tips Place several globes around the classroom. Have students write answers to the questions contained in the activity

steps. (*Step 2: more than one third; Northern Hemisphere / Step 3: at the North Pole; at the South Pole / Step 4: through Europe and Asia*)

Think It Over Accept any reasonable questions about the distribution of Earth's oceans, continents, and mountains.

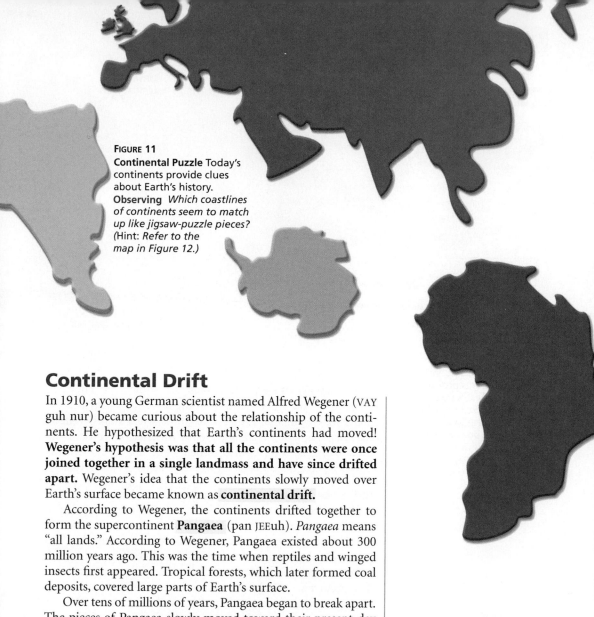

FIGURE 11
Continental Puzzle Today's continents provide clues about Earth's history. **Observing** *Which coastlines of continents seem to match up like jigsaw-puzzle pieces? (Hint: Refer to the map in Figure 12.)*

Continental Drift

In 1910, a young German scientist named Alfred Wegener (VAY guh nur) became curious about the relationship of the continents. He hypothesized that Earth's continents had moved! **Wegener's hypothesis was that all the continents were once joined together in a single landmass and have since drifted apart.** Wegener's idea that the continents slowly moved over Earth's surface became known as **continental drift.**

According to Wegener, the continents drifted together to form the supercontinent **Pangaea** (pan JEEuh). *Pangaea* means "all lands." According to Wegener, Pangaea existed about 300 million years ago. This was the time when reptiles and winged insects first appeared. Tropical forests, which later formed coal deposits, covered large parts of Earth's surface.

Over tens of millions of years, Pangaea began to break apart. The pieces of Pangaea slowly moved toward their present-day locations. These pieces became the continents as they are today.

Wegener gathered evidence from different scientific fields to support his ideas about continental drift. He studied land features, fossils, and evidence of climate change. In 1915, Wegener published his evidence for continental drift in a book called *The Origin of Continents and Oceans.*

Go Online
SciLINKS NSTA

For: Links on continental drift
Visit: www.SciLinks.org
Web Code: scn-1013

Differentiated Instruction

Special Needs [L1]
Continental Drift Flip Books Have each student make a flip book that shows how Pangaea formed and then broke apart. Students draw or trace the positions of continents onto a large note card at several times from about 300 million years ago to present. When assembled and flipped through, the continents will appear to move as they did through geologic time. **learning modality: visual**

Gifted and Talented [L3]
Debating Continental Drift Until the 1960s, the hypothesis of continental drift met with skepticism in Europe and North America. Organize students into two teams for a debate. Have one team act as advocates for the hypothesis, the other as skeptics. Have students assume only the knowledge available to scientists in the early 1900s. **learning modality: verbal**

Continental Drift

Teach Key Concepts [L2]
Pangaea

Focus Remind students about the clues they use to assemble a jigsaw puzzle, such as matching edges of pieces and the continuity of features in the picture. Point out that similar evidence can be used to reconstruct Pangaea.

Teach Show students a current world map. Challenge them to suggest how the continents could be assembled into one large landmass. Use an overhead transparency to mark student suggestions with arrows.

Apply Have students discuss how their reconstructions are similar to or different from a map of Pangaea. **learning modality: visual**

Integrating Life Science [L1]
Drawing Conclusions
Bring a collection of seeds to class, and allow students to examine them closely. Ask: **How are the different seeds moved from place to place?** *(Groups should especially consider whether any seeds could have moved across an ocean.)* **learning modality: kinesthetic**

Independent Practice

All in One Teaching Resources

• Guided Reading and Study Worksheet: *Drifting Continents*

💿 **Student Edition on Audio CD**

Go Online
SciLINKS NSTA

For: Links on continental drift
Visit: www.SciLinks.org
Web Code: scn-1013

Download a worksheet that will guide students' review of Internet resources on continental drift.

Monitor Progress [L2]

Writing Have each student write a summary of Alfred Wegener's hypothesis.

Answer
Figure 11 The most obvious choice is the coastlines of Africa and South America.

Use Visuals: Figure 12

Evidence for Continental Drift

Focus Ask students to describe the differences between the two maps in Figure 12. Make sure they understand that the inset map shows a reconstruction of Pangaea and that the larger map shows the present distribution of continents.

Teach Ask: **How does the location of coal beds differ in the two maps?** *(The beds seem to be spread randomly in the map of present-day continents. When the continents are together, the coal beds create a pattern.)* **Why do the coal beds form a pattern on the map of Pangaea?** *(A generally continuous belt of coal formed, but it was fragmented when Pangaea broke apart.)*

Apply Emphasize that this map shows several types of evidence. Taken together, the evidence provides a strong argument for continental drift. **learning modality: visual**

 **Teaching Resources**

• Transparency F6

Making Models of Continents

Materials 1 sheet of newspaper

Time 15 minutes

Focus Remind students that evidence such as the shape of continent margins, matching mountain belts, and matching rock layers was used to help reconstruct Pangaea.

Teach Organize students in pairs, and provide each student with a sheet of newspaper. Ask students to tear each sheet of newspaper into six or eight pieces and then trade pieces with their partners. Ask students to use evidence from the pieces to reassemble the newspaper pages.

Apply Ask: **What evidence did you use to reconstruct your newspaper page?** *(Students will use the shapes of pieces. They also will match features on the page, such as lines of copy or photographs.)* **How is this similar to some of the evidence that was used to reconstruct Pangaea?** *(Shapes of continents and features on the continents provide evidence for Pangaea.)* **learning modality: visual**

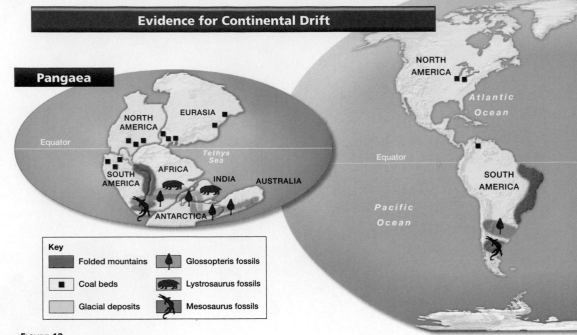

FIGURE 12
Fossils and rocks found on different continents provide evidence that Earth's landmasses once were joined together in the supercontinent Pangaea.
Inferring What do the matching mountain ranges in Africa and South America show, according to Wegener's hypothesis?

Lystrosaurus

20 ◆ F

Evidence From Land Features As shown in Figure 12, mountains and other features on the continents provided evidence for continental drift. For example, when Wegener pieced together maps of Africa and South America, he noticed that mountain ranges on both continents line up. He noticed that European coal fields match up with coal fields in North America.

Evidence From Fossils Wegener also used fossils to support his argument for continental drift. A **fossil** is any trace of an ancient organism that has been preserved in rock. For example, *Glossopteris* (glaw SAHP tuh ris), was a fernlike plant that lived 250 million years ago. *Glossopteris* fossils have been found in rocks in Africa, South America, Australia, India, and Antarctica. The occurrence of *Glossopteris* on these widely separated landmasses convinced Wegener that Pangaea had existed.

Other examples include fossils of the freshwater reptiles *Mesosaurus* and *Lystrosaurus*. These fossils have also been found in places now separated by oceans. Neither reptile could have swum great distances across salt water. Wegener inferred that these reptiles lived on a single landmass that has since split apart.

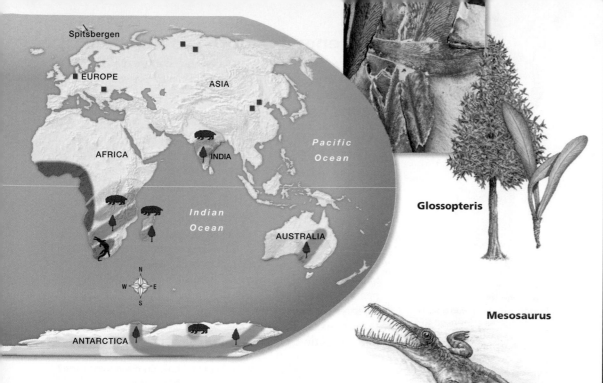

EUROPE
Spitsbergen
ASIA
AFRICA
INDIA
Pacific Ocean
Indian Ocean
AUSTRALIA
ANTARCTICA

Glossopteris

Mesosaurus

Evidence From Climate Wegener used evidence of climate change to support his hypothesis. As a continent moves toward the equator, its climate becomes warmer. As a continent moves toward the poles, its climate becomes colder. But the continent carries with it the fossils and rocks that formed at its previous locations. For example, fossils of tropical plants are found on Spitsbergen, an island in the Arctic Ocean. When these plants lived about 300 million years ago, the island must have had a warm and mild climate. According to Wegener, Spitsbergen must have been located closer to the equator.

Geologists found evidence that when it was warm in Spitsbergen, the climate was much colder in South Africa. Deep scratches in rocks showed that continental glaciers once covered South Africa. Continental glaciers are thick layers of ice that cover hundreds of thousands of square kilometers. But the climate of South Africa is too mild today for continental glaciers to form. Wegener concluded that when Pangaea existed, South Africa was much closer to the South Pole. According to Wegener, the climates of Spitsbergen and South Africa changed because these landmasses had moved.

 Reading Checkpoint How would continental drift affect a continent's climate?

Chapter 1 F ◆ 21

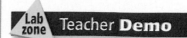
Climate in North America L2

Materials map of United States
Time 10 minutes

Focus Discuss climatic conditions that exist near Earth's equator today.

Teach Using a paper map or transparency, draw a line from San Francisco through the north shore of Lake Superior. This represents the equator when North America was part of Pangaea. Ask: **What climatic conditions existed during this time?** (*Land was humid and tropical or hot and dry; seas were warm.*) Tell students that a shallow ocean covered much of what is now the western U.S. The eastern U.S. generally was above sea level.

Apply Ask: **What types of fossils would you expect to find here?** (*Possible answer: tropical plant fossils*) **learning modality: logical/mathematical**

Wegener's Hypothesis Rejected

Teach Key Concepts L2

Scientific Debate About Drift

Focus Tell students that Wegener believed that the continents could slide over rocks like those that make up the ocean floor.

Teach Ask: **If ocean floor rock is brittle and solid, could the rock of continents slide over it?** (*Student answers will vary. Wegener's hypothesis was rejected because no physical process could slide continents over ocean crust.*)

Apply Tell students that movement of continents is accepted as fact today. **learning modality: logical/mathematical**

Monitor Progress L2

Oral Presentation Call on students to explain the various evidence that Wegener used to support his hypothesis.

Answers
Figure 12 They provide evidence that Africa and South America once were connected.

 Reading Checkpoint A continent moving toward the equator would become warmer; one moving toward the poles would become colder.

Differentiated Instruction

English Learners/Beginning L1
Vocabulary: Link to Visual Explain and clarify what *Pangaea* means by discussing the inset diagram in **Figure 12**. Make an enlarged copy of this map. Cover the labels, and ask students to identify Pangaea and each modern continent within it. Provide students with a word list that includes each term. **learning modality: visual**

English Learners/Intermediate L2
Vocabulary: Link to Visual Ask students to write sentences about the modern continents in Pangaea. Students might include information about the continent's past latitude, past climate, or fossils, and write sentences about the overall distribution or fit of the continents. **learning modality: verbal**

Answer

Reading Checkpoint He thought that mountains formed when continents collided.

Assess

Reviewing Key Concepts

1. a. Alfred Wegener **b.** The continents would have gradually separated to their current positions.
2. a. Matching coastlines of continents, similar land features, evidence from fossils, evidence from climate **b.** Similar fossils occur on different continents. Because many of these organisms could not have crossed an ocean, this provides evidence that the continents once were connected. **c.** If continents drifted through different latitudes, one would expect that the climate would have changed through time. Thus, coal could have formed in Antarctica because at one time the continent may have been in a more tropical region of Earth.
3. a. They could not identify a mechanism by which the continents could move.
b. Answers will vary. Students may suggest that accepting the hypothesis would depend on how much supporting evidence existed. They may also point out that until the cause of continental drift was identified, there was no reason to assume that the new hypothesis was any better than the old one. Accept all reasoned responses.

Reteach

L1

Ask student groups to make concept maps about continental drift. Branches might include *definition, evidence for drift, proposed by,* and *why initially rejected.*

Performance Assessment

L2

Writing Challenge students to write a newspaper article reporting scientists' reactions to Wegener's hypothesis.

All in One Teaching Resources

- Section Summary: *Drifting Continents*
- Review and Reinforce: *Drifting Continents*
- Enrich: *Drifting Continents*

FIGURE 13
Alfred Wegener
Although scientists rejected his theory, Wegener continued to collect evidence on continental drift and to update his book. He died in 1930 on an expedition to explore Greenland's continental glacier.

Wegener's Hypothesis Rejected

Wegener attempted to explain how continental drift took place. He suggested that the continents plowed across the ocean floors. **Unfortunately, Wegener could not provide a satisfactory explanation for the force that pushes or pulls the continents.** Because Wegener could not identify the cause of continental drift, most geologists rejected his idea.

For geologists to accept continental drift, they would also have had to change their ideas about how mountains form. In the early 1900s, many geologists thought that mountains formed because Earth was slowly cooling and shrinking. According to this hypothesis, mountains formed when the crust wrinkled like the skin of a dried-up apple.

Wegener said that if these geologists were correct, then mountains should be found all over Earth's surface. But mountains usually occur in narrow bands along the edges of continents. Wegener developed a hypothesis that better explained where mountains occur and how they form. Wegener proposed that when continents collide, their edges crumple and fold. The folding continents push up huge mountains.

Reading Checkpoint According to Wegener, how do mountains form?

Section 3 Assessment

Target Reading Skill

Identifying Supporting Evidence Refer to your graphic organizer about continental drift as you answer Question 2 below.

Reviewing Key Concepts

1. a. Identifying Who proposed the concept of continental drift?
   b. Summarizing According to the hypothesis of continental drift, how would a world map have changed over the last 250 million years?
2. a. Reviewing What evidence supported the hypothesis of continental drift?
   b. Explaining How did fossils provide evidence for continental drift?
   c. Forming Hypotheses Deposits of coal have been found beneath the ice of Antarctica. But coal only forms in warm swamps. Use Wegener's hypothesis to explain how coal could be found so near to the South Pole.

3. a. Explaining Why did most scientists reject Wegener's hypothesis of continental drift?
   b. Making Judgments Do you think the scientists of Wegener's time should have accepted his hypothesis? Why or why not?

Lab zone At-Home Activity

Moving the Continents Using a world map and tracing paper, trace the outlines of the continents that border the Atlantic Ocean. Label the continents. Then use scissors to carefully cut your map along the edges of the continents. Throw away the Atlantic Ocean. Place the two remaining pieces on a dark surface and ask family members to try to fit the two halves together. Explain to them about continental drift and Pangaea.

Lab zone At-Home Activity

Moving the Continents **L2** Encourage students to do this activity at home. Then "debrief" them in a class discussion. Students can recount how receptive family members and others were to this idea and what any skeptics said in response.

Reading Preview

Key Concepts
• What is the process of sea-floor spreading?
• What is the evidence for sea-floor spreading?
• What happens at deep-ocean trenches?

Key Terms
• mid-ocean ridge • sonar
• sea-floor spreading
• deep-ocean trench
• subduction

Target Reading Skill
Sequencing Make a flowchart to show the process of sea-floor spreading.

| Magma erupts along mid-ocean ridge |

Lab zone Discover **Activity**

What Is the Effect of a Change in Density?
1. Partially fill a sink or dishpan with water.
2. Open up a dry washcloth in your hand. Does the washcloth feel light or heavy?
3. Moisten one edge of the washcloth in the water. Then gently place the washcloth so that it floats on the water's surface. Observe the washcloth carefully (especially at its edges) as it starts to sink.
4. Remove the washcloth from the water and open it up in your hand. Is the mass of the washcloth the same as, less than, or greater than when it was dry?

Think It Over
Observing How did the washcloth's density change? What effect did this change in density have on the washcloth?

Deep in the ocean, the temperature is near freezing. There is no light, and living things are generally scarce. Yet some areas of the deep-ocean floor are teeming with life. One of these areas is the East Pacific Rise. This area forms part of the Pacific Ocean floor off the coasts of Mexico and South America. Here, ocean water sinks through cracks, or vents, in the crust. The water is heated by contact with hot material from the mantle. The hot water then spurts back into the ocean.

Around these hot-water vents live some of the most bizarre creatures ever discovered. Giant, red-tipped tube worms sway in the water. Nearby sit giant clams nearly a meter across. Strange spider-like crabs scuttle by. Surprisingly, the geological features of this strange environment provided some of the best evidence for Wegener's hypothesis of continental drift.

FIGURE 14
The Deep-Ocean Floor
Shrimp, crabs, and other organisms cluster near hot water vents in the ocean floor.

Chapter 1 F ◆ 23

Section
4
Sea-Floor Spreading

Objectives
After completing this lesson, students will be able to
F1.4.1 list the evidence for sea-floor spreading
F1.4.2 explain the process of sea-floor spreading
F1.4.3 describe the process of subduction

Target Reading Skill

Sequencing Explain that organizing information from beginning to end helps students understand a step-by-step process.

Answers
One way students might organize the information is: Magma erupts along mid-ocean ridge ⇒ Magma cools to form new sea floor ⇒ Sea floor spreads away from ridge.

All in One **Teaching Resources**
• Transparency F7

Preteach

Build Background Knowledge L2

Experience with Volcanoes
Ask students: **Where does magma from Earth's interior flow out onto the surface?** (*At volcanoes*) Most students know that lava flows from a volcano and hardens to form a type of rock. Ask: **What causes the lava to harden?** (*It hardens as it cools.*) Have students speculate as to whether there are any places where the opposite process occurs, that is, where material from the surface moves into Earth's interior and some of it melts. Encourage students to discuss the consequences if no such areas existed.

Lab zone Discover **Activity**

Skills Focus Observing L1
Materials sink or large dishpan, water, washcloth
Time 10 minutes
Tips Review with students the difference between mass and density. The washcloth is about the same volume, whether dry or wet. Therefore, the wet washcloth is denser than the dry washcloth.

Expected Outcome The washcloth should float for a short time on the water's surface. As it becomes soaked, the washcloth will gradually sink into the water. When removed from the water, the washcloth will be heavier than when dry.

Think It Over The washcloth's density increased as it became soaked with water. The increased density made the washcloth sink.

Mid-Ocean Ridges

Teach Key Concepts [L2]

Mountains on the Sea Floor

Focus Ask students whether anyone has ever heard an echo of his or her voice. Point out that sonar sends and receives sound waves in a similar way.

Teach Tell students that the ocean floor has mountain chains that are as impressive as those on land. Ask: **How did scientists determine the location and size of the underwater mountain chain?** *(By using sonar)* **What are these underwater mountains called?** *(Mid-ocean ridges)*

Apply Remind students that Iceland is a portion of a mid-ocean ridge that rose above sea level. Ask them to characterize Iceland. *(Students are likely to mention the frequent volcanic activity.)* Tell students that volcanism is characteristic of the entire mid-ocean ridge system. **learning modality: verbal**

Build **Inquiry** [L1]

Visualizing Mid-Ocean Ridges

Materials baseball

Time 20 minutes

Focus Have students compare the shape of a baseball with the shape of Earth.

Teach Allow students to see and feel the seam that circles a baseball. Ask each student to write a short paragraph about how a baseball's seam is similar to the mid-ocean ridge system. *(Students realize that the seam is continuous on a baseball, just as the mid-ocean ridge system is nearly continuous around Earth.)*

Apply Emphasize that a baseball's seam is raised above the rest of the ball and that a "valley" exists at the center of the seam. Draw parallels with the mid-ocean ridge system. **learning modality: visual**

Independent Practice [L2]

All in One Teaching Resources

• Guided Reading and Study Worksheet: *Sea-Floor Spreading*

 Student Edition on Audio CD

Earth's Ocean Floor

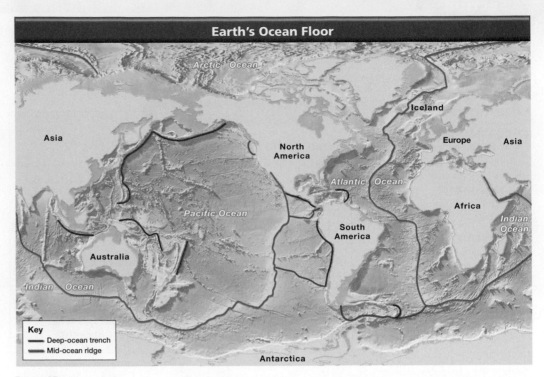

Key
— Deep-ocean trench
━ Mid-ocean ridge

FIGURE 15
The mid-ocean ridge system is more than 50,000 kilometers long.
Interpreting Maps *What is unusual about Iceland?*

Mid-Ocean Ridges

The East Pacific Rise is just one of many **mid-ocean ridges** that wind beneath Earth's oceans. In the mid-1900s, scientists mapped the mid-ocean ridges using sonar. **Sonar** is a device that bounces sound waves off underwater objects and then records the echoes of these sound waves. The time it takes for the echo to arrive indicates the distance to the object.

Mid-ocean ridges curve like the seam of a baseball along the sea floor. They extend into all of Earth's oceans. Figure 15 shows the location of these ridges. Most of the mountains in the mid-ocean ridge system lie hidden under hundreds of meters of water. But in a few places the ridge pokes above the surface. For example, the island of Iceland is a part of the mid-ocean ridge that rises above the surface in the North Atlantic Ocean. A steep-sided valley splits the top of some mid-ocean ridges.

The mapping of mid-ocean ridges made scientists curious to know more about them. What are the ridges? How do they form?

 Reading Checkpoint What device is used to map the ocean floor?

What Is Sea-Floor Spreading?

Harry Hess, an American geologist, was one of the scientists who studied mid-ocean ridges. Hess carefully examined maps of the mid-ocean ridge system. Then he began to think about the ocean floor in relation to the problem of continental drift. Finally, he reached a startling conclusion: Maybe Wegener was right! Perhaps the continents do move.

In 1960, Hess proposed a radical idea. He suggested that a process he called **sea-floor spreading** continually adds new material to the ocean floor. **In sea-floor spreading, the sea floor spreads apart along both sides of a mid-ocean ridge as new crust is added. As a result, the ocean floors move like conveyor belts, carrying the continents along with them.** Look at Figure 16 to see the process of sea-floor spreading.

Sea-floor spreading begins at a mid-ocean ridge, which forms along a crack in the oceanic crust. Along the ridge, molten material that forms several kilometers beneath the surface rises and erupts. At the same time, older rock moves outward on both sides of the ridge. As the molten material cools, it forms a strip of solid rock in the center of the ridge. When more molten material flows into the crack, it forms a new strip of rock.

 Reading Checkpoint How does new oceanic crust form?

Go Online
PHSchool.com

For: More on sea-floor spreading
Visit: PHSchool.com
Web Code: cfd-1014

FIGURE 16
Sea-Floor Spreading
Molten material erupts through the valley that runs along the center of some mid-ocean ridges. This material hardens to form the rock of the ocean floor.
Applying Concepts *What happens to the rock along the ridge when new molten material erupts?*

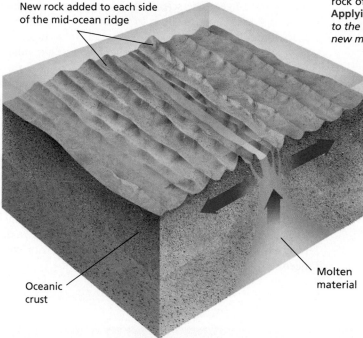

New rock added to each side of the mid-ocean ridge

Oceanic crust

Molten material

Differentiated Instruction

Special Needs L1
Demonstrating Sea-Floor Spreading
To help students better understand the process of sea-floor spreading, place two chairs about a meter apart at the front of the room. Then have students form two lines to the back of the room. At your word, they should move in pairs through the opening and then turn away from each other, spreading out horizontally to the edges of the room. Ask: **What do the chairs represent?** *(The mid-ocean ridge)* **What does the space between the chairs represent?** *(The valley in the center of the ridge)* **What do the students represent?** *(First, the molten material from the mantle; then the spreading sea floor)* **learning modality: kinesthetic**

What Is Sea-Floor Spreading?

Teach Key Concepts L2
Sea-floor Spreading

Focus Review with students Wegener's hypothesis of continental drift.

Teach Work together as a class to summarize the process of sea-floor spreading. *(A crack develops along a mid-ocean ridge. Magma is injected into the space and cools to form new ocean floor. The sea floor spreads more to form a new crack.)* Ask: **How does sea-floor spreading help support the idea that continents drift?** *(It provides a partial explanation of how oceanic crust and continents could move.)* **Why was this not known during Wegener's lifetime?** *(Sonar and deep-diving vessels were not available to identify and explore the mid-ocean ridges.)*

Apply Ask: **Is sea-floor spreading occurring today?** *(Yes)* **Why don't we notice the movement?** *(It is very slow and gradual. The sea floor and the continents generally move at rates of a few centimeters each year.)* **learning modality: verbal**

Go Online
PHSchool.com

For: More on sea-floor spreading
Visit: PHSchool.com
Web Code: cfd-1014

Students can review sea-floor spreading in an online activity.

Monitor Progress L2

Drawing Distribute a map showing the outlines of the world's continents, and challenge students to draw the mid-ocean ridge system on the map. Have them compare their drawings to Figure 15 and make corrections as necessary. Have students place their drawings in their portfolios.

Portfolio

Answers
Figure 15 A mid-ocean ridge cuts through Iceland.
Figure 16 The rock spreads away from the ridge.

 **Reading Checkpoint** Sonar

 Reading Checkpoint It forms when lava is erupted onto the sea floor.

Evidence for Sea-Floor Spreading

Teach Key Concepts L2

Types of Evidence

Focus Remind students that scientific theories must be testable and supported by evidence.

Teach Ask: **What evidence supports the theory of sea-floor spreading?** *(Eruption of molten material along ridges, magnetic stripes, increasing age of oceanic crust away from ridge)* **Why is rock magnetized as it cools?** *(As the rock cools below a certain temperature, iron atoms in some minerals become magnetized.)* **Why does the magnetic polarity of the ocean floor change in stripes?** *(Earth's magnetic field has reversed its polarity many times. Each stripe reflects the magnetic polarity that existed at the time the lava cooled.)* **How is this magnetism measured?** *(A ship tows a magnetometer across the stripes. Where the rock's magnetism parallels Earth's current magnetic field, the two fields add to create a higher value. Where the two are different, a lower magnetic value is recorded.)* **Why does oceanic crust get older away from ridges?** *(Because the ocean floor gradually spreads away from the ridge)*

Apply Ask: **What test of this theory can be done today that wasn't done in the 1960s?** *(Global positioning satellite technology can measure the movement of continents.)*
learning modality: verbal

All in One Teaching Resources
• Transparency F8

Use Visuals: Figure 17 L1

Normal and Reversed Polarity

Focus Tell students that Earth's magnetic field behaves almost as if a huge bar magnet were in its core.

Teach Ask: **What does *normal* mean in the figure?** *(The rock has a magnetic field parallel to Earth's current field.)* **How would a compass behave if Earth's magnetic field were reversed?** *(A compass needle would point south.)*

Apply Flip the poles of a bar magnet held next to a compass needle to reverse the needle's direction. **learning modality: visual**

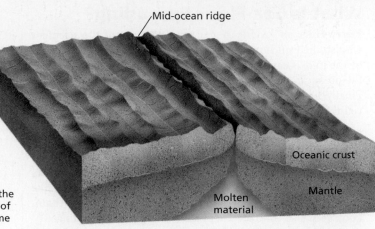

 Rock formed when Earth's magnetic field was normal

 Rock formed when Earth's magnetic field was reversed

FIGURE 17
Magnetic Stripes
Magnetic stripes in the rock of the ocean floor show the direction of Earth's magnetic field at the time the rock hardened.
Interpreting Diagrams *How are these matching stripes evidence of sea-floor spreading?*

Evidence for Sea-Floor Spreading

Several types of evidence supported Hess's theory of sea-floor spreading: eruptions of molten material, magnetic stripes in the rock of the ocean floor, and the ages of the rocks themselves. This evidence led scientists to look again at Wegener's hypothesis of continental drift.

Evidence From Molten Material In the 1960s, scientists found evidence that new material is indeed erupting along mid-ocean ridges. The scientists dived to the ocean floor in *Alvin*, a small submarine built to withstand the crushing pressures four kilometers down in the ocean. In a ridge's central valley, *Alvin's* crew found strange rocks shaped like pillows or like toothpaste squeezed from a tube. Such rocks form only when molten material hardens quickly after erupting under water. These rocks showed that molten material has erupted again and again along the mid-ocean ridge.

Evidence From Magnetic Stripes When scientists studied patterns in the rocks of the ocean floor, they found more support for sea-floor spreading. You read earlier that Earth behaves like a giant magnet, with a north pole and a south pole. Surprisingly, Earth's magnetic poles have reversed themselves many times during Earth's history. The last reversal happened 780,000 years ago. If the magnetic poles suddenly reversed themselves today, you would find that your compass needle points south.

Scientists discovered that the rock that makes up the ocean floor lies in a pattern of magnetized "stripes." These stripes hold a record of reversals in Earth's magnetic field. The rock of the ocean floor contains iron. The rock began as molten material that cooled and hardened. As the rock cooled, the iron bits inside lined up in the direction of Earth's magnetic poles. This locked the iron bits in place, giving the rocks a permanent "magnetic memory."

Using sensitive instruments, scientists recorded the magnetic memory of rocks on both sides of a mid-ocean ridge. They found that stripes of rock that formed when Earth's magnetic field pointed north alternate with stripes of rock that formed when the magnetic field pointed south. As shown in Figure 17, the pattern is the same on both sides of the ridge.

Evidence From Drilling Samples The final proof of sea-floor spreading came from rock samples obtained by drilling into the ocean floor. The *Glomar Challenger,* a drilling ship built in 1968, gathered the samples. The *Glomar Challenger* sent drilling pipes through water six kilometers deep to drill holes in the ocean floor. This feat has been compared to using a sharp-ended wire to dig a hole into a sidewalk from the top of the Empire State Building.

Samples from the sea floor were brought up through the pipes. Then the scientists determined the age of the rocks in the samples. They found that the farther away from a ridge the samples were taken, the older the rocks were. The youngest rocks were always in the center of the ridges. This showed that sea-floor spreading really has taken place.

Reading Checkpoint Why does the rock of the ocean floor have a pattern of magnetic stripes?

FIGURE 18
Sea-Floor Drilling
The *Glomar Challenger* was the first research ship designed to drill samples of rock from the deep-ocean floor.

F ◆ 27

Lab zone **Try This Activity**

Reversing Poles

1. Cut six short pieces, each about 2.5 cm long, from a length of audiotape.
2. Tape one end of each piece of audiotape to a flat surface. The pieces should be spaced 1 cm apart and lined up lengthwise in a single row.
3. Touch a bar magnet's north pole to the first piece of audiotape. Then reverse the magnet and touch its south pole to the next piece.
4. Repeat Step 3 until you have applied the magnet to each piece of audiotape.
5. Sweep one end of the magnet about 1 cm above the line of audiotape pieces. Observe what happens.

Making Models What characteristic of the ocean floor did you observe as you swept the magnet along the line of audiotape pieces?

Lab zone **Try This Activity**

Skills Focus Making models

Materials audiotape, scissors, metric ruler, plastic tape, bar magnet

Time 15 minutes

Tips Have students tape the pieces at least 1 cm apart. Students hold the magnet vertically in Step 5.

L3 **Expected Outcome** The pieces magnetized to the like pole will be attracted; the ones magnetized to the opposite pole will be repelled. Students model the pattern of magnetic stripes.

Extend Have each student write a paragraph that details the analogy suggested by this activity. **learning modality: kinesthetic**

Lab zone **Build Inquiry** **L3**

Making Models of the Ocean Floor

Materials 1 m of roll paper

Time 15 minutes

Focus Remind students that new sea floor is created at ridges and then spreads away from these ridges.

Teach Provide students with a 1-m length of roll paper. Have them mark a pencil line at the 0.5-m mark. This represents the mid-ocean ridge. Ask students to determine the age of the ocean floor at various "drilling locations." Tell students to assume that 1 cm of paper equals 200 km of ocean floor and that this amount of ocean floor formed in 4 million years. Students can then calculate the age at any location on either side of the ridge.

Apply Ask: **Where is the youngest ocean crust?** *(At the ridge center)* **Where is the oldest ocean crust?** *(At both edges of the paper, which are farthest from the ridge)* **What is the relationship between distance from the ridge and age of the crust?** *(Oceanic crust gets older away from the ridge axis.)* **learning modality: visual**

Monitor Progress **L2**

Skills Check Have students make cause-and-effect charts to explain the processes that produced the three types of evidence discussed on these pages.

Answers
Figure 17 The stripes record progressively older polarity reversals of Earth's magnetic field. This could occur only if sea floor were forming at the ridge and spreading away from it.

Reading Checkpoint As rock cooled, it became magnetized parallel to the magnetic field that existed at that time. Through time, sea-floor spreading caused the striped pattern on both sides of the ridge.

Subduction at Trenches

Teach Key Concepts [L2]

Ocean Trenches

Focus Tell students that most of the ocean floor is about 5 km deep. However, trenches often are more than 8 km deep. The Marianas Trench in the Pacific has a depth of 11.2 km. Ask: **Why are ocean trenches so deep?** *(The oceanic lithosphere far from a ridge has cooled and become denser than the asthenosphere below, so it begins to sink into the mantle.)*

Teach Ask: **What happens at mid-ocean ridges?** *(Material from the mantle erupts to Earth's surface.)* **What happens at subduction zones?** *(Material from Earth's surface sinks into the mantle.)* **How is the sea floor like a giant conveyor belt?** *(Material comes up at a ridge, moves across the ocean basin, and sinks at a trench.)*

Apply Show students a relief map of the world that includes the ocean floor. Challenge them to find as many deep-ocean trenches as they can. Ask: **Which ocean is almost completely surrounded by trenches?** *(The Pacific basin)* **Which has very few trenches?** *(The Atlantic basin)* **learning modality: visual**

Video Field Trip

Plate Tectonics

Show the Video Field Trip to let students experience plate tectonics and understand how continents move. Discussion questions: **What are Earth's plates?** *(The lithosphere is broken up into about a dozen sections called tectonic plates that hold all of Earth's continents and the ocean floor.)* **How do plate movements affect Earth's continents and oceans?** *(They break apart and push together continents, create mountain ranges, and create ocean ridges and oceanic crust.)*

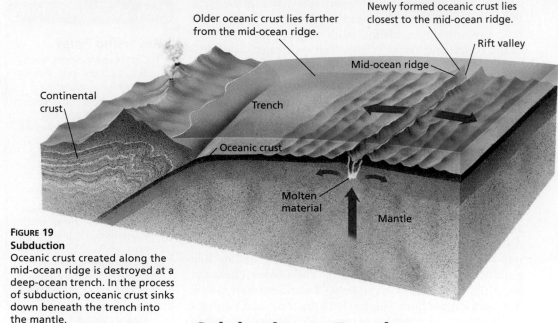

Older oceanic crust lies farther from the mid-ocean ridge.

Newly formed oceanic crust lies closest to the mid-ocean ridge.

Rift valley

Mid-ocean ridge

Continental crust

Trench

Oceanic crust

Molten material

Mantle

FIGURE 19
Subduction
Oceanic crust created along the mid-ocean ridge is destroyed at a deep-ocean trench. In the process of subduction, oceanic crust sinks down beneath the trench into the mantle.
Drawing Conclusions *Where would the densest oceanic crust be found?*

Plate Tectonics

Video Preview
► Video Field Trip
Video Assessment

Subduction at Trenches

How can the ocean floor keep getting wider and wider? The answer is that the ocean floor generally does not just keep spreading. Instead, the ocean floor plunges into deep underwater canyons called **deep-ocean trenches.** At a deep-ocean trench, the oceanic crust bends downward. What occurs at trenches? **In a process taking tens of millions of years, part of the ocean floor sinks back into the mantle at deep-ocean trenches.**

The Process of Subduction The process by which ocean floor sinks beneath a deep-ocean trench and back into the mantle is called **subduction** (sub DUC shun). As subduction occurs, crust closer to a mid-ocean ridge moves away from the ridge and toward a deep-ocean trench. Sea-floor spreading and subduction work together. They move the ocean floor as if it were on a giant conveyor belt.

New oceanic crust is hot. But as it moves away from the mid-ocean ridge, it cools and becomes more dense. Eventually, as shown in Figure 19, gravity pulls this older, denser oceanic crust down beneath the trench. The sinking crust is like the washcloth in the Discover activity at the beginning of this section. As the dry washcloth floating on the water gets wet, its density increases and it begins to sink.

Subduction and Earth's Oceans The processes of subduction and sea-floor spreading can change the size and shape of the oceans. Because of these processes, the ocean floor is renewed about every 200 million years. That is the time it takes for new rock to form at the mid-ocean ridge, move across the ocean, and sink into a trench.

The vast Pacific Ocean covers almost one third of the planet. And yet it is shrinking. How can that be? Sometimes a deep ocean trench swallows more oceanic crust than a mid-ocean ridge can produce. Then, if the ridge does not add new crust fast enough, the width of the ocean will shrink. In the Pacific Ocean, subduction through the many trenches that ring the ocean is occurring faster than new crust can be added.

On the other hand, the Atlantic Ocean is expanding. Unlike the Pacific Ocean, the Atlantic Ocean has only a few short trenches. As a result, the spreading ocean floor has virtually nowhere to go. In most places, the oceanic crust of the Atlantic Ocean floor is attached to the continental crust of the continents around the ocean. So as the Atlantic's ocean floor spreads, the continents along its edges also move. Over time, the whole ocean gets wider.

 Why is the Pacific Ocean shrinking?

FIGURE 20
Growing an Ocean
Because of sea-floor spreading, the distance between Europe and North America is increasing by a few centimeters per year.

Section 4 Assessment

Target Reading Skill Sequencing Refer to your flowchart on sea-floor spreading as you answer the questions below.

Reviewing Key Concepts

1. **a. Naming** What scientist helped to discover the process of sea-floor spreading?
   b. Identifying Along what feature of the ocean floor does sea-floor spreading begin?
   c. Sequencing What are the steps in the process of sea-floor spreading?
2. **a. Reviewing** What three types of evidence provided support for the theory of sea-floor spreading?
   b. Applying Concepts How do rocks along the central valley of the mid-ocean ridge provide evidence of sea-floor spreading?
   c. Predicting Where would you expect to find the oldest rock on the ocean floor?

3. **a. Defining** What is a deep-ocean trench?
   b. Relating Cause and Effect What happens to oceanic crust at a deep-ocean trench?

Writing in Science

Description Write a description of what you might see if you could explore a mid-ocean ridge in a vessel like the *Alvin.* In your description, be sure to include the main features of the ocean floor along and near the ridge.

Modeling Sea-Floor Spreading

L2

Prepare for Inquiry

Key Concept
Sea-floor spreading at the mid-ocean ridge continuously adds new material to the ocean floor.

Skills Objectives
After this lab, students will be able to
• make a model of sea-floor spreading

 Prep Time 15 minutes
Class Time 30 minutes

Advance Planning
Gather all of the materials at least one day before the activity. Prepare two sample sheets: a sheet with stripes predrawn, and a sheet folded and marked for cutting.

Alternative Materials
Instead of having small groups making several models, you could divide the class into larger groups and have each group use butcher paper to make a large model.

Safety
Students should exercise caution when cutting paper with scissors. Review Safety Guidelines in Appendix A.

All in One Teaching Resources
• Lab Worksheet: *Modeling Sea-Floor Spreading*

Guide Inquiry

Invitation
Help students focus on the key concept by asking: **What happens at the mid-ocean ridge?** (*Molten material rises from the mantle and erupts.*) **What forms when the molten material hardens?** (*New ocean floor*) **What happens to the new ocean floor?** (*It moves outward on both sides of the ridge.*) **How are magnetic stripes evidence of this process?** (*The magnetic stripes show that material has moved away from the ridge over time.*) **What happens at deep-ocean trenches?** (*Oceanic crust sinks back into the mantle.*)

Lab zone Skills Lab

Modeling Sea-Floor Spreading

Problem
How does sea-floor spreading add material to the ocean floor?

Skills Focus
making models

Materials
• scissors
• colored marker
• metric ruler
• 2 sheets of unlined paper

Procedure

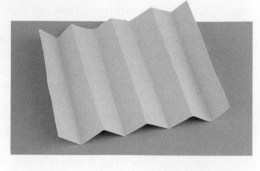

1. Draw stripes across one sheet of paper, parallel to the short sides of the paper. The stripes should vary in spacing and thickness.

2. Fold the paper in half lengthwise and write the word "Start" at the top of both halves of the paper. Using the scissors, carefully cut the paper in half along the fold line to form two strips.

3. Lightly fold the second sheet of paper into eighths. Then unfold it, leaving creases in the paper. Fold this sheet in half lengthwise.

4. Starting at the fold, draw lines 5.5 cm long on the middle crease and the two creases closest to the ends of the paper.

5. Now carefully cut along the lines you drew. Unfold the paper. There should be three slits in the center of the paper.

6. Put the two striped strips of paper together so their Start labels touch one another. Insert the Start ends of the strips up through the center slit and then pull them toward the side slits.

Introduce the Procedure
Have students read through the entire activity. Then ask: **What is the purpose of this activity?** (*To make a model of sea-floor spreading*) **Why do you cut the first sheet in half?** (*The sea floor spreads in both directions from the mid-ocean ridge. Cutting the sheet in half allows the model to represent movement on both sides of the ridge.*) **After you've cut the sheet in half, how does the pattern of stripes on one half compare with the pattern on the other half?** (*The pattern is the same on both halves.*)

Troubleshooting the Experiment
Demonstrate how to begin to make each of the two sheets. Then show students your samples of the finished products. Allow them to refer to these sheets as they make their own. Ensure that students make the slits large enough to pull the paper through easily. They should cut a little more than halfway through the width of the sheet.

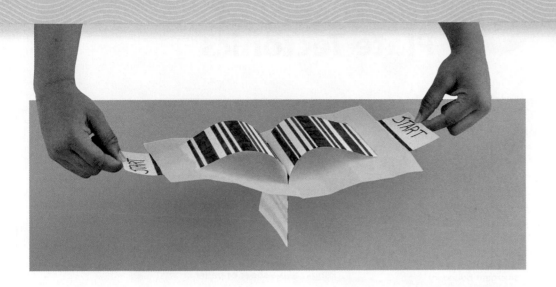

7. Insert the ends of the strips into the side slits. Pull the ends of the strips and watch what happens at the center slit.

8. Practice pulling the strips until you can make the two strips come up through the center and go down through the sides at the same time.

Analyze and Conclude

1. **Making Models** What feature of the ocean floor does the center slit stand for? What prominent feature of the ocean floor is missing from the model at this point?

2. **Making Models** What do the side slits stand for? What does the space under the paper stand for?

3. **Comparing and Contrasting** As shown by your model, how does the ocean floor close to the center slit differ from the ocean floor near a side slit? How does this difference affect the depth of the ocean?

4. **Making Models** What do the stripes on the strips stand for? Why is it important that your model have an identical pattern of stripes on both sides of the center slit?

5. **Applying Concepts** Explain how differences in density and temperature provide some of the force needed to cause sea-floor spreading and subduction.

6. **Communicating** Use your own words to describe the process of sea-floor spreading. What parts of the process were not shown by your model?

More to Explore

How could you modify your model to show an island that formed where a large amount of molten rock erupted from the mid-ocean ridge? How could you show what would happen to the island over a long period of time?

Expected Outcome

Students will build a model that shows the formation of new sea floor at a mid-ocean ridge, the spreading of the sea floor on both sides of the ridge, and the subduction of the sea floor at deep-ocean trenches.

Analyze and Conclude

1. The center slit represents the central valley of the mid-ocean ridge. The missing feature is the mountainous ridge.

2. The side slits represent deep-ocean trenches. The space beneath the paper stands for the asthenosphere.

3. The ocean floor as shown by the strip near the center slit is younger, hotter, and less dense than the ocean floor farther away. As the floor moves away from the ridge, it cools and becomes denser. The ocean floor as shown by the part near a side slit is older, cooler, and denser. The increased density causes the depth of the ocean to increase.

4. The stripes represent the magnetic stripes in the rock of the ocean floor. The pattern of magnetic stripes is the same on both sides of the mid-ocean ridge.

5. Temperature differences cause convection currents. These currents cause molten rock to erupt through the valley along the center of the mid-ocean ridge. As material erupts, the sea floor spreads, cools, and becomes denser. The denser material sinks back into the mantle when it reaches a trench.

6. Answers will vary. A typical answer should mention the eruption of molten material at the mid-ocean ridge, the spreading of the sea floor, and the subduction of oceanic crust at deep-ocean trenches. Parts of the process not shown by the model include changes in density and the melting that occurs at subduction zones.

Extend Inquiry

More to Explore Answers will vary. A typical answer might suggest drawing an island near the Start label on one of the strips. Then, through the movement of the strip through the model, the island's position would change. It would sink below sea level and eventually be subducted.

Objectives

After this lesson, students will be able to
F1.5.1 explain the theory of plate tectonics
F1.5.2 describe the three types of plate boundaries

Target Reading Skill

Building Vocabulary Explain that knowing the definitions of key-concept words helps students understand what they read.

Answers

Have students make and practice with flashcards.

Preteach

Build Background Knowledge `L2`

Defining Plates

Ask: **What is a plate?** (*A typical answer will describe a dinner plate.*) Challenge students to think of other plates, such as metal plates that cover machinery, home plate in baseball, and the plates or scales that cover a reptile. Form a general definition for *plate*: a broad, flat sheet of material.

Help Students Read `L1`

Relating Cause and Effect

Encourage students to list cause-and-effect relationships while reading about plate tectonics and then compare their lists.
learning modality: logical/mathematical

Reading Preview

Key Concepts

- What is the theory of plate tectonics?
- What are the three types of plate boundaries?

Key Terms

- plate
- scientific theory
- plate tectonics
- fault
- divergent boundary
- rift valley
- convergent boundary
- transform boundary

Target Reading Skill

Building Vocabulary A definition states the meaning of a word or phrase by telling about its most important feature or function. After you read the section, reread the paragraphs that contain definitions of Key Terms. Use all the information you have learned to write a definition of each Key Term in your own words.

Lab zone Discover Activity

How Well Do the Continents Fit Together?

1. Using a world map in an atlas, trace the shape of each continent and Madagascar on a sheet of paper. Also trace the shape of India and the Arabian Peninsula.
2. Carefully cut apart the landmasses, leaving Asia and Europe as one piece. Separate India and the Arabian Peninsula from Asia.
3. Piece together the continents as they may have looked before the breakup of Pangaea. Then attach your reconstruction of Pangaea to a sheet of paper.

Think It Over
Drawing Conclusions How well did the pieces of your continents fit together? Do your observations support the idea that today's landmasses were once joined together? Explain.

Have you ever dropped a hard-boiled egg? If so, you may have noticed that the eggshell cracked in an irregular pattern of pieces. Earth's lithosphere, its solid outer shell, is not one unbroken layer. It is more like that cracked eggshell. It's broken into pieces separated by jagged cracks.

A Canadian scientist, J. Tuzo Wilson, observed that there are cracks in the continents similar to those on the ocean floor. In 1965, Wilson proposed a new way of looking at these cracks. According to Wilson, the lithosphere is broken into separate sections called **plates.** The plates fit together along cracks in the lithosphere. As shown in Figure 22, the plates carry the continents or parts of the ocean floor, or both. Wilson combined what geologists knew about sea-floor spreading, Earth's plates, and continental drift into a single theory. A **scientific theory** is a well-tested concept that explains a wide range of observations.

FIGURE 21
A Cracked Eggshell
Earth's lithosphere is broken into plates like the cracked shell of a hard-boiled egg.

Lab zone Discover Activity

Skills Focus Drawing conclusions `L1`

Materials world map in an atlas, tracing paper, scissors, sheet of paper, tape

Time 20 minutes

Tips To shorten the activity, provide each student with a photocopy of the continent outlines.

Expected Outcome Students can easily fit some of the continents together, such as South America and Africa. It will be more difficult to imagine how the other continents fit together. Accept all plausible configurations.

Think It Over A typical answer might be that some of the continents fit together quite well, while others did not. The general fit between some continents suggests that the continents might once have been joined.

How Plates Move

The theory of **plate tectonics** (tek TAHN iks) states that pieces of Earth's lithosphere are in slow, constant motion, driven by convection currents in the mantle. **The theory of plate tectonics explains the formation, movement, and subduction of Earth's plates.**

How can Earth's plates move? What force is great enough to move the heavy continents? Geologists think that movement of convection currents in the mantle is the major force that causes plate motion. During subduction, gravity pulls one edge of a plate down into the mantle. The rest of the plate also moves. This slow movement is similar to what happens in a pot of soup when gravity causes the cooler, denser soup near the surface to sink.

As the plates move, they collide, pull apart, or grind past each other, producing spectacular changes in Earth's surface. These changes include volcanoes, mountain ranges, and deep-ocean trenches.

Lab zone Skills Activity

Predicting

Study the map of Earth's plates in Figure 22. Notice the arrows that show the direction of plate movement. Now find the Nazca plate on the map. Which direction is it moving? Find the South American plate and describe its movement. What do you think will happen as these plates continue to move?

FIGURE 22
Plate boundaries divide the lithosphere into large plates.
Interpreting Maps *Which plates include only ocean floor? Which plates include both continents and ocean floor?*

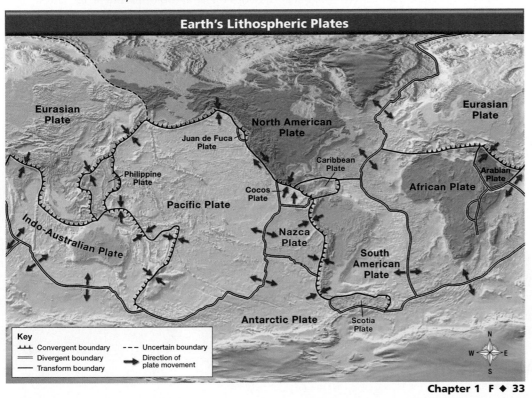

Earth's Lithospheric Plates

Eurasian Plate
North American Plate
Juan de Fuca Plate
Eurasian Plate
Caribbean Plate
Arabian Plate
Philippine Plate
Cocos Plate
African Plate
Pacific Plate
Indo-Australian Plate
Nazca Plate
South American Plate
Antarctic Plate
Scotia Plate

Key
— Convergent boundary   - - - Uncertain boundary
═══ Divergent boundary   → Direction of plate movement
— Transform boundary

Lab zone Skills Activity

Skills Focus Predicting

Materials Figure 22

Time 10 minutes

Tips Before the activity, show students that some arrows point toward each other, some away, and some point past each other in opposite directions.

Expected Outcome The Nazca plate is moving east, and the South American plate is

[L3] moving west. This creates a convergent plate boundary. Because the Nazca plate carries dense oceanic crust and the South American plate carries less dense continental crust, the Nazca plate will sink beneath the South American plate.

Extend Challenge students to describe each of the boundaries associated with the North American plate and predict what will happen to each one. **learning modality: logical/ mathematical**

Instruct

How Plates Move

Teach Key Concepts [L2]

Earth's Plates

Focus Review the definitions of *lithosphere* and *asthenosphere* with students.

Teach Ask: **What are characteristics of the lithosphere?** *(Relatively cool, solid, brittle)* **What are characteristics of the asthenosphere?** *(Hot, capable of flow)* Refer students to Figure 22. Show them that Earth's lithosphere is fragmented into pieces called plates. Ask: **How could hard, solid plates of lithosphere move?** *(By sliding over the asthenosphere)*

Apply Point out how large plates can be, and that they can be covered by ocean, continent, or both. Ask students to identify the plate on which they live. **learning modality: visual**

All in One Teaching Resources
• Transparency F10

Lab zone Teacher Demo

Making Models of Plates [L1]

Materials grapefruit with its peel cut into segments

Time 5 minutes

Focus Remind students that Earth is a sphere and that the lithosphere is broken into plates.

Teach Show students the grapefruit. Explain that Earth's plates also cover a sphere.

Apply Ask: **What do the cracks between pieces of peel represent?** *(Plate boundaries)* **learning modality: visual**

Independent Practice

All in One Teaching Resources
• Guided Reading and Study Worksheet: *The Theory of Plate Tectonics*

 Student Edition on Audio CD

Monitor Progress _____ [L2]

Writing Have each student write a paragraph explaining the theory of plate tectonics.

Answer
Figure 22 Ocean floor: Nazca, Cocos, Scotia; both: all other labeled plates

Plate Boundaries

Teach Key Concepts $\quad$ L2
Modeling Plate Boundaries

Focus Remind students that two adjacent plates can move toward each other, away from each other, or past each other.

Teach Have students model the movement along the three types of boundaries with their hands. *(One hand sinks beneath the other, two hands separate, and two hands slide past each other.)*

Apply Identify plate boundaries around the globe. Ask students to describe the motion and the effects of the motion. For example: **San Andreas Fault, transform boundary** *(Plates slide past each other, earthquakes)* **Coast of Washington state, ocean-continent convergent boundary** *(Ocean plate sinks beneath continent, volcanoes and earthquakes)* **Himalayas, continent-continent collision** *(Two continents collide and crust folds and thickens, earthquakes)* **learning modality: kinesthetic**

Use Visuals: Figure 23 $\quad$ L1
Landforms and Plate Boundaries

Focus Remind students that each plate boundary has characteristic landforms.

Teach Direct students' attention to each plate boundary shown in the figure. Ask students to identify the landforms associated with each boundary. *(Subduction zone: mountains, volcanoes; mid-ocean ridge: mountain range, central valley; rift valley: fault block valley, volcanoes; transform fault: marked fracture in crust, offset features; continent-continent collision: folded mountains)*

Apply Using a world map, have students identify areas on Earth where each boundary type occurs. *(From left to right, examples are the Peru-Chile Trench, the Mid-Atlantic Ridge, the East African Rift Valley, the San Andreas Fault, and the Himalayas.)* **learning modality: visual**

Plate Boundaries

The edges of Earth's plates meet at plate boundaries. Plate boundaries extend deep into the lithosphere. **Faults** —breaks in Earth's crust where rocks have slipped past each other— form along these boundaries. **As shown in Figure 23, there are three kinds of plate boundaries: divergent boundaries, convergent boundaries, and transform boundaries. A different type of plate movement occurs along each type of boundary.**

Scientists have used instruments on satellites to measure plate motion very precisely. The plates move at amazingly slow rates: from about 1 to 24 centimeters per year. The North American and Eurasian plates are moving apart at a rate of 2.5 centimeters per year. That's about as fast as your fingernails grow. This may not seem like much, but these plates have been moving apart for tens of millions of years.

Divergent Boundaries The place where two plates move apart, or diverge, is called a **divergent boundary** (dy VUR junt). Most divergent boundaries occur along the mid-ocean ridges where sea-floor spreading occurs.

Divergent boundaries also occur on land. When a divergent boundary develops on land, two of Earth's plates slide apart. A deep valley called a **rift valley** forms along the divergent boundary. For example, the Great Rift Valley in East Africa marks a deep crack in the African continent.

FIGURE 23
Plate Tectonics

Plate movements have built many of the features of Earth's land surfaces and ocean floors.
Predicting *What will eventually happen if a rift valley continues to pull apart?*

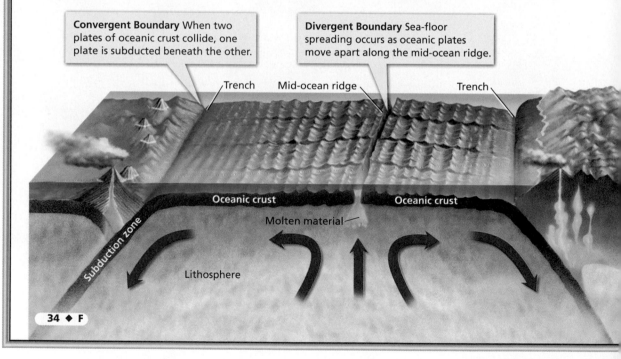

Convergent Boundary When two plates of oceanic crust collide, one plate is subducted beneath the other.

Divergent Boundary Sea-floor spreading occurs as oceanic plates move apart along the mid-ocean ridge.

Trench $\quad$ Mid-ocean ridge $\quad$ Trench

Oceanic crust $\quad$ Oceanic crust

Subduction zone

Molten material

Lithosphere

Convergent Boundaries The place where two plates come together, or converge, is called a **convergent boundary** (kun VUR junt). When two plates converge, the result is called a collision. When two plates collide, the density of the plates determines which one comes out on top.

Oceanic crust becomes cooler and denser as it spreads away from the mid-ocean ridge. Where two plates carrying oceanic crust meet at a trench, the plate that is more dense sinks under the other plate.

Sometimes a plate carrying oceanic crust collides with a plate carrying continental crust. Oceanic crust is more dense than continental crust. The less dense continental crust can't sink under the more dense oceanic crust. Instead, subduction occurs as the oceanic plate sinks beneath the continental plate.

When two plates carrying continental crust collide, subduction does not take place. Neither piece of crust is dense enough to sink very far into the mantle. Instead, the collision squeezes the crust into mighty mountain ranges.

Transform Boundaries A **transform boundary** is a place where two plates slip past each other, moving in opposite directions. Earthquakes often occur along transform boundaries, but crust is neither created nor destroyed.

 Reading Checkpoint What features form where two continental plates come together?

 **Math Skills**

Calculating a Rate
To calculate the rate of plate motion, divide the distance the plate moves by the time it takes to move that distance.

$$\text{Rate} = \frac{\text{Distance}}{\text{Time}}$$

For example, a plate takes 2 million years to move 156 km. Calculate its rate of motion.

$$\frac{156 \text{ km}}{2{,}000{,}000 \text{ years}} = 7.8 \text{ cm per year}$$

Practice Problem The Pacific plate is sliding past the North American plate. It has taken 10 million years for the plate to move 600 km. What is the Pacific plate's rate of motion?

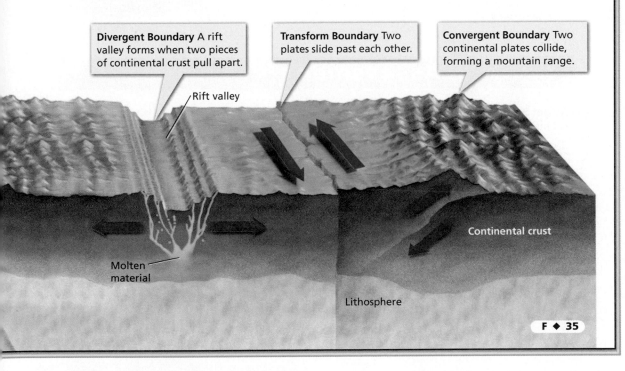

Divergent Boundary A rift valley forms when two pieces of continental crust pull apart.

Transform Boundary Two plates slide past each other.

Convergent Boundary Two continental plates collide, forming a mountain range.

Rift valley

Molten material

Continental crust

Lithosphere

 **Skills**

Math Skill Calculating a Rate

Focus Students calculate average rates of plate motion using the equation r = d/t, where *r* is rate, *d* is distance, and *t* is time.

Teach In the example problem, kilometers must be converted into centimeters. Remind students that one kilometer is equal to 100,000 centimeters.

Answer
6 cm/year

 **Build Inquiry**   L1

Continent-Continent Collisions

Materials 2 cloth towels

Time 10 minutes

Focus Review with students that Earth's continental crust varies in thickness.

Teach Ask students to place two cloth towels end-to-end on a table. The students then should slowly move the towels toward each other. As the towels collide, material will fold and the towels will be shortened and thickened. Ask students to compare the original length of the two towels with the length after the collision. Also ask them to compare the height of the towels in the collision area with the height elsewhere.

Apply Ask: **What happens to continental crust when two continents collide?** (*The crust is shortened and thickened to form a mountain belt.*) **learning modality: kinesthetic**

All in One Teaching Resources
• Transparency F11

Differentiated Instruction

Less Proficient Readers   L1
Interpreting Diagrams Much important information is contained in **Figure 23**. Ask students to look at the figure and read the caption. Help them define difficult vocabulary by relating the information in the caption to what they see in the figure.
learning modality: verbal

Gifted and Talented   L3
Creating a Time Line Have each student research and prepare a visual display that illustrates the formulation of the Himalayas. Displays should show events from about 60 or 70 million years ago to the present. (*India began colliding with Asia about 45 million years ago. The collision compressed and uplifted rock layers to form the Himalayas. The mountains still are rising today.*)
learning modality: visual

Monitor Progress   L2

Oral Presentation Call on students at random to explain what occurs at each of the different types of plate boundaries.

Answers
Figure 23 The valley eventually will become an ocean basin with a mid-ocean ridge.

 Reading Checkpoint Mountain ranges

Assess

Reviewing Key Concepts
1. a. Plates are sections of Earth's lithosphere. **b.** a theory that explains the formation, movement, and subduction of Earth's plates. **c.** convection currents in Earth's mantle.
2. a. convergent, divergent, transform. **b.** Plates move away from each other at a divergent boundary, move toward each other at a convergent boundary, or slide past each other at a transform boundary. **c.** The oceanic plate will subduct beneath the continental plate.

Reteach   **L1**
Have each student make a table comparing the three types of plate boundaries. The tables should include all possibilities for each boundary type.

Performance Assessment   **L2**
Drawing Organize students in small groups, and give each group a piece of posterboard. Tell each group to make a poster that includes all of the information students have learned about sea-floor spreading and plate tectonics. Students may use colored pencils, chalk, or water paints to make the posters.

All in One **Teaching Resources**
• Section Summary: *The Theory of Plate Tectonics*
• Review and Reinforce: *The Theory of Plate Tectonics*
• Enrich: *The Theory of Plate Tectonics*
• Transparency F12

Monitor Progress _____ **L2**
Answer
Figure 24
You would need answers to how fast and in what direction each plate is moving.

225 Million Years Ago

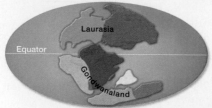
180–200 Million Years Ago

135 Million Years Ago

Earth Today

Plate Motions Over Time The movement of Earth's plates has greatly changed Earth's surface. Geologists have evidence that, before Pangaea existed, other supercontinents formed and split apart over billions of years. Pangaea itself formed when Earth's landmasses drifted together about 260 million years ago. Then, about 225 million years ago, Pangaea began to break apart. Figure 24 shows how major landmasses have moved since the breakup of Pangaea.

FIGURE 24
Continental Drift
It has taken the continents about 225 million years since the breakup of Pangaea to move to their present locations. **Posing Questions** *What questions would you need to answer in order to predict where the continents will be in 50 million years?*

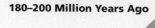
Section 5 Assessment

🎯 **Target Reading Skill** Building Vocabulary Use your definitions to help answer the questions.

Reviewing Key Concepts
1. a. Defining What are plates?
  b. Summarizing In your own words, what is the theory of plate tectonics?
  c. Relating Cause and Effect What do scientists think causes the movement of Earth's plates?
2. a. Listing What are the three types of plate boundaries?
  b. Describing Describe the type of movement that occurs at each type of plate boundary.
  c. Predicting What is likely to occur at a plate boundary where oceanic crust collides with continental crust?

36 ◆ F

Math ▸ Practice

3. Calculating a Rate There are two islands on opposite sides of a mid-ocean ridge in the Atlantic Ocean. During the last 8 million years, the distance between the islands has increased by 200 kilometers. Calculate the rate at which the two plates are diverging.

Math ▸ Practice
Math Skill Calculating a Rate
Answer

3. $\dfrac{200 \text{ km}}{8{,}000{,}000 \text{ years}} = 2.5 \text{ cm/year}$

Lab zone ▸ Chapter Project

Keep Students on Track Ask students to add examples of plate boundaries to their models. Students complete their models by adding surface features and labeling features on the model. Offer guidance about which materials to use and about how students should prepare their presentations for the class.

Modeling Mantle Convection Currents

Problem

How might convection in Earth's mantle affect tectonic plates?

Skills Focus

making models, observing

Materials

- large plastic bottle • food coloring • small glass jar • aluminum foil or plastic wrap
- rubber band • several paper hole punches or small pieces of paper • tap water

Procedure

1. Fill the large bottle about half full with cold tap water.
2. Partly fill the small jar with hot tap water and stir in 6 drops of food coloring. Carefully add enough hot water to fill the jar to the brim.
3. Cover the top of the jar with aluminum foil or plastic wrap and secure with a rubber band.
4. Carefully lower the jar into the bottle of tap water.
5. Place the pieces of paper on the surface of the water.
6. Without disturbing the water, use the tip of the pencil to make two small holes about 2–4 mm in diameter in the material covering the jar.
7. Predict what will happen to the colored water and to the pieces of paper floating on the surface.
8. Observe the contents of the jar, as well as the paper pieces on the surface of the water.

Analyze and Conclude

1. **Observing** Describe what happened to the colored water and to the pieces of paper after the holes were punched in the material covering the jar.
2. **Drawing Conclusions** How did your prediction compare with what actually happened to the colored water and pieces of paper?
3. **Inferring** What type of heat transfer took place in the bottle? Describe how the transfer occurred.
4. **Making Models** Which part of your model represents a tectonic plate? Which part represents Earth's mantle?
5. **Communicating** How well do you think this lab modeled the movement of Earth's plates? What similarities exist between this model and actual plate movement? What factors weren't you able to model in this lab?

Designing Experiments

Repeat this activity, but develop a plan to measure the temperature of the water inside the large bottle. Is there a difference in temperature between the water's surface and the water near the top of the small jar? Do you observe any change in the convection currents as the water temperature changes? With your teacher's approval, carry out your plan.

Analyze and Conclude

1. Most students will describe the colored water's rising and traveling across the surface of the cold water. The pieces of paper will move away from the rising colored water and toward the edges of the surface of the cold water.
2. Student answers will vary. Look for specific or detailed descriptions of how their predictions compared.
3. The type of heat transfer was convection. The warm, colored water was less dense and was forced to rise, creating a convection current.
4. The pieces of paper represent tectonic plates. The cold water and the colored water represent Earth's mantle.
5. Student answers will vary. Accept answers that detail similarities between the movement of paper pieces and the movement of actual tectonic plates. One aspect of the process that can't be modeled with this setup is convection currents in the solid, but pliable, movement of the mantle.

Modeling Mantle Convection Currents L2

Prepare for Inquiry

Skills Objectives

After this lab, students will be able to
- make a model of convection in Earth's mantle
- observe convection currents in their model

Prep Time 20 minutes
Class Time: 40 minutes

Advance Planning

To save class time, fill the large bottles with cold water in advance.

Alternative Materials

If ice is available, ice water may be used in place of the cold tap water.

Safety

Stress the importance of immediately reporting and cleaning up any spills or broken glassware. Review the safety guidelines in Appendix A.

All in One Teaching Resources
- Lab Worksheet: *Modeling Mantle Convection Currents*

Guide Inquiry

Invitation

Remind students that convection is a common method of heat transfer. Ask them to list some examples of convection in their daily lives. *(Answers might include heating fluids on a stovetop or in a heating system.)*

Introduce the Procedure

Have students read the entire procedure. Then ask: **What is the purpose of the food coloring?** *(The food coloring shows the path of the convection currents that form.)*

Troubleshooting the Experiment

Sometimes a bubble of air can form at the top of the small container, preventing the escape of hot water. If that happens, gently push on the foil and force the air out.

Extend Inquiry

Designing Experiments Check

students' plans. Make sure students address both questions before proceeding.

The BIG Idea

Have students read the answer to the Essential Question. Encourage them to evaluate and revise their own answers as needed.

Help Students Read

Developing Vocabulary

Vocabulary Rating Chart Have each student construct a chart with four columns labeled Term, Can Define or Use It, Have Heard or Seen It, and Don't Know. Have students copy the key terms from this chapter into the first column and rate their knowledge by putting a check in one of the other columns. Then, have them reread the parts that pertain to key terms in question.

Word-Part Analysis Explain that the root is the key to a word's meaning. Ask students to compare the key terms *conduction* and *subduction*. Have them separate the parts in each word and find the definitions of each part. Ask what these two words have in common and how they are different. (*Sub-* means "beneath," *con-* means "with" or "together," *-duct-* means "to carry," and *-tion* means "a state" or "condition." The words are similar in that they describe a state of movement. The first means to be carried beneath, the second means to be carried with.) Ask: **What is the root word that these two terms have in common?** (*duct*)

Connecting Concepts

Concept Maps Help students develop one way to show how the information in this chapter is related. Convection currents in Earth's mantle are the driving force that causes the movement of Earth's plates. Have students brainstorm to identify the key concepts, key terms, details, and examples. Then tell them to write each item on a sticky note and attach it at random to chart paper or to the board.

Tell students that this concept map will be organized in hierarchical order, and have them begin at the top with the key concepts. Ask students these questions to guide them in categorizing the information on the

stickies: **What are Earth's main layers? How do convection currents affect the crust? What happens at plate boundaries?**

Prompt students by using such connecting words or phrases as "consists of," "results in," and "occurs at," to indicate the basis for the organization of the map. The phrases should form a sentence between or among a set of concepts.

Chapter 1 Study Guide

The BIG Idea **Energy Transfer and Earth's Structure** Mantle convection causes the movement of pieces of the lithosphere called plates. Plate motions produce faults, mountain ranges, earthquakes, and volcanoes.

① Earth's Interior

Key Concepts

- Geologists have used two main types of evidence to learn about Earth's interior: direct evidence from rock samples and indirect evidence from seismic waves.
- The three main layers of Earth are the crust, the mantle, and the core. These layers vary in size, composition, temperature, and pressure.
- The crust is a layer of solid rock that includes both dry land and the ocean floor.
- Earth's mantle is made up of rock that is very hot, but solid. Scientists divide the mantle into layers based on physical characteristics.
- The core is made mostly of the metals iron and nickel. It consists of two parts—a liquid outer core and a solid inner core.

Key Terms

- seismic waves • pressure • crust • basalt
- granite • mantle • lithosphere
- asthenosphere • outer core • inner core

② Convection and the Mantle

Key Concepts

- There are three types of heat transfer: radiation, conduction, and convection.
- Heating and cooling of the fluid, changes in the fluid's density, and the force of gravity combine to set convection currents in motion.
- Heat from the core and the mantle itself causes convection currents in the mantle.

Key Terms

- radiation • conduction • convection
- density • convection current

③ Drifting Continents

Key Concepts

- Wegener's hypothesis was that all the continents had once been joined together in a single landmass and have since drifted apart.

- Wegener gathered evidence from different scientific fields to support his ideas about continental drift. He studied land features, fossils, and evidence of climate change.
- Wegener could not provide a satisfactory explanation for the force that pushes or pulls the continents.

Key Terms

- continental drift • Pangaea • fossil

④ Sea-Floor Spreading

Key Concepts

- In sea-floor spreading, the sea floor spreads apart along both sides of a mid-ocean ridge as new crust is added. As a result, the ocean floors move like conveyor belts, carrying the continents along with them.
- Several types of evidence supported Hess's theory of sea-floor spreading: eruptions of molten material, magnetic stripes in the rock of the ocean floor, and the ages of the rocks.
- In a process taking tens of millions of years, part of the ocean floor sinks back into the mantle at deep-ocean trenches.

Key Terms

- mid-ocean ridge • sonar • sea-floor spreading
- deep-ocean trench • subduction

⑤ The Theory of Plate Tectonics

Key Concepts

- The theory of plate tectonics explains the formation, movement, and subduction of Earth's plates.
- There are three kinds of plate boundaries: divergent boundaries, convergent boundaries, and transform boundaries. A different type of plate movement occurs along each.

Key Terms

- plate • scientific theory • plate tectonics
- fault • divergent boundary • rift valley
- convergent boundary • transform boundary

Answer

Accept logical presentations by students.

All in One Teaching Resources

- Key Terms Review: *Plate Tectonics*
- Connecting Concepts: *Plate Tectonics*

Review and Assessment

Organizing Information

Comparing and Contrasting Fill in the compare-and-contrast table to compare the characteristics of the different types of plate boundaries. Then give it a title.

Type of Plate Boundary	Type of Motion	Effect on Crust	Feature(s) Formed
a. ___?___ boundary	Plates slide past each other.	b. ___?___	c. ___?___
d. ___?___ boundary	e. ___?___	Subduction or mountain building	f. ___?___
g. ___?___ boundary	h. ___?___	i. ___?___	Mid-ocean ridge, ocean floor

Reviewing Key Terms

Choose the letter of the best answer.

1. The relatively soft layer of the upper mantle is the
   a. asthenosphere.
   b. lithosphere.
   c. inner core.
   d. continental crust.

2. The transfer of heat by the direct contact of particles of matter is
   a. pressure.
   b. radiation.
   c. conduction.
   d. convection.

3. Subduction of the ocean floor takes place at
   a. the lower mantle.
   b. mid-ocean ridges.
   c. rift valleys.
   d. trenches.

4. The process that powers plate tectonics is
   a. radiation.
   b. convection.
   c. conduction.
   d. subduction.

5. Two plates collide with each other at
   a. a divergent boundary.
   b. a convergent boundary.
   c. the boundary between the mantle and the crust.
   d. a transform boundary.

If the statement is true, write *true*. If it is false, change the underlined word or words to make the statement true.

6. Continental <u>crust</u> is made of rocks such as granite.

7. Slow movements of mantle rock called <u>radiation</u> transfer heat in the mantle.

8. The single landmass that broke apart 250 million years ago was <u>Pangaea</u>.

9. <u>Mid-ocean ridges</u> are places where oceanic crust sinks back to the mantle.

10. When two continental plates diverge, a <u>transform boundary</u> forms.

Writing in Science

Prediction Now that you have learned about the theory of plate tectonics, write a paragraph predicting what the shape and positions of Earth's continents will be 50 million years in the future. Include what would happen to the oceans if continental landmasses became connected in new ways or drifted from their present locations.

Discovery CHANNEL SCHOOL

Plate Tectonics
Video Preview
Video Field Trip
▶ Video Assessment

Go Online
PHSchool.com
For: Self-Assessment
Visit: PHSchool.com
Web Code: cfa-1010

Students can take an online practice test that is automatically scored.

All in One Teaching Resources
- Transparency F13
- Chapter Test
- Performance Assessment Teacher Notes
- Performance Assessment Teacher Worksheet
- Performance Assessment Scoring Rubric

ExamView® **Computer Test Bank CD-ROM**

Review and Assessment

Organizing Information
a. transform
b. Crust is sheared.
c. strike-slip fault
d. convergent
e. Plates move together.
f. mountains, volcanoes
g. divergent
h. Plates move apart.
i. crust pulled apart by tension forces

Reviewing Key Terms
1. a   2. c   3. d   4. b   5. b
6. true
7. convection currents
8. true
9. Deep-ocean trenches
10. rift valley or divergent boundary

Discovery CHANNEL SCHOOL Video Assessment

Plate Tectonics

Show the Video Assessment to review chapter content and as a prompt for the writing assignment. Discussion questions: **What forces cause the plates to move?** (*The plates move continuously in response to slow-moving convection currents in the mantle.*) **What was Pangaea?** (*A huge super-continent that existed 250 million years ago*)

Writing in Science

Writing Skill Explanation

Scoring Rubric
4 Includes a prediction of the shape and position of Earth's continents and the effects on the oceans; states additional information, such as secondary effects on plants and animals
3 Includes all criteria
2 Includes only brief description
1 Includes prediction that is not based on facts learned in this chapter

Checking Concepts

11. Geologists study rocks from Earth's mantle and deep crust and the speeds and directions of seismic waves.

12. They increase.

13. Earth's core moves (spins). Movement of the liquid outer core causes the magnetic field.

14. Rock near the bottom of the mantle gets very hot and, over millions of years, moves upward. Meanwhile, rock near the top of the mantle cools and sinks.

15. The older parts of the sea floor are subducted at trenches while new sea floor is produced at mid-ocean ridges.

16. Iron-bearing minerals acquire a weak magnetic field parallel to Earth's field at the time the rock forms. Rock magnetized in one direction forms along the mid-ocean ridge until Earth's magnetic poles reverse. Then rock magnetized in the opposite direction forms a new stripe of rock along each side of the mid-ocean ridge. The stripes provide support for the theory of sea-floor spreading.

Thinking Critically

17. Both continental crust and oceanic crust are parts of Earth's outer layer. Continental crust consists mainly of less dense rocks such as granite, whereas oceanic crust consists mainly of denser rock such as basalt. Oceanic crust is denser than continental crust.

18. lithosphere, asthenosphere, lower mantle, outer core, inner core

19. A subduction zone forms. The oceanic crust is more dense and therefore slides underneath the continental crust.

20. Heat from Earth's interior is the driving force of plate tectonics. The plates move over Earth's asthenosphere. Earth's internal heat causes convection currents in the mantle. The flow of these currents causes plate movement.

21. A theory is a well-tested concept that explains a wide range of observations. Plate tectonics is a theory because it is supported by much evidence and explains a wide range of observations, such as the locations of volcanoes and earthquakes. Continental drift was supported by some evidence, but it could not explain many observations. It lacked a viable mechanism to explain how plates move.

Math Practice

22. 14 cm/year

Review and Assessment

Checking Concepts

11. What kinds of indirect evidence do geologists use to study the structure of Earth?

12. How do temperature and pressure change as you go deeper into Earth?

13. What happens in Earth's interior to produce Earth's magnetic field? Describe the layer where the magnetic field is produced.

14. Why are there convection currents in the mantle?

15. Why are the oldest parts of the ocean floor no older than about 200 million years old?

16. How do magnetic stripes form on the ocean floor? Why are these stripes significant?

Thinking Critically

17. **Comparing and Contrasting** How are oceanic and continental crust alike? How do they differ?

18. **Sequencing** Place these terms in correct order so they begin at Earth's surface and move toward the center: inner core, asthenosphere, lower mantle, lithosphere, outer core.

19. **Predicting** In the diagram below, a plate of oceanic crust is colliding with a plate of continental crust. What will happen? Why?

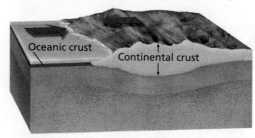

Oceanic crust   Continental crust

20. **Relating Cause and Effect** What do many geologists think is the driving force of plate tectonics? Explain.

21. **Making Judgments** Scientists refer to plate tectonics as a *theory*. What is a theory? How is plate tectonics a theory? Why isn't continental drift considered a theory? (*Hint:* Refer to the Skills Handbook for more on theories.)

Math Practice

22. **Calculating a Rate** It takes 100,000 years for a plate to move about 14 kilometers. Calculate the rate of plate motion.

Applying Skills

Use the map to answer Questions 23–25.

Geologists think that a new plate boundary is forming in the Indian Ocean. The part of the plate carrying Australia is twisting away from the part of the plate carrying India.

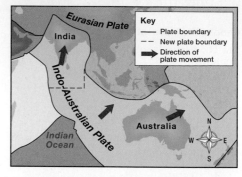

23. **Interpreting Maps** In what direction is the part of the plate carrying Australia moving? In what direction is the part carrying India moving?

24. **Predicting** As India and Australia move in different directions, what type of plate boundary will form between them?

25. **Inferring** What features could occur where the northern part of the Indo-Australian plate is colliding with the Eurasian plate?

Lab zone Chapter **Project**

Performance Assessment Present your model to the class. Point out the types of plate boundaries on your model. Discuss the plate motions and landforms that result in these areas.

Lab zone Chapter **Project**   L3

Project Wrap Up As each group presents its model of a cut-away Earth, assess how well the model reflects the concepts of Earth's layers, sea-floor spreading, and plate tectonics. Also assess the model for proper construction and eye appeal. Students explain what their model shows and how Earth's interior relates to the surface.

Reflect and Record Have students compare their model with other groups' models and consider how differences might have affected the final product. Other items to include in their reflections are which concepts were difficult to show in the model, what materials worked best, and what improvements could be made. Have students write their reflections in their journals.

Standardized Test Prep

Choose the letter that best answers the question or completes the statement.

1. Which of the following is evidence for sea-floor spreading?

   A matching patterns of magnetic stripes in the ocean floor

   B volcanic eruptions along mid-ocean ridges

   C older rock found farther from mid-ocean ridges

   D all of the above

2. Wegener thought the continents moved because fossils of the same organisms are found on widely separated continents. Wegener's use of fossil evidence is an example of a(n)

   F prediction.

   G observation.

   H inference.

   J controlled experiment.

3. The table below shows the movement of rock away from a mid-ocean ridge, and the time in years it takes sea-floor spreading to move the rock that distance.

Distance (meters)	Time (years)
50	4,000
100	8,000
150	12,000

What is the speed of the rock?

   A 0.0125 m per year   **B** 12.5 m per year

   C 80 m per year   **D** 200,000 m per year

4. Which of the following best describes the process in the diagram below?

   F Converging plates form a transform boundary.

   G Converging plates form volcanoes.

   H Diverging plates form a mid-ocean ridge.

   J Diverging plates form a rift valley.

Constructed Response

5. Today, the Mediterranean Sea lies between Europe and Africa. But the African plate is moving toward the Eurasian plate at a rate of a few centimeters per year. Predict how this area will change in 100 million years. In your answer, first explain how the Mediterranean Sea will change. Then explain what will happen on land.

Applying Skills

23. The part carrying Australia is moving to the northeast; the part carrying India is moving to the north.

24. Because the plates are moving in different directions, a divergent boundary will form between them.

25. Students infer that this is a convergent plate boundary where two plates made of continental crust are colliding. When the plates converge, the collision squeezes the crust into mountain ranges.

Standardized Test Prep

1. D   **2.** H   **3.** A   **4.** J

5. The Mediterranean will gradually decrease in size and there will be some mountain-building and volcanic activity in Eurasia. Eventually Africa will touch Eurasia.

Chapter at a Glance

Chapter Project — *Design and Build an Earthquake-Safe House*

Discovery CHANNEL SCHOOL
Video Preview

 **Teaching Resources**
- Chapter Project Teacher Notes, pp. 112–113
- Chapter Project Student Overview, pp. 114–115
- Chapter Project Student Worksheets, pp. 116–117
- Chapter Project Scoring Rubric, p. 118

Section 1

Forces in Earth's Crust

F.2.1.1 Explain how stress in the crust changes Earth's surface.

3 periods
1 1/2 blocks

F.2.1.2 Describe where faults are usually found and why they form.

F.2.1.3 Identify the land features that result from plate movement.

Go Online
SCI LINKS NSTA

Section 2

Earthquakes and Seismic Waves

F.2.2.1 Describe how the energy of an earthquake travels through Earth.

3 periods
1 1/2 blocks

F.2.2.2 Identify the scales used to measure the strength of an earthquake.

F.2.2.3 Explain how scientists locate the epicenter of an earthquake.

Go Online
active art

Discovery CHANNEL SCHOOL
Video Field Trip

Section 3

Monitoring Earthquakes

F.2.3.1 Explain how seismographs work.

2 periods
1 block

F.2.3.2 Describe how geologists monitor faults.

F.2.3.3 Explain how seismographic data are used.

Go Online
SCI LINKS NSTA

Section 4

Earthquake Safety

F.2.4.1 Explain how geologists determine earthquake risk.

1 period
1/2 block

F.2.4.2 Identify the kinds of damage an earthquake can cause.

F.2.4.3 Provide suggestions to increase earthquake safety and reduce earthquake damage.

Go Online
PHSchool.com

 **Teaching Resources**
- Key Terms Review, p. 153
- Transparency F23
- Performance Assessment Teacher Notes, p. 160
- Performance Assessment Scoring Rubric, p. 161
- Performance Assessment Student Worksheet, p. 162
- Chapter Test, pp.163–166

Go Online
PHSchool.com

Discovery CHANNEL SCHOOL
Video Assessment

Test Preparation Blackline Masters

Lab zone Chapter Activities Planner

For more activities

LAB ZONE
Easy Planner
CD-ROM

Student Edition	Inquiry	Time	Materials	Skills	Resources
Chapter Project, p. 43	Open-Ended	Ongoing (2–3 weeks)	**All in One** Teaching Resources, p. 112	Making models, relating cause and effect	**Lab zone Easy Planner**
Section 1					
Discover Activity, p. 44	Guided	5 minutes	Craft stick	Predicting	**Lab zone Easy Planner**
Try This, p. 48	Directed	10 minutes	Plastic putty	Classifying	**Lab zone Easy Planner**
Section 2					
Discover Activity, p. 51	Directed	10 minutes	Spring toy	Observing	**Lab zone Easy Planner**
Skills Activity, p. 55	Directed	5 minutes	None	Classifying	**Lab zone Easy Planner**
Skills Lab, pp. 58–59	Directed	Prep: 5 minutes Class: 35–40 minutes	Drawing compass with pencil, outline map of the United States	Interpreting data, drawing conclusions	**Lab zone Easy Planner** **Lab Activity Video** **All in One** Teaching Resources Skills Lab: *Finding the Epicenter, pp. 134–136*
Section 3					
Discover Activity, p. 60	Guided	15 minutes	Pan with 2–3 cm of gelatin, 4 plastic stirrers, pencil with eraser	Drawing conclusions	**Lab zone Easy Planner**
Skills Activity, p. 64	Directed	10 minutes	Small weight, spring scale, sandpaper, masking tape	Measuring	**Lab zone Easy Planner**
Technology Lab, pp. 66–67	Open-Ended	Prep: 20 minutes Class: 45–50 minutes	Large book, pencil, pen, 2 strips of paper, alternative materials such as the following: cardboard boxes, paper towel tubes, rubber bands, and wooden dowels	Designing, evaluating, troubleshooting	**Lab zone Easy Planner** **Lab Activity Video** **All in One** Teaching Resources Technology Lab: *Design a Seismograph, pp. 144–145*
Section 4					
Discover Activity, p. 68	Guided	10 minutes	5 straws, tape	Predicting	**Lab zone Easy Planner**
Try This Activity, p. 70	Directed	10 minutes	10 books ranging from light to heavy, 2 dishtowels	Predicting	**Lab zone Easy Planner**

Section 1 Forces in Earth's Crust

 *3 periods, 1 1/2 blocks*

ABILITY LEVELS
L1 Basic to Average
L3 For All Students
L3 Average to Advanced

Objectives

F.2.1.1 Explain how stress in the crust changes Earth's surface.
F.2.1.2 Describe where faults are usually found and why they form.
F.2.1.3 Identify the land features that result from plate movement.

Key Terms

• stress • tension • compression • shearing • normal fault • hanging wall
• footwall • reverse fault • strike-slip fault • anticline • syncline • plateau

Local Standards

Preteach

Build Background Knowledge

Students share their experiences about earthquakes or what they have learned from media and other sources.

 Lab zone Discover Activity *How Does Stress Affect Earth's Crust?* **L1**

Targeted Print and Technology Resources

All in One Teaching Resources

L2 Reading Strategy p. 121

⊙ **PresentationExpress™ CD-ROM**

Instruct

Types of Stress Use visuals and paper-folding techniques to demonstrate how stress in the crust changes Earth's surface.

Kinds of Faults Guide students to use their hands to demonstrate how types of faults depend on forces at work.

Changing Earth's Surface Use leading questions to open discussion of the surface changes that cause landforms and the types of landforms in the United States.

Targeted Print and Technology Resources

All in One Teaching Resources

L2 Guided Reading, pp. 121–124
L2 Transparencies F14, F15

www.SciLinks.org Web Code: scn-1021

⊙ **Student Edition on Audio CD**

Assess

Section Assessment Questions

 Have students use their definitions of vocabulary terms in this section to answer the questions.

Reteach

Students sketch the movement of each type of fault and list the landforms created by this type of fault.

Targeted Print and Technology Resources

All in One Teaching Resources

• Section Summary, p. 120
L1 Review and Reinforce, p. 125
L3 Enrich, p. 126

Section 2 Earthquakes and Seismic Waves

3 periods, 1 1/2 blocks

ABILITY LEVELS
L1 Basic to Average
L3 For All Students
L3 Average to Advanced

Objectives

F.2.2.1 Describe how the energy of an earthquake travels through Earth.
F.2.2.2 Identify the scales used to measure the strength of an earthquake.
F.2.2.3 Explain how scientists locate the epicenter of an earthquake.

Key Terms

• earthquake • focus • epicenter • P wave • S wave • surface wave
• Mercalli scale • magnitude • Richter scale • seismograph
• moment magnitude scale

Local Standards

Preteach

Build Background Knowledge

Students discuss waves they have observed and describe how waves move through water.

 **Discover Activity** *How Do Seismic Waves Travel Through Earth?* L1

Targeted Print and Technology Resources

 Teaching Resources

L2 Reading Strategy Transparency F16: Identifying Main Ideas

⊙ **PresentationExpress™ CD-ROM**

Instruct

Types of Seismic Waves Use the spring toy in the Discover activity to explain the different types of seismic waves and connect the movements of these waves.

Measuring Earthquakes Lead students to discuss and compare the different types of scales used to measure earthquakes.

Locating the Epicenter Use the map in the text to open discussion of how geologists determine the epicenter by using data from several seismograms.

 Skills Lab *Finding the Epicenter* L2

Targeted Print and Technology Resources

 Teaching Resources

L2 Guided Reading, pp. 129–131
L2 Transparency F17
L2 Skills Lab: *Finding the Epicenter,* pp. 134–136

📼 **Lab Activity Video/DVD**
Skills Lab: *Finding the Epicenter*

www.PHSchool.com Web Code: cfp-1022

⊙ **Student Edition on Audio CD**

Assess

Section Assessment Questions

Have students use their completed graphic organizers with main ideas and details to answer the questions.

Reteach

Students illustrate how seismic waves travel and how an earthquake is located by using waves.

Targeted Print and Technology Resources

Teaching Resources

• Section Summary, p. 128
L1 Review and Reinforce, p. 132
L3 Enrich, p. 133

Section 3 Monitoring Earthquakes

ABILITY LEVELS
L1 Basic to Average
L3 For All Students
L3 Average to Advanced

🕐 *2 periods, 1 block*

Objectives

F.2.3.1 Explain how seismographs work.

F.2.3.2 Describe how geologists monitor faults.

F.2.3.3 Explain how seismographic data are used.

Key Terms

• seismogram • friction

Local Standards

Preteach

Build Background Knowledge

Students discuss why predicting earthquakes is important and whether predictions will ever be accurate.

 **Discover Activity** *How Can Seismic Waves Be Detected?* **L1**

Targeted Print and Technology Resources

All in One **Teaching Resources**

L2 Reading Strategy Transparency F18: Sequencing

 PresentationExpress™ CD-ROM

Instruct

The Modern Seismograph Use visuals to examine and discuss how a seismograph works.

Instruments That Monitor Faults Guide students to compare and contrast instruments that detect phenomena that may indicate an impending earthquake.

Using Seismographic Data Describe how friction influences movements of rocks and allow students to demonstrate the concept by interlocking their hands and then pulling free.

 **Technology Lab** *Design a Seismograph* **L2**

Targeted Print and Technology Resources

All in One **Teaching Resources**

L2 Guided Reading, pp. 139–141

L2 Transparencies F19, F20

L2 Technology Lab: *Design a Seismograph*, pp. 144–145

📼 **Lab Activity Video/DVD**
Skills Lab: *Technology Lab: Design a Seismograph*

www.SciLinks.org Web Code: scn-1023

 Student Edition on Audio CD

Assess

Section Assessment Questions

Have students use their graphic organizers with their sequence information to answer the questions.

Reteach

Students name and describe the types of monitoring devices used to predict earthquakes.

Targeted Print and Technology Resources

All in One **Teaching Resources**

• Section Summary, p. 138

L1 Review and Reinforce, p. 142

L3 Enrich, p. 143

Section 4 Earthquake Safety

1 period, 1/2 block

ABILITY LEVELS
L1 Basic to Average
L3 For All Students
L3 Average to Advanced

Objectives

F.2.4.1 Explain how geologists determine earthquake risk.

F.2.4.2 Identify the kinds of damage an earthquake can cause.

F.2.4.3 Provide suggestions to increase earthquake safety and reduce earthquake damage.

Key Terms

• liquefaction • aftershock • tsunami • base-isolated building

Local Standards

Preteach

Build Background Knowledge

Students discuss structures they have seen in the context of the support the structures would lend to buildings, bridges, and the like that have been damaged by earthquakes.

 **Discover Activity** *Can Bracing Prevent Building Collapse?* L1

Targeted Print and Technology Resources

 Teaching Resources

L2 Reading Strategy Transparency F21: Asking Questions

 PresentationExpress™ CD-ROM

Instruct

Earthquake Risk Help students to examine plate boundaries in relation to earthquake risk.

How Earthquakes Cause Damage Ask leading questions to open discussion of how shaking, liquefaction, aftershocks, and tsunamis can cause damage, and apply those concepts to how damage to buildings could have been prevented.

Steps to Earthquake Safety Guide students to discuss safety measures in real-life scenarios and brainstorm supplies needed in an emergency kit.

Designing Safer Buildings Use models to demonstrate methods to help buildings withstand earthquakes and make homes safer.

Targeted Print and Technology Resources

Teaching Resources

L2 Guided Reading, pp. 148–150

L2 Transparency F22

www.PHSchool.com Web Code: cfd-1024

www.PHSchool.com Web Code: cfh-1020

Student Edition on Audio CD

Assess

Section Assessment Questions

Have students use their completed graphic organizers with their questions and answers to answer the questions.

Reteach

Students list the ways that earthquakes cause damage and how to make homes safer.

Targeted Print and Technology Resources

Teaching Resources

• Section Summary, p. 147

L1 Review and Reinforce, p. 151

L3 Enrich, p. 152

Chapter 2 Content Refresher

Go Online

NSTA-PDLINKS

For: Professional development support
Visit: www.SciLinks.org/PDLinks
Web Code: scf-1020

Professional
Development

Section 1 Forces in Earth's Crust

Thrust Faults One of the most common types of faults is a thrust fault. A thrust fault is a low-angle reverse fault in which the fault plane dips less than 45° and usually dips about 10°. The dip of the fault is the angle that the fault plane is tilted down from horizontal. Most of the displacement in a thrust fault is in a horizontal direction rather than in a vertical direction, as in reverse faults. Thrust faults can displace rocks over large high-angle horizontal distances. In some cases rocks can be moved hundreds of kilometers by thrust faults.

As in high-angle reverse faults, the hanging wall of a thrust fault has been moved up relative to the footwall. Thrust faults displace older rocks in the hanging wall over younger rocks in the footwall. In any fault or fold, wherever older rocks are found next to younger rocks, the older rocks have been displaced upward relative to the younger rocks. If you move over a fault, on the ground or on a map, from a younger rock unit to an older rock unit, you know which side of the fault has been moved up—the older side has moved up relative to the younger side. For example, the center of the fold in an anticline has been bent or folded upwards. In an anticline, the older rocks will be found in the center of the fold, with younger rocks along the outside of the fold.

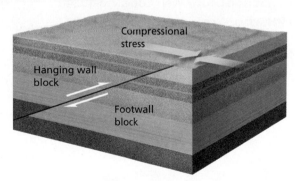

Section 2 Earthquakes and Seismic Waves

New Madrid Earthquakes From December 1811 to February 1812, three large earthquakes struck near New Madrid, Missouri. The earthquakes were felt over an area of at least 2 million square miles, from Canada to New Orleans. The earthquakes toppled chimneys as far away as Richmond, Virginia, and Cincinnati, Ohio. The shaking rang church bells in Washington, D.C., and in Boston, 1,100 miles away.

The land surface underwent significant changes over an area of 30,000 to 50,000 square miles. The ground was observed to move in long, low waves. As these waves rolled across the surface, large parallel fissures opened in the ground. Some of these were 600 to 700 feet long, with one reported to have a length of 5 miles. The land surface was raised several feet in some areas and lowered in others. Some of the lowered areas flooded to form lakes. Reelfoot Lake in Tennessee is one of these lakes. It is 8–10 miles long and 2–3 miles wide.

Since only about 3,000 people lived in the region, the damage was less than would be expected from such large earthquakes. No seismographs recorded the earthquakes. But scientists have estimated the strength of the earthquakes from eyewitness damage reports as measuring 7.2, 7.1, and 7.45 on the moment magnitude scale.

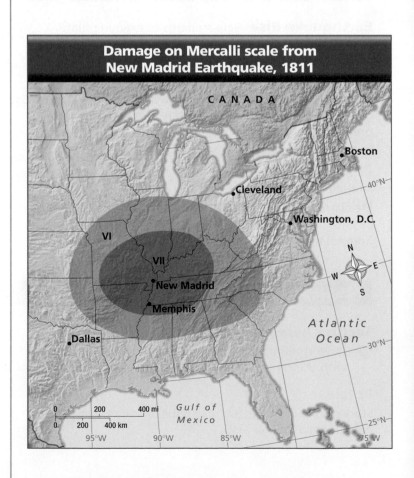

Damage on Mercalli scale from New Madrid Earthquake, 1811

Section 3
Monitoring Earthquakes

Predicting Earthquakes

One way the USGS estimates earthquake probability is to study the earthquake history of an area. Studying the history allows scientists to identify seismic gaps, which are

Address Misconceptions

Tsunamis are sometimes referred to as tidal waves. However, they have nothing to do with the tides. For a strategy for overcoming this misconception, see **Address Misconceptions** on page 70.

sections along active faults that have not experienced an earthquake in a long time. These gaps might be the most likely places for future earthquakes to occur. Scientists can then concentrate monitoring equipment, such as tiltmeters, creep meters, seismographs, and laser-ranging devices, in these gaps. So far, forecasting earthquakes based on the seismic gaps has not been successful.

Accidentally, scientists may have discovered a potential method to release the energy accumulated in rocks along a fault. In the late 1980s, wastewater was pumped down a disposal well near Denver, Colorado. The well was located near the Front Range fault, which runs along the front of the Rocky Mountains in this area. The water lubricated the fault and reduced the friction built up in the rocks. This triggered several small earthquakes. Scientists are now studying whether this method could be used to reduce friction along the dangerous portion of a major fault, such as the San Andreas. The costs and liability problems associated with this method of "controlling earthquakes" may make its practical use difficult.

Section 4 Earthquake Safety

Tsunami Warning System One of the greatest dangers associated with earthquakes is a tsunami. A tsunami is a seismic sea wave that is commonly but incorrectly called a tidal wave. These waves are caused when an earthquake occurs near or at the ocean floor. Tsunamis can also be caused by undersea volcanic eruptions and landslides. In the deep ocean, a tsunami can travel at speeds of over 1,000 km/h (600 mph). Wavelengths may be 200 km (124 miles) in the open ocean, but the wave heights may be only a few tens of centimeters.

Ships at sea commonly do not feel even potentially destructive tsunamis. Only when the waves reach shallow areas near shore do they become dangerous. In coastal areas, the waves can reach 10 m (30 feet) or more.

The Pacific Ocean is especially prone to tsunamis because of the high degree of seismic activity in and around the basin. In 1965, the Pacific Tsunami Warning System (PTWS) was established to monitor and study tsunamis and to provide early warning of a wave's approach. The PTWS consists of 25 member countries and is based in Honolulu, Hawaii. Seismograph stations and sea-level monitoring stations are located throughout the Pacific basin. Once a seismograph detects an earthquake, sea-level stations near the epicenter determine whether a tsunami has been generated. Not all undersea earthquakes produce tsunamis. If a tsunami is detected, a warning is issued to all the PTWS members. A similar warning system in the Indian Ocean was established in 2006, in response to the 2004 tsunami that killed more than 200,000 people.

Help Students Read

Relating Cause and Effect
Understanding How and Why Things Occur

Strategy Help students read and understand relationships between events. Cause-and-effect relationships are integral to science, so it is very important that students understand the cause-and-effect relationship developed in the text. Before students begin, assign a passage in the chapter for them to read, such as the section called *Changing Earth's Surface*.

Example
1. Remind students that a cause is what makes something happen and the effect is what happens as a result. Point out that in science, many actions cause other actions to occur.
2. Have students identify cause-and-effect relationships in the passage. Remind them that the text does not always directly state the cause-and-effect relationship, but in many cases clue words or phrases such as *because, so, results, therefore, cause,* and *lead to* do point out such a connection.
3. Explain that causes and effects often occur in chains, with effects becoming causes of later effects. Have students find a cause-and-effect chain and show it in the form of a flowchart.

The BIG Idea

The Big Idea is the major scientific concept of the chapter. It is followed by the Essential Question. Read aloud the question to students. As students study the chapter, tell them to think about the Essential Question. Explain that they will discover the answer to the question as they read. The chapter Study Guide provides a sample answer.

 **Chapter Project** L3

Objectives

This project will enhance students' knowledge of design features and materials that make structures more earthquake-resistant. After this Chapter Project, students will be able to

- make a model that incorporates construction methods and materials used to reduce damage to actual structures during an earthquake
- relate cause and effect to evaluate "earthquake" damage to the model
- apply concepts from the text to improve the model
- communicate how the design and materials used for the model help make it earthquake-resistant
- predict how well an actual structure built on the model's design would survive an earthquake

Skills Focus

Making models, relating cause and effect, applying concepts, communicating, predicting

Project Time Line 2 to 3 weeks

All in One Teaching Resources

- Chapter Project Teacher Notes
- Chapter Project Overview
- Chapter Project Worksheet 1
- Chapter Project Worksheet 2
- Chapter Project Scoring Rubric

Developing a Plan

Have each student first sketch a design for the model structure, choose materials, and discuss the design with classmates. Have students complete the first design, build the model, and test it in a simulated earthquake. Students can then use what they have learned to improve their models, test them, and make any final changes.

Chapter 2
Earthquakes

The BIG Idea
Energy Transfer and Earth's Structure

Q What force deforms Earth's crust and causes earthquakes?

Chapter Preview

❶ **Forces in Earth's Crust**
Discover How Does Stress Affect Earth's Crust?
Try This Modeling Stress
At-Home Activity Modeling Faults

❷ **Earthquakes and Seismic Waves**
Discover How Do Seismic Waves Travel Through Earth?
Active Art Seismic Waves
Skills Activity Classifying
Analyzing Data Seismic Wave Speeds
Skills Lab Finding the Epicenter

❸ **Monitoring Earthquakes**
Discover How Can Seismic Waves Be Detected?
Skills Activity Measuring Friction
Technology Lab Design a Seismograph

❹ **Earthquake Safety**
Discover Can Bracing Prevent Building Collapse?
Try This Stable or Unstable?

An earthquake destroyed this freeway in Oakland, California, in 1989. ▶

42 ◆ F

Possible Materials

- Provide a wide variety of materials, such as craft sticks, pretzels, toothpicks, wooden dowels, straws, uncooked pasta, bread sticks, washers, tissue paper, foam plastic, glue, aluminum foil, tape, rubber, gumdrops, clay, staples, paper clips, foam rubber, rubber, cotton batting, small springs, and cement.

- Discourage students from using materials that would not behave realistically—for example, modeling walls with index cards that would not tear during shaking. Also, construction toys would make the structures too solid.
- To simulate earthquakes, students could place the model structures on a cafeteria tray, a piece of plywood, a small table, or an other base and then hold the base at opposite ends while shaking it back and forth.

Lab zone™ Chapter **Project**

Design and Build an Earthquake-Safe House

Earthquakes like the ones that caused the damage in this picture are proof that our planet is subject to great forces from within. Earthquakes remind us that we live on the moving pieces of Earth's crust. In this Chapter Project you will design a structure that can withstand earthquakes.

Your Goal To design, build, and test a model structure that is earthquake resistant

Your structure must
● be made of materials that have been approved by your teacher
● be built to specifications agreed on by your class
● be able to withstand several "earthquakes" of increasing intensity
● be built following the safety guidelines in Appendix A

Plan It! Before you design your model, find out how earthquakes damage structures such as homes, office buildings, and highways. Preview the chapter to find out how engineers design structures to withstand earthquakes. Then choose materials for your structure and sketch your design. When your teacher has approved your design, build and test your structure.

Chapter 2 F ◆ 43

Earthquakes

Show the Video Preview to introduce the Chapter Project and present an overview of the chapter content. Ask: **What do you think causes earthquakes?** (*Accept student responses that show some connection between the forces exerted and plate tectonics.*)

Launching the Project

To introduce the project, have each student build a simple structure from toothpicks and tape, subject it to a simulated earthquake, and observe what happens to it. Ask: **How could you improve your structure so that it would be stronger in an earthquake?** (*Accept all responses at this time, and encourage creative thinking.*) Encourage discussion of the different kinds of structures students could model and the materials they could use.

Performance Assessment

The Chapter Project Scoring Rubric will help you evaluate how well students complete the Chapter Project. You may want to share the scoring rubric with your students so that they are clear about what is expected of them. Students will be assessed on

● designing their models, including the selection of appropriate building materials and effective construction methods
● their creativity and neatness in building the models
● how well they work with others in testing the models and devising improvements
● how well they present their models to the class

Portfolio

Objectives

After this lesson, students will be able to

F2.1.1 Explain how stress in the crust changes Earth's surface

F2.1.2 Describe where faults are usually found and why they form

F2.1.3 Identify the land features that result from plate movement

Target Reading Skill 🎯

Building Vocabulary Explain that knowing the definitions of key-concept words helps students understand what they read.

Answers

As students read each passage that contains a key term, encourage them to write a few descriptive phrases that will help them remember the key term. Invite students to share their definitions.

Preteach

Build Background Knowledge   L2

Experience with Earthquakes

Encourage any students who have experienced an earthquake to describe the event—where they were at the time, how they first became aware that an earthquake was occurring, what happened to the buildings and objects around them, how they felt during and after the quake, and so on. If students have not experienced an earthquake, let them relate what they have learned from television reports, movies, newspaper and magazine articles, and other sources.

Reading Preview

Key Concepts

- How does stress in the crust change Earth's surface?
- Where are faults usually found, and why do they form?
- What land features result from the forces of plate movement?

Key Terms

- stress • tension
- compression • shearing
- normal fault • hanging wall
- footwall • reverse fault
- strike-slip fault • anticline
- syncline • plateau

🎯 Target Reading Skill

Building Vocabulary
A definition states the meaning of a word or phrase. As you read, write a definition of each Key Term in your own words.

FIGURE 1
Effects of Stress
Powerful forces in Earth's crust caused the ground beneath this athletic field in Taiwan to change its shape.

44 ◆ F

Lab zone Discover **Activity**

How Does Stress Affect Earth's Crust?

1. Put on your goggles.
2. Holding a popsicle stick at both ends, slowly bend it into an arch.
3. Release the pressure on the popsicle stick and observe what happens.
4. Repeat Steps 1 and 2. This time, however, keep bending the ends of the popsicle stick toward each other. What happens to the wood?

Think It Over
Predicting Think of the popsicle stick as a model for part of Earth's crust. What do you think might eventually happen as the forces of plate movement bend the crust?

The movement of Earth's plates creates enormous forces that squeeze or pull the rock in the crust as if it were a candy bar. These forces are examples of **stress,** a force that acts on rock to change its shape or volume. (A rock's volume is the amount of space the rock takes up.) Because stress is a force, it adds energy to the rock. The energy is stored in the rock until the rock changes shape or breaks.

If you try to break a caramel candy bar in two, it may only bend and stretch at first. Like a candy bar, many types of rock can bend or fold. But beyond a certain limit, even these rocks will break.

Lab zone Discover **Activity**

Skills Focus Predicting   L1

Materials craft stick

Time 5 minutes

Tips In Step 2, advise students to increase the pressure on the stick slowly and gradually. In Step 3, caution students to maintain a firm grip on one end of the craft stick as they release the pressure so that the stick does not fly into the air and cause injury.

Expected Outcome When students release the pressure in Step 3, the stick will spring back and straighten. As they continue bending in Step 4, the stick will break.

Think It Over The crust will break.

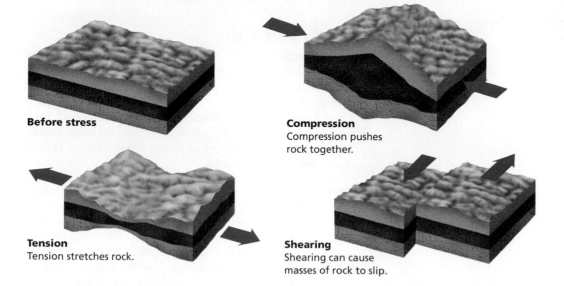

Before stress

Compression
Compression pushes rock together.

Tension
Tension stretches rock.

Shearing
Shearing can cause masses of rock to slip.

Types of Stress

Three different kinds of stress can occur in the crust—tension, compression, and shearing. **Tension, compression, and shearing work over millions of years to change the shape and volume of rock.** These forces cause some rocks to become brittle and snap. Other rocks bend slowly, like road tar softened by the sun. Figure 2 shows how stress affects the crust.

Most changes in the crust occur so slowly that they cannot be observed directly. But if you could speed up time so a billion years passed by in minutes, you could see the crust bend, stretch, break, tilt, fold, and slide. The slow shift of Earth's plates causes these changes.

Tension The stress force called **tension** pulls on the crust, stretching rock so that it becomes thinner in the middle. The effect of tension on rock is somewhat like pulling apart a piece of warm bubble gum. Tension occurs where two plates are moving apart.

Compression The stress force called **compression** squeezes rock until it folds or breaks. One plate pushing against another can compress rock like a giant trash compactor.

Shearing Stress that pushes a mass of rock in two opposite directions is called **shearing**. Shearing can cause rock to break and slip apart or to change its shape.

 Reading Checkpoint How does shearing affect rock in Earth's crust?

FIGURE 2
Stress in Earth's Crust
Stress forces push, pull, or twist the rocks in Earth's crust.
Relating Cause and Effect Which type of stress tends to shorten part of the crust?

Differentiated Instruction

English Learners/Beginning L1
Comprehension: Link to Visual
Use **Figure 2** to help students contrast the three types of stress forces in Earth's crust. Review the terms *tension, compression,* and *shearing.* Point to the arrows and ask students to describe what is happening in each illustration. **learning modality: visual**

English Learners/Intermediate L2
Comprehension: Link to Visual
Have each student construct a three-column table that describes the characteristics of the different types of stress. Under each heading, students can write key terms that define each type of stress and then draw a sketch of that type. **learning modality: visual**

Instruct

Types of Stress

Teach Key Concepts L2
Stress in Earth's Crust

Focus Remind students that the motion of magma just under Earth's crust causes the movement of plates.

Teach Ask: **How does stress in the crust change Earth's surface?** (*Stress pushes, pulls, or twists the rocks in Earth's crust.*) Have students examine the types of stress in Figure 2. **What type of landform results from tension?** (*Valley*) **What type of landform results from compression?** (*Mountain*)

Apply Have students demonstrate the three kinds of stress with a piece of paper. **Shearing:** (Fold the piece of paper in half and rub the two sides together.) **Compression:** (Crumple the paper.) **Tension:** (Pull the paper in opposite directions.) **learning modality: kinesthetic**

All in One Teaching Resources
• Transparency F14

Independent Practice L2
• Guided Reading and Study Worksheet: *Forces in Earth's Crust*

 Student Edition on Audio CD

Help Students Read L1
Relating Cause and Effect Encourage students to list cause-and-effect relationships as they read about stress, faults, and Earth's surface. Then have students compare their lists. **learning modality: logical/ mathematical**

Monitor Progress L2

Oral Presentation Ask each student to explain, with the aid of a diagram, how the directions of force differ in compression, tension, and shearing.

Answers
Figure 2 Compression

 Reading Checkpoint Shearing can cause rock to break and slip apart.

Kinds of Faults

Teach Key Concepts

How Faults Form

Focus Point out that the type of fault that occurs depends on the kinds of forces acting on the rocks. **NOTE:** When geologists say that the hanging wall lies "above" the footwall, they are referring to the positions of the hanging wall and footwall in relation to the fault, not the elevation of the land surface.

Teach As students read the description of each type of fault and examine its diagram, ask them how they would show each type of fault. **Strike-slip fault** *(Hold the edges of the open hands against each other with the palms down, the fingers pointing away from the body, and the thumbs tucked below; then slide one hand away from the body and the other hand toward the body.)* **Normal fault** *(Hold the open hands with the fingers pointing toward one another, lay the fingers of one hand over the fingers of the other hand, and then move the hands away from each other.)* **Reverse fault** *(Hold the hands as described for a normal fault, but move them toward each other.)*

Apply Remind students that there are places where plates are converging. Ask: **What do you think happens to Earth's crust in those places as the plates move toward each other?** *(Over long periods of time, the crust compresses, forming mountains and other landforms.)* **What type of stress force is occurring along those boundaries between plates?** *(Compression)* **What type of fault would you expect to find there?** *(Reverse faults)* **learning modality: kinesthetic**

All in One Teaching Resources

• Transparency F15

Use Visuals: Figure 3

Kinds of Faults

Focus Direct students' attention to the illustrations of the different faults.

Teach Ask: **How can you tell by looking at the photograph in which direction the hanging wall has moved?** *(You can match up the rock layers on each side of the fault.)*

Apply Ask: **Would you use the same method to determine how rocks on either side of the strike-slip fault have moved? Why or why not?** *(No, you would need to use another method because the rock has not moved up or down.)* **learning modality: visual**

Kinds of Faults

When enough stress builds up in rock, the rock breaks, creating a fault. Recall that a fault is a break in the rock of the crust where rock surfaces slip past each other. The rocks on both sides of a fault can move up or down or sideways. **Most faults occur along plate boundaries, where the forces of plate motion push or pull the crust so much that the crust breaks. There are three main types of faults: normal faults, reverse faults, and strike-slip faults.**

Normal Faults Tension in Earth's crust pulls rock apart, causing **normal faults.** In a normal fault, the fault is at an angle, so one block of rock lies above the fault while the other block lies below the fault. The block of rock that lies above is called the **hanging wall.** The rock that lies below is called the **footwall.** Look at Figure 3 to see how the hanging wall lies above the footwall. When movement occurs along a normal fault, the hanging wall slips downward. Normal faults occur where plates diverge, or pull apart. For example, normal faults are found along the Rio Grande rift valley in New Mexico, where two pieces of Earth's crust are under tension.

FIGURE 3
Kinds of Faults

There are three main kinds of faults: normal faults, reverse faults, and strike-slip faults.
Inferring *Which half of a normal fault would you expect to form the floor of a valley? Why?*

Key

→ Force deforming the crust

→ Movement along the fault

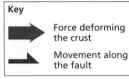

Footwall   Hanging wall

Normal fault
In a normal fault, the hanging wall slips down relative to the footwall.

Reverse Faults In places where the rock of the crust is pushed together, compression causes reverse faults to form. A **reverse fault** has the same structure as a normal fault, but the blocks move in the opposite direction. Look at Figure 3 to see how the rocks along a reverse fault move. As in a normal fault, one side of a reverse fault lies at an angle above the other side. The rock forming the hanging wall of a reverse fault slides up and over the footwall. Movement along reverse faults produced part of the northern Rocky Mountains in the western United States and Canada.

Strike-Slip Faults In places where plates move past each other, shearing creates strike-slip faults. In a **strike-slip fault**, the rocks on either side of the fault slip past each other sideways, with little up or down motion. A strike-slip fault that forms the boundary between two plates is called a transform boundary. The San Andreas fault in California is an example of a strike-slip fault that is a transform boundary.

For: Links on faults
Visit: www.SciLinks.org
Web Code: scn-1021

> **Reading Checkpoint** What is the difference between a hanging wall and a footwall?

Reverse fault
In a reverse fault, the hanging wall moves up relative to the footwall.

Strike-slip fault
Rocks on either side of a strike-slip fault slip past each other.

Differentiated Instruction

Gifted and Talented [L3]
Analyzing Visuals The San Andreas fault is particularly interesting because the deformations it produces in surface features are so clearly visible. Encourage students who need additional challenges to look through books and magazines to find photographs of such deformations and make multiple photocopies for the class to examine. Tell students to use the evidence in the photographs to locate and mark the fault line in each photograph and draw arrows to show the directions in which the two opposing rock slabs moved. **learning modality: visual**

For: Links on faults
Visit: www.SciLinks.org
Web Code: scn-1021

Download a worksheet that will guide students' review of Internet resources on faults.

Lab zone Build **Inquiry** [L2]

Modeling Faults

Materials 3 colors of modeling clay, thin plastic spatula

Time 20 minutes

Focus Have students draw a quick sketch of each type of fault. This will help them make their three-dimensional models.

Teach Ask student groups to use the clay to model each type of fault. They should layer the three colors of clay in three separate "blocks." They then can cut a different type of fault through each of the clay blocks and model the appropriate motion. Students can use the spatula to taper back the cliffs that form so that they look like real fault scarps. They also might make a "fence" or "road" that can be offset during strike-slip motion.

Apply Ask: **What formed when you modeled normal fault motion?** (*a cliff, or fault scarp*) **Would you expect to see similar features in nature?** (*Yes, there are many in the Rio Grande Rift, for example*) **learning modality: kinesthetic**

Monitor Progress [L2]

Drawing Have each student make a simple sketch of each type of fault without referring to the diagrams on these pages. Ask students to use arrows to show the block movements. Have them label each sketch with the name of the fault it shows. Have students place their drawings in their portfolios.

Answers
Figure 3 The hanging wall; it slips downward when movement occurs.

> **Reading Checkpoint** A hanging wall is the rock that lies above a fault; a footwall is the rock that lies below the fault.

Changing Earth's Surface

Teach Key Concepts

L2

Land Features

Focus Review with students the three kinds of stress: compression, tension, and shearing.

Teach Ask: **How can Earth's surface be changed over time?** (*It can be folded, stretched, and uplifted by plate movement.*) **Which type of land feature sometimes consists of anticlines and synclines?** (*Folded mountains*) **How can tension create mountains?** (*As Earth's crust is stretched, normal faults form. High areas occur between down-dropped blocks.*) **Which landform forms when a large area of land is uplifted without much folding or faulting?** (*Plateaus*)

Apply Ask: **Where in the United States are folded mountains, normal-fault mountains, and a plateau?** (*Folded mountains: parts of the Appalachians, such as the Valley and Ridge Province; normal-fault mountains: the Basin and Range region of Nevada and neighboring states; a plateau: the Colorado Plateau in the "Four Corners" region*) **learning modality: logical/mathematical**

Help Students Read

L1

Relating Cause and Effect Refer to the Reading Comprehension Skills in the Skills Handbook for guidance in relating cause and effect.

Help students understand how plate movement shapes Earth's surface. Ask them to create a flowchart beginning with two plates moving toward each other. **learning modality: logical/mathematical**

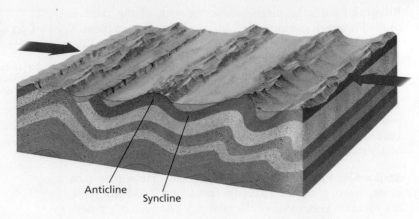

FIGURE 4
Effects of Folding Compression and folding of the crust produce anticlines, which arch upward, and synclines, which dip downward. Over millions of years, folding can push up high mountain ranges.
Predicting *If the folding in the diagram continued, what kind of fault might form?*

Anticline   Syncline

Changing Earth's Surface

The forces produced by the movement of Earth's plates can fold, stretch, and uplift the crust. **Over millions of years, the forces of plate movement can change a flat plain into landforms such as anticlines and synclines, folded mountains, fault-block mountains, and plateaus.**

Folding Earth's Crust Sometimes plate movement causes the crust to fold. Have you ever skidded on a rug that wrinkled up as your feet pushed it across the floor? Much as the rug wrinkles, rock stressed by compression may bend without breaking. Folds are bends in rock that form when compression shortens and thickens part of Earth's crust. A fold can be only a few centimeters across or hundreds of kilometers wide. You can often see small folds in the rock exposed where a highway has been cut through a hillside.

Geologists use the terms anticline and syncline to describe upward and downward folds in rock. A fold in rock that bends upward into an arch is an **anticline,** shown in Figure 4. A fold in rock that bends downward to form a valley is a **syncline.** Anticlines and synclines are found in many places where compression forces have folded the crust. The central Appalachian Mountains in Pennsylvania are folded mountains made up of anticlines and synclines.

The collision of two plates can cause compression and folding of the crust over a wide area. Folding produced some of the world's largest mountain ranges. The Himalayas in Asia and the Alps in Europe formed when pieces of the crust folded during the collision of two plates.

Lab zone — Try This **Activity**

Modeling Stress

You can model the stresses that create faults.

1. Knead a piece of plastic putty until it is soft.
2. Push the ends of the putty toward the middle.
3. Pull the ends apart.
4. Push half of the putty one way and the other half in the opposite direction.

Classifying Which step in this activity models the type of stress that would produce anticlines and synclines?

Lab zone — Try This **Activity**

Skills Focus Classifying

Materials plastic putty

Time 10 minutes

Tips After students soften the putty in Step 1, tell them to form it into a tube shape before they perform each subsequent step.

L1

Expected Outcome Step 2 represents compression, Step 3 represents tension, and Step 4 represents shearing.

Extend Have students repeat the activity with a stiffer material, such as modeling clay, and compare the results. **learning modality: kinesthetic**

Stretching Earth's Crust When two normal faults cut through a block of rock, a fault-block mountain forms. You can see a diagram of this process in Figure 5. How does this process begin? Where two plates move away from each other, tension forces create many normal faults. When two of these normal faults form parallel to each other, a block of rock is left lying between them. As the hanging wall of each normal fault slips downward, the block in between moves upward, forming a fault-block mountain.

If you traveled by car from Salt Lake City to Los Angeles, you would cross the Great Basin. This region contains many ranges of fault-block mountains separated by broad valleys, or basins.

✓ **Reading Checkpoint** What type of plate movement causes fault-block mountains to form?

FIGURE 5
Fault-Block Mountains
As tension forces pull the crust apart, two parallel normal faults can form a range of fault-block mountains, like this mountain range in Idaho.

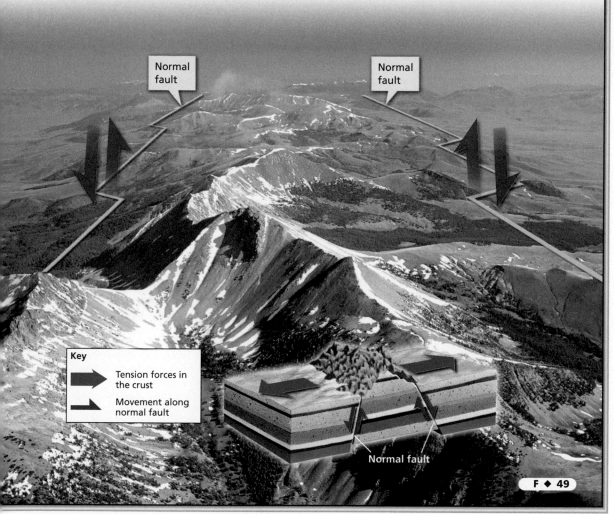

Normal fault

Normal fault

Key
→ Tension forces in the crust
→ Movement along normal fault

Normal fault

F ◆ 49

Lab zone Teacher **Demo**

Modeling Anticlines and Synclines L2

Materials stack of several sheets of construction paper of different colors

Focus Tell students that the different colors represent different rock layers.

Teach Model an anticline by laying the stack of papers on a desktop and pushing the two shorter ends toward each other; the stack will bend upward in the middle. To model a syncline, lay the stack across a space between two desks and push the ends; the stack will bend downward in the middle.

Apply Ask: **Why do hills often show different kinds of rocks?** *(Different kinds of rocks that once lay on top of one another were pushed up so that they now appear side by side.)* **learning modality: visual**

Monitor Progress ——— L2

Skills Check Have students compare and contrast the ways in which folded mountains, fault-block mountains, and plateaus are formed.

Answers
Figure 4 Reverse fault

✓ **Reading Checkpoint** Tension as plates pull apart

Assess

Reviewing Key Concepts

1. a. shearing, tension, and compression
b. Tension pulls on the crust, stretching rock so that it becomes thinner in the middle.
c. Compression squeezes rock; tension pulls on rock.
2. a. A break in the rock of the crust where rock surfaces slip past each other **b.** The forces of plate motion push and pull the crust so much that the crust eventually breaks. **c.** Normal, reverse
3. a. Anticlines, synclines, folded mountains, fault-block mountains, and plateaus **b.** Compression produces anticlines, synclines, and folded mountains; tension produces fault-block mountains.

Reteach   L1

Write the three types of stress on the board: *Tension, Compression,* and *Shearing.* As a class, discuss the types of faults each stress creates and have students sketch the movement of the rocks. Ask students to list the landforms created by each stress force.

Performance Assessment   L2

Skills Check To evaluate students' understanding of different types of faults and their ability to represent those concepts in a model, have each student use two dry kitchen sponges to show the movements involved in strike-slip, normal, and reverse faulting and explain the processes as they demonstrate them.

All in One Teaching Resources

- Section Summary: *Forces in Earth's Crust*
- Review and Reinforce: *Forces in Earth's Crust*
- Enrich: *Forces in Earth's Crust*

FIGURE 6
The Kaibab Plateau
The flat land on the horizon is the Kaibab Plateau, which forms the North Rim of the Grand Canyon in Arizona. The Kaibab Plateau is part of the Colorado Plateau.

Uplifting Earth's Crust The forces that raise mountains can also uplift, or raise, plateaus. A **plateau** is a large area of flat land elevated high above sea level. Some plateaus form when forces in Earth's crust push up a large, flat block of rock. Like a fancy sandwich, a plateau consists of many different flat layers, and is wider than it is tall.

Forces deforming the crust uplifted the Colorado Plateau in the "Four Corners" region of Arizona, Utah, Colorado, and New Mexico. Much of the Colorado Plateau lies more than 1,500 meters above sea level. Figure 6 shows one part of that plateau in northern Arizona.

Section 1 Assessment

Target Reading Skill **Building Vocabulary** Refer to your definitions of the Key Terms to help you answer the following questions.

Reviewing Key Concepts

1. a. Reviewing What are the three main types of stress in rock?
   b. Relating Cause and Effect How does tension change the shape of Earth's crust?
   c. Comparing and Contrasting Compare the way that compression affects the crust to the way that tension affects the crust.
2. a. Describing What is a fault?
   b. Explaining Why do faults often occur along plate boundaries?
   c. Relating Cause and Effect What type of fault is formed when plates diverge, or pull apart? What type of fault is formed when plates are pushed together?

3. a. Listing Name five kinds of landforms caused by plate movement.
   b. Relating Cause and Effect What are three landforms produced by compression in the crust? What landform is produced by tension?

Lab zone At-Home Activity

Modeling Faults To model Earth's crust, roll modeling clay into layers and then press the layers together to form a rectangular block. Use a plastic knife to slice through the block at an angle, forming a fault. Explain which parts of your model represent the land surface, the hanging wall, and the footwall. Then show the three ways in which the sides of the fault can move.

50 ◆ F

Lab zone At-Home Activity

Modeling Faults L2 Some students may prefer to use objects other than modeling clay to show movement along faults. After students have done the activity at home, discuss how they made their models.

Lab zone Chapter Project

Keep Students on Track Provide graph paper so that students can draw their models to scale. Suggest that students list the materials they plan to use and attach the lists to their scale drawings. Allow time for students to show their drawings to classmates and explain how they plan to build the models, as well as for classmates to ask questions and offer suggestions. Meet with students individually to offer guidance if they are having difficulty devising plans.

Reading Preview

Key Concepts
- How does the energy of an earthquake travel through Earth?
- What are the scales used to measure the strength of an earthquake?
- How do scientists locate the epicenter of an earthquake?

Key Terms
- earthquake • focus
- epicenter • P wave
- S wave • surface wave
- Mercalli scale • magnitude
- Richter scale • seismograph
- moment magnitude scale

Target Reading Skill
Identifying Main Ideas As you read Types of Seismic Waves, write the main idea in a graphic organizer like the one below. Then write three supporting details. The supporting details further explain the main idea.

Main Idea

Seismic waves carry the energy of an earthquake.

Detail	Detail	Detail

Lab zone — Discover Activity

How Do Seismic Waves Travel Through Earth?

1. Stretch a spring toy across the floor while a classmate holds the other end. Do not overstretch the toy.
2. Gather together about four coils of the spring toy and release them. In what direction do the coils move?
3. Once the spring toy has stopped moving, jerk one end of the toy from side to side once. Be certain your classmate has a secure grip on the other end. In what direction do the coils move?

Think It Over
Observing Describe the two types of wave motion that you observed in the spring toy.

Earth is never still. Every day, worldwide, there are several thousand earthquakes. An **earthquake** is the shaking and trembling that results from the movement of rock beneath Earth's surface. Most earthquakes are too small to notice. But a large earthquake can produce dramatic changes in Earth's surface and cause great damage.

The forces of plate movement cause earthquakes. Plate movements produce stress in Earth's crust, adding energy to rock and forming faults. Stress increases along a fault until the rock breaks. An earthquake begins. In seconds, the earthquake releases an enormous amount of stored energy.

Most earthquakes begin in the lithosphere within about 100 kilometers of Earth's surface. The **focus** (FOH kus) is the area beneath Earth's surface where rock that is under stress breaks, triggering an earthquake. The point on the surface directly above the focus is called the **epicenter** (EP uh sen tur).

Chapter 2 F ◆ 51

Objectives
After this lesson, students will be able to
F2.2.1 Describe how the energy of an earthquake travels through Earth
F2.2.2 Identify the scales used to measure the strength of an earthquake
F2.2.3 Explain how scientists locate the epicenter of an earthquake

Target Reading Skill

Identifying Main Ideas Explain that it is easier to understand something if you can identify the main idea as well as the details that support this idea.

Answers
Possible answers:
Detail: P waves compress and expand the ground.
Detail: S waves vibrate from side to side as well as up and down.
Detail: Surface waves produce the most severe ground movements.

All in One Teaching Resources
- Transparency F16

Preteach

Build Background Knowledge L2

Experience with Waves
Ask: **What kinds of waves have you observed?** *(Students probably will mention ocean waves and waves in a lake, a pond, a swimming pool, or even a bathtub.)* **How do waves move in water?** *(They probably will say that the waves move outward from a "push" on the water.)*

Lab zone — Discover Activity

Skills Focus Observing   **L1**

Materials spring toy

Time 10 minutes

Tips Advise students to hold both ends of the spring securely as they make the waves. If they have difficulty observing differences in the two wave types, allow them to repeat each step several times.

Expected Outcome In Step 2, the coils will move forward and backward along the spring in a straight line. In Step 3, the coils will move from side to side.

Think It Over In Step 2, the coils move forward and back as a wave moves from the compressed end of the spring to the other end in a straight line. In Step 3, the coils move from side to side as a wave moves in a bulge from the jerked end of the spring to the other end.

F ● 51

Instruct

Types of Seismic Waves

Teach Key Concepts L1
Movements of Waves

Focus Set up a row of dominoes, and touch one at one end so that each domino strikes its neighbor and all of the dominoes fall. Explain that energy was transferred first from your hand to the first domino, then to the second domino, and so on. This action is similar to the way that waves carry the energy that is released when rocks move.

Teach Remind students of their experience of creating waves with the spring toy in the Discover activity. Ask: **When the wave moved straight ahead along the spring, which type of earthquake wave did it model?** (*A P wave*) **When the spring moved from side to side, which type of wave did it model?** (*An S wave*) **When you used the spring, where was the focus of the model earthquake?** (*At the end that was compressed and jerked*)

Apply Ask: **Why do surface waves produce more severe ground movements than P waves and S waves do?** (*Because the surface consists of loose soil, sand, gravel, mud, small rocks, and similar materials, rather than solid rock, it is susceptible to greater movement as the particles shift and slide.*)

Extend The Active Art will show students how seismic waves behave and the damage they cause. **learning modality: logical/ mathematical**

All in One Teaching Resources
- Transparency F17

Independent Practice L2

All in One Teaching Resources
- Guided Reading and Study Worksheet: *Earthquakes and Seismic Waves*

 Student Edition on Audio CD

Types of Seismic Waves

Like a pebble thrown into a pond, an earthquake produces vibrations called waves. These waves carry energy as they travel outward. During an earthquake, seismic waves race out from the focus in all directions. Seismic waves are vibrations that travel through Earth carrying the energy released during an earthquake. The seismic waves move like ripples in a pond. **Seismic waves carry energy from an earthquake away from the focus, through Earth's interior, and across the surface.** That's what happened in 2002, when a powerful earthquake ruptured the Denali fault in Alaska, shown in Figure 7.

There are three main categories of seismic waves: P waves, S waves, and surface waves. An earthquake sends out two types of waves from its focus: P waves and S waves. When these waves reach Earth's surface at the epicenter, surface waves develop.

FIGURE 7
Seismic Waves
This diagram shows an earthquake along the Denali fault. An earthquake occurs when rocks fracture deep in the crust. The seismic waves move out in all directions from the focus. *Interpreting Diagrams* *At what point do seismic waves first reach the surface?*

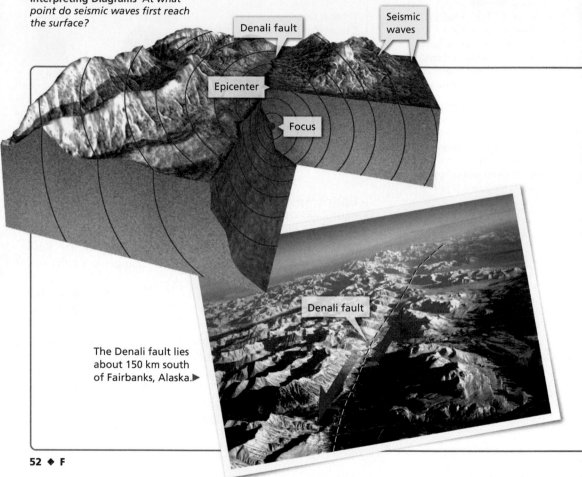

The Denali fault lies about 150 km south of Fairbanks, Alaska.▶

P Waves The first waves to arrive are primary waves, or P waves. **P waves** are seismic waves that compress and expand the ground like an accordion. Like the other types of seismic waves, P waves can damage buildings. Look at Figure 7 to see how P waves move.

S Waves After P waves come secondary waves, or S waves. **S waves** are seismic waves that vibrate from side to side as well as up and down. They shake the ground back and forth. When S waves reach the surface, they shake structures violently. Unlike P waves, which travel through both solids and liquids, S waves cannot move through liquids.

Surface Waves When P waves and S waves reach the surface, some of them become surface waves. **Surface waves** move more slowly than P waves and S waves, but they can produce severe ground movements. Some surface waves make the ground roll like ocean waves. Other surface waves shake buildings from side to side.

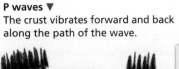 **Reading Checkpoint** Which type of seismic wave causes the ground to roll like ocean waves?

Go Online
active art
For: Seismic Waves activity
Visit: PHSchool.com
Web Code: cfp-1022

P waves ▼
The crust vibrates forward and back along the path of the wave.

Particle motion

Direction of waves ⟶

S waves ▼
The crust vibrates from side to side and up and down.

Particle motion

Direction of waves ⟶

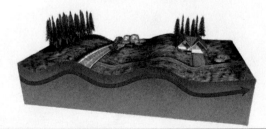

◄ **Surface waves**
The ground surface rolls with a wavelike motion.

F ◆ 53

Differentiated Instruction

Less Proficient Readers **L1**
Identifying Root Words and Suffixes
Students may wonder about the origins of the terms *seismic, seismograph, seismologist,* and *seismology.* Encourage students to look up these terms to find their common root. (*From* seismos, *the Greek word for earthquake,*

derived from seiein, *meaning "to shake"*) Also discuss the meanings of the suffixes
-graph (*a device that writes or records*),
-ology (*"the study of" something*), and
-ologist (*"a person who studies" something*).
learning modality: verbal

Go Online
active art
For: Seismic Waves activity
Visit: PHSchool.com
Web Code: cfp-1022
Students can interact with earthquake seismic waves and watch them move through the crust.

 Lab zone **Teacher Demo**

Comparing Types of Waves

Materials dishpans or other wide, shallow containers; water; pebbles

Time 10 minutes

Focus Ask students to recall how waves move when an earthquake occurs. (*They travel outward in all directions.*)

Teach Drop a pebble or another small object into a container filled from six to eight centimeters deep with water. Ask: **How did the waves move when a pebble hit the water?** (*The waves moved outward from the pebble in concentric rings.*) Draw students' attention to the pattern of seismic waves shown in the diagram. Ask: **How are seismic waves like the wave I made when I dropped a pebble into water?** (*Seismic waves also move outward in concentric rings.*) **How are they different?** (*Seismic waves move outward three-dimensionally in all directions, whereas the water waves moved only on the surface. Seismic waves move through solid materials.*)

Apply Using a paper clip, demonstrate P and S waves in the container of water. Have students identify which wave is occurring. Make sure that students understand the two types of waves and that they can accurately identify the differences in the movements they create. **learning modality: visual**

Monitor Progress _____ **L2**

Drawing Have each student draw and label a sketch showing an earthquake's focus underground, its epicenter on the surface, the different motions of P waves and S waves moving outward from the focus, and surface waves moving outward from the epicenter.

Answers
Figure 7 The epicenter

 Reading Checkpoint Surface waves

Instruct

Video Field Trip — Discovery Channel School

Earthquakes

Show the Video Field Trip to let students experience earthquakes and understand the different ways earthquakes are measured. Discussion questions: **How do the different seismic waves travel?** (*The primary, or P, waves travel fast through the ground and arrive first. The secondary, or S, waves arrive next with side-to-side and up-and-down motions.*) **What kind of ground movement does each one cause?** (*P: initial jolt; S: swaying ground*)

Teach Key Concepts   L1

Scales to Measure Earthquakes

Focus Most students probably have heard of the Richter scale. Ask them to share what they know. (*Students may say that the higher the number, the more destructive the earthquake.*)

Teach Ask: **How are the Mercalli scale and the Richter scale similar?** (*Both describe the "strength" of an earthquake.*) **How are they different?** (*The Mercalli scale describes an earthquake's strength in terms of its effects—to what extent people notice it and the amount of damage it causes. The Richter scale describes an earthquake's strength in terms of the size of its seismic waves.*)

Apply Ask: **On which scale would an earthquake's strength vary from one place to another, and why?** (*The Mercalli scale; the amount of shaking that people would feel and the damage to objects would be greater in a place closer to the quake's epicenter and less in a place farther away, so the intensity ratings in the two places would be different.*) **learning modality: logical/mathematical**

Help Students Read

Comparing and Contrasting   L1   Have students compare and contrast the methods of measuring earthquakes. Ask: **What are we asking when we say, "How big was the earthquake?"** (*Answers should include amount of damage, strength, and energy.*) **learning modality: logical/mathematical**

54 ● F

Earthquakes
- Video Preview
- ▶ Video Field Trip
- Video Assessment

Measuring Earthquakes

When an earthquake occurs, people want to know "How big was the quake?" and "Where was it centered?" When geologists want to know the size of an earthquake, they must consider many factors. As a result, there are at least 20 different measures for rating earthquakes, each with its strengths and shortcomings. **Three commonly used methods of measuring earthquakes are the Mercalli scale, the Richter scale, and the moment magnitude scale.**

The Mercalli Scale The **Mercalli scale** was developed to rate earthquakes according to the level of damage at a given place. The 12 steps of the Mercalli scale, shown in Figure 9, describe an earthquake's effects. The same earthquake can have different Mercalli ratings because it causes different amounts of ground motion at different locations.

The Richter Scale An earthquake's **magnitude** is a number that geologists assign to an earthquake based on the earthquake's size. Geologists determine magnitude by measuring the seismic waves and fault movement that occur during an earthquake. The **Richter scale** is a rating of an earthquake's magnitude based on the size of the earthquake's seismic waves. The seismic waves are measured by a **seismograph.** A seismograph is an instrument that records and measures seismic waves. The Richter scale provides accurate measurements for small, nearby earthquakes. But it does not work well for large or distant earthquakes.

Slight Damage

Moderate Damage

FIGURE 8
Levels of Earthquake Damage
The level of damage caused by an earthquake varies depending on the magnitude of the earthquake and the distance from the epicenter.

54 ◆ F

Great Destruction

Differentiated Instruction

Gifted and Talented   L3
Making a Time Line Have students investigate the ten largest earthquakes ever recorded around the world. They can make a banner for each that shows the location, magnitude, and a brief description of the damage. Have students find out whether scientists know what caused each earthquake; for example, experts may know that a large fault lay beneath the area. **learning modality: visual**

FIGURE 9
The Mercalli Scale
The Mercalli scale uses Roman numerals to rank earthquakes by how much damage they cause.
Applying Concepts *How would you rate the three examples of earthquake damage in Figure 8?*

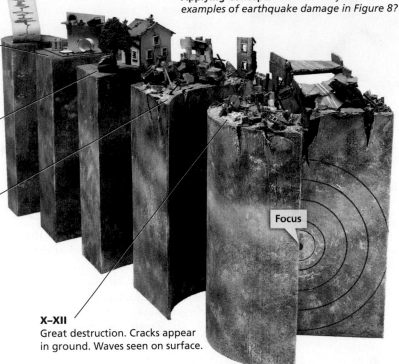

I–III
People notice vibrations like those from a passing truck. Unstable objects disturbed.

IV–VI
Slight damage. People run outdoors.

VII–IX
Moderate to heavy damage. Buildings jolted off foundations or destroyed.

Focus

X–XII
Great destruction. Cracks appear in ground. Waves seen on surface.

The Moment Magnitude Scale Geologists today often use the **moment magnitude scale,** a rating system that estimates the total energy released by an earthquake. The moment magnitude scale can be used to rate earthquakes of all sizes, near or far. You may hear news reports that mention the Richter scale. But the number they quote is almost always the moment magnitude for that earthquake.

To rate an earthquake on the moment magnitude scale, geologists first study data from seismographs. The data show what kinds of seismic waves the earthquake produced and how strong they were. The data also help geologists infer how much movement occurred along the fault and the strength of the rocks that broke when the fault slipped. Geologists use all this information to rate the quake on the moment magnitude scale.

 Reading Checkpoint What evidence do geologists use to rate an earthquake on the moment magnitude scale?

Lab zone Skills Activity

Classifying
Classify the earthquake damage at these locations using the Mercalli scale.

1. Many buildings are destroyed; cracks form in the ground.
2. Several old brick buildings and a bridge collapse.
3. Canned goods fall off shelves; walls crack; people go outside to see what's happening.

Lab zone Skills Activity

Skills Focus Classifying

Materials none

Time 5 minutes

Tips Have students refer to the Mercalli Scale figure to help them answer questions.

Expected Outcome 1. X–XII great destruction; 2. VII–IX moderate to heavy damage; 3. IV–VI slight damage

Extend Have students look at pictures from recent earthquakes and rate the damage, using the Mercalli scale in the figure above. **learning modality: visual**

Lab zone Build Inquiry L2

Inferring How to Locate the Epicenter

Materials None

Time 15 minutes

Focus Do the following activity in a large area such as a gym. Choose two students to role-play a P wave and an S wave. Position both students at a starting point, and position a third student some distance away to represent a seismograph.

Teach When you say "Earthquake!" have the two students start walking toward the third student, with the "P wave" student taking long forward strides and the "S wave" student taking shorter steps in a waddling gait to represent the side-to-side vibration of S waves. After a few seconds, say "Stop." Then ask: **Which wave is closer to the seismograph?** (*The P wave*) Repeat the activity with six students role-playing three pairs of P and S waves. Assign a number to each pair, and have all three pairs start walking at your signal. Say "One, stop," "Two, stop," and "Three, stop" at intervals. Have the students who are observing compare the distances between the P-wave and S-wave students in the three pairs. Ask: **Are all three distances the same?** (*No*) **How do they vary?** (*The P and S students who were walking for the shortest time are the closest together. The P and S students who were walking for the longest time are the farthest apart.*)

Apply Ask: **How would this difference help a geologist tell how far away an earthquake's epicenter is?** (*If the S waves arrive at a seismograph a very short time after the P waves, the epicenter is close to the seismograph; the longer the interval between the arrival times of the P waves and those of S waves, the farther away the epicenter is.*) **learning modality: kinesthetic**

Monitor Progress L2

Skills Check Have students compare and contrast the three types of seismic waves.

Answers
Figure 9 Top photo: I–III; middle photos: IV–VI, VII–IX; bottom photo: X–XII

 **Reading Checkpoint** The moment magnitude scale estimates the total energy released by an earthquake by recording the kinds of seismic waves produced and their strength.

Locating the Epicenter

Teach Key Concepts L1

Mapping an Earthquake's Location

Focus Ask students whether they have listened for thunder after seeing lightning. Ask: **Why do you hear thunder after you see lightning?** (*The sound waves of thunder travel more slowly than the light waves of lightning.*) Remind students that the time it takes for thunder to be heard after lightning flashes is an indication of how far away the lightning is. The same principle is used to find the location of an earthquake's epicenter.

Teach Review the meaning of the word *radius* (the distance from the center of a circle to its circumference), and have students find radii on the map in Figure 11. Ask: **Why have three circles been drawn on this map?** (*Each of the three circles was drawn on the basis of data from a different seismograph. The center of each circle is the location of one seismograph. The point at which the three circles intersect marks the epicenter of the earthquake.*)

Apply Ask: **Why would two circles not be enough to determine the epicenter?** (*Two circles would intersect at two points, not one, identifying two possible epicenters.*) **learning modality: visual**

Math ► Analyzing Data

Math Skill Making and Interpreting Graphs

Focus Point out the line graph, and discuss why this is an appropriate representation of the data.

Teach Review with students what the axes mean and how the grid is structured. Ask: **What is on the vertical axis?** (*Arrival time in minutes*) **What is on the horizontal axis?** (*Distance from epicenter in kilometers*) **What do the points on the graph show?** (*Plotted data*)

Answers
1. *x*-axis: distance from the epicenter; *y*-axis: arrival time
2. 7.5 minutes
3. 4 minutes
4. 2,000 = 3.5 minutes
4,000 = 4.5 minutes

FIGURE 10
Collecting Seismic Data
This geologist is checking data collected after an earthquake. These data can be used to pinpoint the epicenter of an earthquake.

Comparing Magnitudes An earthquake's magnitude tells geologists how much energy was released by the earthquake. Each one-point increase in magnitude represents the release of roughly 32 times more energy. For example, a magnitude 6 quake releases 32 times as much energy as a magnitude 5 quake, and about 1,000 times as much as a magnitude 4 quake.

The effects of an earthquake increase with magnitude. People scarcely notice earthquakes with magnitudes below 3. Earthquakes with a magnitude below 5 are small and cause little damage. Those with a magnitude between 5 and 6 can cause moderate damage. Earthquakes with a magnitude above 6 can cause great damage. Fortunately, the most powerful earthquakes, with a magnitude of 8 or above, are rare. During the twentieth century, only two earthquakes measured above 9 on the moment magnitude scale. These earthquakes occurred in Chile in 1960 and in Alaska in 1964.

Locating the Epicenter

Geologists use seismic waves to locate an earthquake's epicenter. Seismic waves travel at different speeds. P waves arrive at a seismograph first, with S waves following close behind. To tell how far the epicenter is from the seismograph, scientists measure the difference between the arrival times of the P waves and S waves. The farther away an earthquake is, the greater the time between the arrival of the P waves and the S waves.

Math ► Analyzing Data

Seismic Wave Speeds

Seismographs at five observation stations recorded the arrival times of the P and S waves produced by an earthquake. These data are shown in the graph.

1. **Reading Graphs** What variable is shown on the *x*-axis of the graph? The *y*-axis?

2. **Reading Graphs** How long did it take the S waves to travel 2,000 km?

3. **Estimating** How long did it take the P waves to travel 2,000 km?

4. **Calculating** What is the difference in the arrival times of the P waves and the S waves at 2,000 km? At 4,000 km?

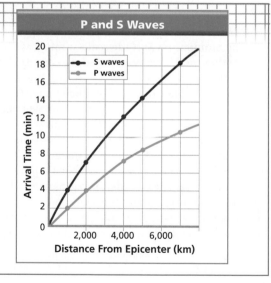

P and S Waves

(Legend: ● S waves ● P waves)

y-axis: Arrival Time (min)
x-axis: Distance From Epicenter (km)

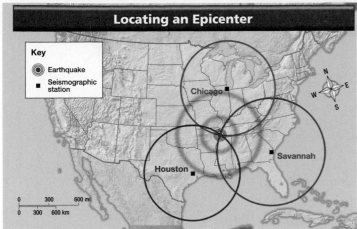

Locating an Epicenter

Key
- ◉ Earthquake
- ■ Seismographic station

Chicago

Houston

Savannah

0 300 600 mi
0 300 600 km

FIGURE 11
The map shows how to find the epicenter of an earthquake using data from three seismographic stations. **Measuring** *Use the map scale to determine the distances from Savannah and Houston to the epicenter. Which is closer?*

Geologists then draw at least three circles using data from different seismographs set up at stations all over the world. The center of each circle is a particular seismograph's location. The radius of each circle is the distance from that seismograph to the epicenter. As you can see in Figure 11, the point where the three circles intersect is the location of the epicenter.

 Reading Checkpoint What do geologists measure to determine the distance from a seismograph to an epicenter?

Section 2 Assessment

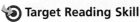 **Target Reading Skill**
Identifying Main Ideas Use your graphic organizer to help you answer Question 1 below.

Reviewing Key Concepts
1. **a. Reviewing** How does energy from an earthquake reach Earth's surface?
   b. Describing What kind of movement is produced by each of the three types of seismic waves?
   c. Sequencing When do P waves arrive at the surface in relation to S waves and surface waves?
2. **a. Defining** What is an earthquake's magnitude?
   b. Describing How is magnitude measured using the Richter scale?
   c. Applying Concepts What are the advantages of using the moment magnitude scale to measure an earthquake?

3. **a. Explaining** What type of data do geologists use to locate an earthquake's epicenter?
   b. Interpreting Maps Study the map in Figure 11 above. Then describe the method that scientists use to determine the epicenter of an earthquake.

Writing in Science

News Report As a television news reporter, you are covering an earthquake rated between IV and V on the Mercalli scale. Write a short news story describing the earthquake's effects. Your lead paragraph should tell *who, what, where, when,* and *how.* (*Hint:* Refer to Figure 9 for examples of earthquake damage.)

Lab zone Chapter Project

Keep Students on Track Encourage volunteers to describe any changes they made in their initial designs. Have students review their agreed-upon criteria for simulating earthquakes so that all models are subjected to the same degree of shaking. Emphasize the importance of taking notes about any damage that the models sustain and any weaknesses that are revealed.

Writing in Science

Writing Skill Cause-and-effect
Scoring Rubric
4 includes descriptions of earthquake effects and the who, what, where, when, and how of a news account; reads like an actual news account
3 includes all criteria
2 includes one or two of the criteria
1 includes inaccurate details

Monitor Progress _____ **L2**

Answers
Figure 11 Houston (about 800 km compared with about 900 km for Savannah)

 Reading Checkpoint The difference between the arrival times of the P waves and S waves

Assess

Reviewing Key Concepts
1. a. Seismic waves carry the energy of an earthquake away from the focus. Some of those waves reach the surface and become surface waves. **b.** *P waves:* Compress and expand the ground as they travel; move through solids and liquids; are the fastest-moving seismic waves. *S waves:* Vibrate from side to side and up and down as they travel; move only through solids. *Surface waves:* Move along the surface; move more slowly than P and S waves; can produce violent ground movements. **c.** P waves are the first waves to arrive during an earthquake, followed by S waves. As P and S waves reach the surface, they are transformed into surface waves.
2. a. A measurement of earthquake strength based on seismic waves and movement along faults **b.** The Richter scale describes an earthquake's strength in terms of the size of its seismic waves. **c.** It can rate all sizes of earthquakes, near or far.
3. a. Seismic waves **b.** Geologists measure the difference between arrival times of the P and S waves, using data from three seismographs. They then draw three circles, using the data from the seismographs. The point at which the circles intersect is the location of the epicenter.

Reteach **L1**
Ask students to illustrate how primary, secondary, and surface waves travel, and how seismologists use the waves' characteristics to determine the distance to an earthquake epicenter.

╳ All in One Teaching Resources
- Section Summary: *Earthquakes and Seismic Waves*
- Review and Reinforce: *Earthquakes and Seismic Waves*
- Enrich: *Earthquakes and Seismic Waves*

Finding the Epicenter [L3]

Prepare for Inquiry

Key Concept
Data from seismographs in three different locations can be used to identify an earthquake's epicenter.

Skills Objectives
Students will be able to
- interpret data to determine the distances of three seismographs from an earthquake's epicenter
- draw a conclusion about the location of the earthquake's epicenter

 Prep Time 5 minutes
Class Time 35–40 minutes

Advance Planning
Make a photocopy of the map for each student.

All in One Teaching Resources
- Lab Worksheet: *Finding the Epicenter*

Guide Inquiry

Invitation
Ask: **Why is it important for scientists to know where an earthquake's epicenter is located?** (*Accept all reasonable responses, such as the usefulness of this information in predicting future earthquakes.*) Then have students refer to Figure 11 on the previous page. Explain that in this activity, they will use the same technique to find an earthquake's epicenter.

Introducing the Procedure
Before students begin, review the use of a drawing compass and a map scale. Ask: **What do the numbers on the compass represent?** (*The distance in centimeters between the compass's metal point and the pencil point*) **If you set the compass at 7 and drew a circle, what would the circle's diameter be?** (*14 cm*) **What would its radius be?** (*7 cm*)
Next, ask: **What does a map scale show?** (*The distance on the map that represents a certain number of kilometers or miles on the real land surface*) **What is this map's scale?** (*Each centimeter on the map represents 300 km on land. If students cannot answer your*

Finding the Epicenter

Problem
How can you locate an earthquake's epicenter?

Skills Focus
interpreting data, drawing conclusions

Materials
- drawing compass with pencil
- outline map of the United States

Data Table

City	Difference in P and S Wave Arrival Times	Distance to Epicenter
Denver, Colorado	2 min 40 s	
Houston, Texas	1 min 50 s	
Chicago, Illinois	1 min 10 s	

Procedure

1. Make a copy of the data table showing differences in earthquake arrival times.

2. The graph shows how the difference in arrival time between P waves and S waves depends on the distance from the epicenter of the earthquake. Find the difference in arrival time for Denver on the *y*-axis of the graph. Follow this line across to the point at which it crosses the curve. To find the distance to the epicenter, read down from this point to the *x*-axis of the graph. Enter this distance in the data table.

3. Repeat Step 2 for Houston and Chicago.

4. Set your compass at a radius equal to the distance from Denver to the earthquake epicenter that you previously recorded in your data table.

5. Draw a circle with the radius determined in Step 4, using Denver as the center. Draw the circle on your copy of the map. (*Hint:* Draw your circles carefully. You may need to draw some parts of the circles off the map.)

6. Repeat Steps 4 and 5 for Houston and Chicago.

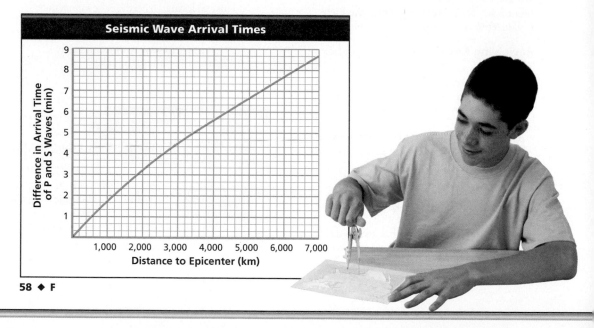

Seismic Wave Arrival Times

Difference in Arrival Time of P and S Waves (min) vs *Distance to Epicenter (km)*

---

question, have them lay a metric ruler along the scale line to see how many kilometers are represented by each centimeter.) **Suppose that you wanted to show a distance of 1800 km away from Denver on this map. How would you determine the length of that map measurement in centimeters?** (*Divide the distance you want to show by the number of kilometers represented by 1 cm on the map: 1800 km ÷ 300 km = 6 cm on the map.*) Then ask: **How would you use the compass to measure that distance?** (*Set the compass*

arm at 6 cm, hold the metal point on the dot for Denver, and draw a circle. To determine the compass setting, students also could hold the metal point on the 0 end of the scale line and adjust the compass arm so that the pencil point is at 1800 km on the line.*) **What does the circle show?** (*All the points 1800 km away from Denver*) If students need more practice, give them additional examples, not including the distances they will use in the activity.

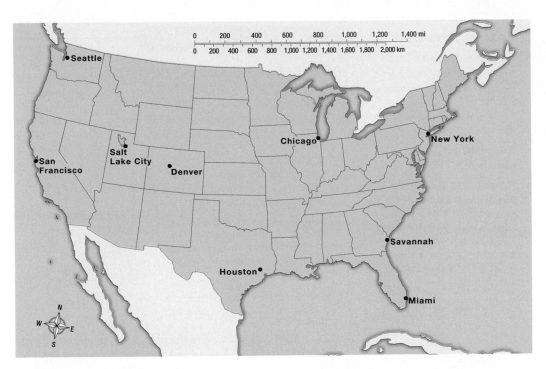

Analyze and Conclude

1. **Drawing Conclusions** Observe the three circles you have drawn. Where is the earthquake's epicenter?

2. **Measuring** Which city on the map is closest to the earthquake epicenter? How far, in kilometers, is this city from the epicenter?

3. **Inferring** In which of the three cities listed in the data table would seismographs detect the earthquake first? Last?

4. **Estimating** About how far from San Francisco is the epicenter that you found? What would be the difference in arrival times of the P waves and S waves for a recording station in San Francisco?

5. **Interpreting Data** What happens to the difference in arrival times between P waves and S waves as the distance from the earthquake increases?

6. **Communicating** Review the procedure you followed in this lab and then answer the following question. When you are trying to locate an epicenter, why is it necessary to know the distance from the epicenter for at least three recording stations?

More to Explore

You have just located an earthquake's epicenter. Find this earthquake's location on the map of Earthquake Risk in the United States (Figure 18). What is the risk of earthquakes in the area of this quake?

Now look at the map of Earth's Lithospheric Plates (Figure 22 in the chapter "Plate Tectonics"). What conclusions can you draw from this map about the cause of earthquakes in this area?

Troubleshooting the Experiment

• In Step 2, point out that the arrival-time differences listed in the table include seconds as well as minutes, whereas the labels on the *y*-axis give only whole minutes. Therefore, students will need to use the lighter lines on the graph to estimate the partial-minute differences as closely as they can. (Because there are two lighter lines dividing each whole-minute interval into three parts, each lighter line represents 20 seconds.)

• Remind students that they must use the map scale to determine where to set the compass arm for each distance in Steps 4 and 6.

Expected Outcome

The correct compass settings are 5.2 centimeters for Denver, 3.4 centimeters for Houston, and 2 centimeters for Chicago. The point on the map at which all three circles intersect will be about 600 kilometers south of Chicago.

Analyze and Conclude

1. The epicenter is located east of the Mississippi River on the border of Kentucky and Tennessee.

2. Chicago; 600 kilometers

3. *First:* Denver; *Last:* Miami

4. 2,900 kilometers from San Francisco; 4 minutes 25 seconds

5. The difference in arrival times also increases.

6. Using three recording stations enables you to identify one actual epicenter location, whereas using only two stations identifies two possible epicenter locations.

Extend the Inquiry

More to Explore This earthquake was not a freak event because it occurred in an area of moderate risk. Earthquakes in this area are caused by movement along the boundary between the Pacific and North American plates.

Objectives

After this lesson, students will be able to

F2.3.1 Explain how seismographs work

F2.3.2 Describe how geologists monitor faults

F2.3.3 Explain how seismographic data are used

Target Reading Skill

Sequencing Explain that sequencing means listing events in the order of their occurrence and that sequencing can help clarify a process.

Answers

One possible answer is this:
Incoming seismic waves
Drum vibrates
Pen traces a record of the vibrations

All in One Teaching Resources

• Transparency F18

Preteach

Build Background Knowledge

L2

Predicting Earthquakes

Ask: **Why is it important for scientists to develop ways to predict earthquakes?** (*A warning would allow people who live in the area to protect themselves by reinforcing buildings and other structures, by obtaining emergency supplies, and by taking other precautionary measures.*) **Do you think earthquake predictions will ever be very accurate? Why or why not?** (*Accept divergent responses so long as students support their views with well-reasoned explanations.*)

Reading Preview

Key Concepts
• How do seismographs work?
• How do geologists monitor faults?
• How are seismographic data used?

Key Terms
• seismogram • friction

Target Reading Skill

Sequencing As you read, make a flowchart like the one below that shows how a seismograph produces a seismogram. Write each step of the process in a separate box in the order in which it occurs.

How a Seismograph Works

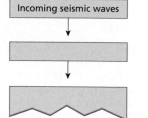

Incoming seismic waves

Lab zone | Discover Activity

How Can Seismic Waves Be Detected?

1. ✂ Using scissors, cut 4 plastic stirrers in half. Each piece should be about 5 cm long.
2. Your teacher will give you a pan containing gelatin. Gently insert the 8 stirrer pieces into the gelatin, spacing them about 2–3 cm apart in a row. The pieces should stand upright, but not touch the bottom of the pan.
3. At the opposite end of the pan from the stirrers, gently tap the surface of the gelatin once with the eraser end of a pencil. Observe the results.

Think It Over
Inferring What happened to the stirrer pieces when you tapped the gelatin? What was responsible for this effect?

Look at the beautiful vase in the photo. You might be surprised to learn that the vase is actually a scientific instrument. Can you guess what it was designed to do? Zhang Heng, an astronomer, designed and built this earthquake detection device in China nearly 2,000 years ago. It is said to have detected an earthquake centered several hundred kilometers away.

Earthquakes are dangerous, so people want to monitor them. To *monitor* means to "watch closely." Like the ancient Chinese, many societies have used technology to determine when and where earthquakes have occurred. During the late 1800s, scientists developed seismographs that were much more sensitive and accurate than any earlier devices.

FIGURE 12
Earthquake Detector
Nearly 2,000 years ago, a Chinese scientist invented this instrument to detect earthquakes.

Lab zone | Discover Activity

Skills Focus Inferring   **L1**

Materials pan with about 2–3 cm of gelatin, 4 plastic stirrers, pencil with eraser

Prep Time 30 minutes

Class Time 15 minutes

Tips Make the gelatin well in advance so that it will set. You will observe the best results if the gelatin is held at room

temperature 15 minutes before the activity. If kept too long at room temperature, the gelatin will become a liquid. Insert the stirrers most of the way through the gelatin, but make sure that they do not touch the bottom of the pan.

Expected Outcome Striking the gelatin with the pencil eraser will cause the plastic stirrers to vibrate. Students will observe

that the vibrations begin at the stirrer closest to the point that was tapped and then quickly move down the row of stirrers.

Think It Over The stirrers move after the eraser strikes the surface of the gelatin. Students infer that vibrations or waves traveling through the gelatin cause the stirrers to move.

The Seismograph

A simple seismograph can consist of a heavy weight attached to a frame by a spring or wire. A pen connected to the weight rests its point on a drum that can rotate. As the drum rotates slowly, the pen draws a straight line on paper wrapped tightly around the drum. **Seismic waves cause the seismograph's drum to vibrate. But the suspended weight with the pen attached moves very little. Therefore, the pen stays in place and records the drum's vibrations.**

Measuring Seismic Waves When you write a sentence, the paper stays in one place while your hand moves the pen. But in a seismograph, it's the pen that remains stationary while the paper moves. Why is this? All seismographs make use of a basic principle of physics: Whether it is moving or at rest, every object resists any change to its motion. A seismograph's heavy weight resists motion during a quake. But the rest of the seismograph is anchored to the ground and vibrates when seismic waves arrive.

Reading a Seismogram You have probably seen a zigzag pattern of lines used to represent an earthquake. The pattern of lines, called a **seismogram,** is the record of an earthquake's seismic waves produced by a seismograph. Study the seismogram in Figure 13 and notice when the P waves, S waves, and surface waves arrive. The height of the jagged lines drawn on the seismograph's drum is greater for a more severe earthquake or for an earthquake close to the seismograph.

 Reading Checkpoint What is a seismogram?

FIGURE 13
Recording Seismic Waves
A seismograph records seismic waves, producing a seismogram. Today, electronic seismographs contain sensors instead of pens.
Interpreting Diagrams *What is the function of the weight in the seismograph?*

Seismograph

- Wire
- Weight
- Pen
- Rotating Drum

Ground motion due to seismic waves

Seismogram

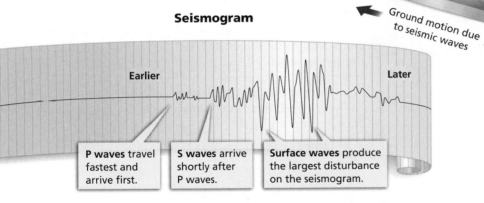

Earlier — Later

P waves travel fastest and arrive first.

S waves arrive shortly after P waves.

Surface waves produce the largest disturbance on the seismogram.

Differentiated Instruction

Less Proficient Readers
Describing Monitoring Devices
Have students describe each monitoring device in their own words rather than copy the text information. Let students share their sentences in a follow-up class

L1 discussion. Guide students to agree on one "best sentence" for each device that incorporates the most important points mentioned in students' sentences. **learning modality: verbal**

The Seismograph

Teach Key Concepts

Measuring Seismic Waves **L1**

Focus Review with students the three categories of seismic waves.

Teach Have students examine Figure 13 as a volunteer reads the passage aloud. Ask: **Which part of the seismograph moves as the ground shakes during an earthquake?** (*The rotating drum*) **How are the heights of the lines related to the strength of an earthquake?** (*The more the ground moves, the farther back and forth the lines trace.*)

Apply Ask: **How do geologists use a seismogram to determine when an earthquake started?** (*They note the difference in arrival times of P waves and S waves.*)
learning modality: logical/mathematical

All in One Teaching Resources
- Transparency F19

Independent Practice **L2**

All in One Teaching Resources
- Guided Reading and Study Worksheet: *Monitoring Earthquakes*

◉ Student Edition on Audio CD

Help Students Read **L1**

Outlining Have students create an outline of the section *Monitoring Earthquakes*. Outlines should follow the head structure used in the section. Ask: **Based on your outline, what are four types of motion detectors?** (*tiltmeter, creep meter, laser-ranging device, GPS satellite*)

Monitor Progress _____ **L2**

Drawing Have each student draw and label a simple diagram explaining how a mechanical seismograph works.

Answers
Figure 13 The weight holds the pen steady. When the ground shakes, the pen stays in place.

Reading Checkpoint The pattern of lines that is the record of an earthquake's seismic waves produced by a seismograph

Instruments That Monitor Faults

Teach Key Concepts L1

Monitoring Devices

Focus In order to measure stress in Earth's crust, geologists have developed sensitive instruments to record ground movement.

Teach Ask: **What kind of equipment do geologists use to monitor the movement of faults?** (*Creep meters, laser-ranging devices, tiltmeters, satellites*) **How are a laser-ranging device and a creep meter similar? How are they different?** (*Similarity: Both measure movement along a fault. Differences: A creep meter measures horizontal movement only; a laser-ranging device measures any change in distance from the reflector. A creep meter provides gross measurements; a laser-ranging device provides precise measurements.*)

Apply Ask: **What might be happening deep underground to cause small changes in the elevation or tilt of the land surface before an earthquake?** (*The blocks of rock might be moving just slightly along a normal or reverse fault. In a normal fault, the hanging wall's surface would fall. In a reverse fault, its surface would rise.*) **What types of changes might indicate movement along a strike-slip fault?** (*Sideways distortions in objects that cross the fault, such as roads or fences*)
learning modality: logical/mathematical

All in One Teaching Resources

• Transparency F20

Go Online
SciLINKS NSTA

For: Links on earthquake measurement
Visit: www.SciLinks.org
Web Code: scn-1023

Download a worksheet to guide students' review of Internet resources on earthquake measurement.

Instruments That Monitor Faults

Along a fault, scientists may detect a slight rise or fall in the elevation and tilt of the land. Geologists hypothesize that such changes signal a buildup of stress in rock. Increasing stress could eventually lead to an earthquake. **To monitor faults, geologists have developed instruments to measure changes in elevation, tilting of the land surface, and ground movements along faults.** Some of the instruments that geologists use to monitor these movements include tiltmeters, creep meters, laser-ranging devices, and satellites.

Tiltmeters A tiltmeter measures tilting or raising of the ground. If you have ever used a carpenter's level, you have used a type of tiltmeter. The tiltmeters used by geologists consist of two bulbs that are filled with a liquid and connected by a hollow stem. Notice that if the land rises or falls slightly, the liquid will flow from one bulb to the other. Each bulb contains a measuring scale to measure the depth of the liquid in that bulb. Geologists read the scales to measure the amount of tilt occurring along the fault.

Creep Meters A creep meter uses a wire stretched across a fault to measure horizontal movement of the ground. On one side of the fault, the wire is anchored to a post. On the other side, the wire is attached to a weight that can slide if the fault moves. Geologists determine how much the fault has moved by measuring how much the weight has moved against a scale.

Laser-Ranging Devices A laser-ranging device uses a laser beam to detect horizontal fault movements. The device times a laser beam as it travels to a reflector and back. Thus, the device can detect any change in distance to the reflector.

GPS Satellites Scientists can monitor changes in elevation as well as horizontal movement along faults using a network of Earth-orbiting satellites called GPS. GPS, the Global Positioning System, was developed to help ships and planes find their routes. As shown in Figure 14, GPS can also be used to locate points on Earth's surface with great precision. Using GPS, scientists measure tiny movements of markers set up on the opposite sides of a fault.

 Reading Checkpoint How does a creep meter work?

Go Online
SciLINKS NSTA

For: Links on earthquake measurement
Visit: www.SciLinks.org
Web Code: scn-1023

FIGURE 14
Motion Detectors

To detect slight motions along faults, geologists use several types of devices.
Comparing and Contrasting *Which of these devices measure horizontal movement? Which ones measure vertical movement?*

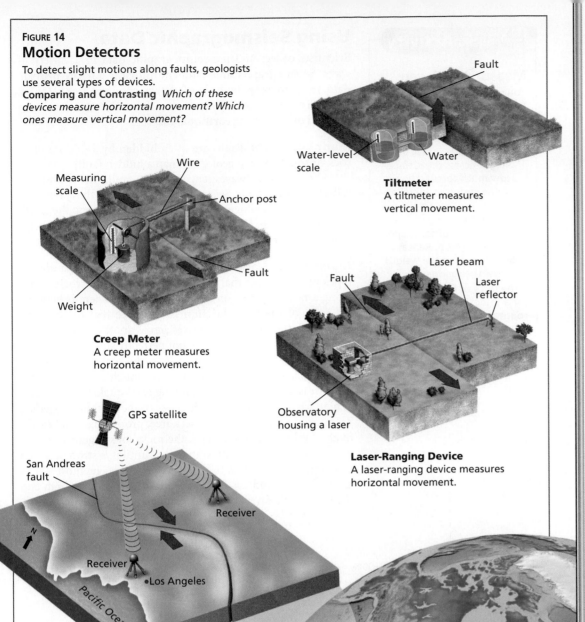

Creep Meter
A creep meter measures horizontal movement.

Wire
Measuring scale
Anchor post
Fault
Weight

Tiltmeter
A tiltmeter measures vertical movement.

Fault
Water-level scale
Water

Laser-Ranging Device
A laser-ranging device measures horizontal movement.

Laser beam
Laser reflector
Fault
Observatory housing a laser

GPS satellite
San Andreas fault
Receiver
Receiver
•Los Angeles
Pacific Ocean
N

GPS Satellites
Ground-based receivers use the GPS satellite system to measure changes in elevation and tilt of the land as well as horizontal movement along a fault.

F ◆ 63

Differentiated Instruction

Less Proficient Readers
Identifying Motion Detectors Have students review the different motion detectors in Figure 14. See whether students can identify the fault and stress types in Figure 14. Any student having trouble identifying the fault types and kinds of stress and the monitors used to detect them can keep a chart in his or her **L1**

portfolio. Have each student divide a sheet of paper into three columns. At the top of each column, have the student write the name of one type of fault. Under each heading, a student can enter the type of movement associated with that fault and the device used to measure motion.
learning modality: visual

Motion Detectors

Materials clay or other material to represent fault blocks; craft sticks, wooden matchsticks, or paper clips for posts; metal washer or other small weight; string or wire; mirror; penlight

Time 20 minutes

Focus Review with students the four types of fault-monitoring devices. Discuss the devices' similarities and differences.

Teach Challenge students to devise a simple model of a creep meter or a laser-ranging device according to a description and diagram on this page.

Apply Have students use the model to demonstrate how the device indicates land movements along a strike-slip fault, a normal fault, and a reverse fault. **learning modality: logical/mathematical**

Monitor Progress _____ L2

Writing Have each student write a paragraph explaining how measuring changes in the land along a fault might help scientists predict earthquakes. Have students place their paragraphs in their portfolios. Portfolio

Answers
Figure 14 *Horizontal:* creep meter, laser-ranging device, GPS satellite; *vertical:* tiltmeter and GPS satellite

✓ **Reading Checkpoint** A creep meter measures horizontal movement through the use of a wire attached to either side of a fault. On one side, the wire is anchored to a post. On the other side, the wire is attached to a weight that slides when the fault moves. Geologists measure how much the weight has moved to determine how much movement along the fault has occurred.

Using Seismographic Data

Teach Key Concepts L1

Friction Along Faults

Focus Tell students that the rock on either side of a fault can sometimes resist movement and that these locked portions of faults cause geologists the most concern.

Teach Ask students to clasp their hands together, locking their fingers. Then have students raise their hands above their heads, palms facing upward. Tell each student to push one hand slowly forward while pulling the other hand backward. (*Stress should build, and students' fingers should bend until finally the fault breaks, and the fingers come apart with a release of energy*). Tell students that this demonstration is similar to what occurs along a locked region of a fault.

Apply Ask: **Why would earthquakes along locked regions of a fault cause more damage?** (*The rocks have absorbed a great deal of energy, bending as the students' fingers did. When the earthquake occurs, the rocks snap back and release all of this energy. If a fault is not locked, the rock on either side can creep along rather than breaking apart in earthquakes.*) Students can demonstrate this by sliding their palms past each other.
learning modality: kinesthetic

Using Seismographic Data

Scientists collect and use seismographic data in a variety of ways. **Seismographs and fault-monitoring devices provide data used to map faults and detect changes along faults. Geologists are also trying to use these data to develop a method of predicting earthquakes.**

Mapping Faults Faults are often hidden by a thick layer of rock or soil. How can geologists map a hidden fault?

When seismic waves encounter a fault, the waves are reflected off the fault. Seismographs can detect these reflected seismic waves. Geologists then use these data to map the fault's length and depth. Knowing the location of hidden faults helps scientists determine the earthquake risk for the area.

Monitoring Changes Along Faults Geologists study the types of movement that occur along faults. How rocks move along a fault depends on how much friction there is between the sides of the fault. **Friction** is the force that opposes the motion of one surface as it moves across another surface. Friction exists because surfaces are not perfectly smooth.

Where friction along a fault is low, the rocks on both sides of the fault slide by each other without much sticking. Therefore stress does not build up, and big earthquakes are unlikely. Where friction is moderate, the sides of the fault jam together. Then from time to time they jerk free, producing small earthquakes. Where friction is high, the rocks lock together and do not move. In this case, stress increases until it is strong enough to overcome the friction force. For example, in most places along the San Andreas fault in California, friction is high and the plates lock. Stress builds up until an earthquake occurs.

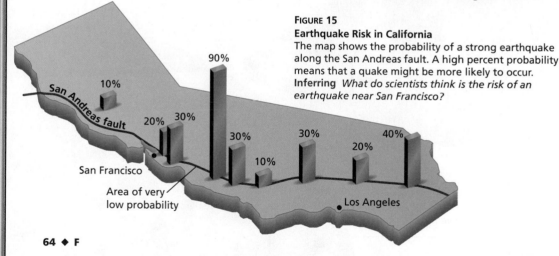

FIGURE 15
Earthquake Risk in California
The map shows the probability of a strong earthquake along the San Andreas fault. A high percent probability means that a quake might be more likely to occur.
Inferring *What do scientists think is the risk of an earthquake near San Francisco?*

90%
10%
20% 30%
San Andreas fault
30%
10%
30%
20%
40%
San Francisco
Area of very low probability
Los Angeles

64 ◆ F

Figure 15 shows how geologists in California have used data about how the San Andreas fault moves. They have tried to estimate the earthquake risk along different parts of the fault. Unfortunately, this attempt at forecasting earthquakes has not worked yet.

Trying to Predict Earthquakes Even with data from many sources, geologists can't predict when and where a quake will strike. Usually, stress along a fault increases until an earthquake occurs. Yet sometimes stress builds up along a fault, but an earthquake fails to occur. Or, one or more earthquakes may relieve stress along another part of the fault. Exactly what will happen remains uncertain.

The problem of predicting earthquakes is one of many scientific questions that remain unsolved. If you become a scientist, you can work to find answers to these questions. Much remains to be discovered!

 Reading Checkpoint Why is it difficult to predict earthquakes?

FIGURE 16
Seismographic Data
A geologist interprets a seismogram. Understanding changes that precede earthquakes may help in efforts to predict them.

Section 3 Assessment

Target Reading Skill Sequencing Refer to your flowchart about seismographs as you answer Question 1.

Reviewing Key Concepts

1. **a. Defining** What is a seismograph?
   b. Explaining How does a seismograph record seismic waves?
   c. Predicting A seismograph records a strong earthquake and a weak earthquake. How would the seismograms for the two earthquakes compare?
2. **a. Reviewing** What four instruments are used to monitor faults?
   b. Describing What changes does each instrument measure?
   c. Inferring A satellite that monitors a fault detects an increasing tilt in the land surface along the fault. What could this change in the land surface indicate?
3. **a. Listing** What are three ways in which geologists use seismographic data?
   b. Explaining How do geologists use seismographic data to make maps of faults?
   c. Making Generalizations Why do geologists collect data on friction along the sides of faults?

Writing in Science

Patent Application You are an inventor who has created a simple device that can detect an earthquake. To protect your rights to the invention, you apply for a patent. In your patent application, describe your device and how it will indicate the direction and strength of an earthquake. You may include a sketch.

Writing in Science

Writing Skill Explanation
Scoring Rubric
4 includes a description of how the device works and how it will indicate direction and strength of an earthquake; ideas are logical and well developed
3 includes all criteria
2 includes one or two criteria only
1 includes one or two criteria and inaccurate information

Monitor Progress [L2]
Answers
Figure 15 20%

Reading Checkpoint Sometimes stress builds up along a fault but an earthquake fails to occur, or several small earthquakes along the fault relieve the stress.

Assess

Reviewing Key Concepts
1. **a.** A device that records seismic waves **b.** A simple seismograph has a heavy weight attached to a frame by a spring or wire. A pen connected to the weight rests its point on a drum that can rotate. As the drum rotates, the pen draws a straight line on paper that is wrapped tightly around the drum. **c.** The seismogram for the strong earthquake would have jagged lines with more height between the top and the bottom.
2. **a.** Creep meters, tiltmeters, laser-ranging devices, satellite monitors **b.** Creep meter: horizontal movement; tiltmeter: tilting of the ground; laser-ranging device: horizontal movement; satellite monitor: movement along faults. **c.** Stress building up along the fault, which will eventually cause an earthquake
3. **a.** Mapping faults, monitoring changes along faults, and trying to predict earthquakes **b.** They measure how faults reflect seismic waves. These data are used to map the fault's length and depth. **c.** Friction determines how rocks move along a fault. If geologists know whether a fault is locked by friction or sliding, they can predict where severe earthquakes are most likely to occur.

Reteach [L1]
Have students name the four types of fault-monitoring devices described in this section. Have them describe what each detects and how the data collected can be used to predict earthquakes.

All in One Teaching Resources
• Section Summary: *Monitoring Earthquakes*
• Review and Reinforce: *Monitoring Earthquakes*
• Enrich: *Monitoring Earthquakes*

Design a Seismograph

L2

Prepare for Inquiry

Key Concept
By designing a seismograph, the student will experience the 3-step design process: Research, Design and Build, Evaluate and Redesign.

Skills Objectives
Students will be able to
- design an experiment
- evaluate their results
- troubleshoot problems that occur during the design and build stages

 Prep Time 20 min

Class Time 45–50 min

Advance Planning
You can make the strips of paper by cutting 8 1/2 × 11 sheets of paper into strips and taping them into strips that measure one meter each. Adding machine paper also can be used.

Safety
Students should exercise caution when using scissors. Review the Safety Guidelines in Appendix A.

Alternative Materials
Student seismographs can be built from cardboard boxes, paper towel tubes, rubber bands, wooden dowels, and other common materials.

All in One Teaching Resources
- Lab Worksheet: *Design a Seismograph*

Guide Inquiry

Invitation
Everyone is likely to have seen videos of seismographs wildly reacting to an earthquake. This lab will model the basic principles that make the seismograph work.

Introduce the Procedure
Ask students to recall times when they have seen instruments that use pens and rolling graph paper. Students may recall having seen movies of lie detectors or other devices. Explain that in a seismograph, the pen stands still while the paper moves beneath it. In fact, for a seismograph to work, the pen

must be isolated from the vibrations caused by the moving ground. The paper, however, is part of a recording drum that is fixed securely to bedrock.

Troubleshooting the Experiment
- Have students repeat Part 1 as often as necessary to become familiar with the concept of how the strip of paper moves beneath the pen during a simulated earthquake.

Design a Seismograph

Problem
Can you design and build a seismograph that can record the movements of simulated earthquakes?

Skills Focus
designing, evaluating, troubleshooting

Materials
- large book
- pencil
- pen
- 2 strips of paper
- optional materials provided by your teacher

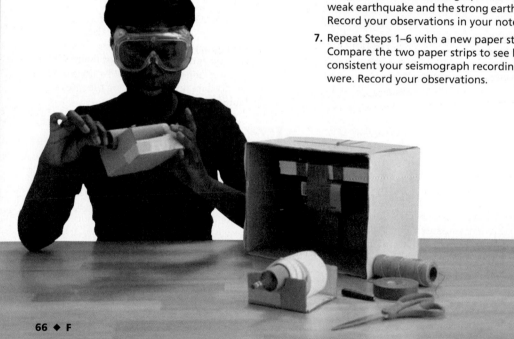

Procedure

PART 1 Research and Investigate

1. With two lab partners, create a model of a seismograph. Begin by placing a large book on a table.

2. Wind a strip of paper about one meter long around a pencil.

3. Hold the pencil with the paper wound around it in one hand. In your other hand, hold a pen against the paper.

4. As you hold the pen steady, have one lab partner slowly pull on the paper so that it slides across the book.

5. After a few seconds, the other lab partner should jiggle the book gently for 10 seconds to model a weak earthquake, and then for 10 seconds to model a strong earthquake.

6. Observe the pen markings on the paper strip. Compare how the seismograph recorded the weak earthquake and the strong earthquake. Record your observations in your notebook.

7. Repeat Steps 1–6 with a new paper strip. Compare the two paper strips to see how consistent your seismograph recordings were. Record your observations.

- Students will work in small groups to design their own seismograph, using their results from Part 1. Be sure students realize that the strip of paper and the pen need to move independently from each other.

PART 2 Design and Build

8. Using what you learned from the seismograph model in Part 1, develop your own design for a seismograph. Your seismograph should be able to
   - record vibrations continuously for 30 seconds
   - produce a seismogram that can distinguish between gentle and strong earthquakes
   - record seismic readings consistently from trial to trial

9. Sketch your design on a sheet of paper. Then make a list of the materials you will need. Materials might include a heavy weight, a roll of paper, a pen, wood blocks, wood dowels, and duct tape.

10. Obtain your teacher's approval for your design. Then construct your seismograph.

PART 3 Evaluate and Redesign

11. Test your seismograph in a series of simulated earthquakes of different strengths. Evaluate how well your seismograph functions. Does it meet the criteria outlined in Step 8? Make note of any problems.

12. Based on your tests, decide how you could improve the design of your seismograph. Then make any necessary changes to your seismograph and test how it functions.

Analyze and Conclude

1. **Evaluating** What problems or shortcomings did you encounter with the seismograph you tested in Part 1? Why do you think these problems occurred?

2. **Designing a Solution** How did you incorporate what you learned in Part 1 into your seismograph design in Part 2? For example, what changes did you make to improve consistency from trial to trial?

3. **Troubleshooting** As you designed, built, and tested your seismograph, what problems did you encounter? How did you solve these problems?

4. **Working With Design Constraints** What limitations did factors such as gravity, materials, costs, time, or other factors place on the design and function of your seismograph? Describe how you adapted your design to work within these limitations.

5. **Evaluating the Impact on Society** Why is it important for scientists around the world to have access to accurate and durable seismographs?

Communicate

Write an advertisement trying to "sell" your seismograph. In your ad, explain how your design and evaluation process helped you improve your seismograph. Include a labeled sketch of your design.

Expected Outcome

The small earthquake should result in small oscillations of the pen markings, and the large earthquake should result in larger oscillations.

Analyze and Conclude

1. Student answers will vary. It's important that students analyze their results from Part 1 so that they can design and build a working seismograph. Look for a list of problems and an accurate analysis of why each problem occurred.

2. Student answers will vary. Look for descriptions that mention specific lessons learned in Part 1 and how those lessons influenced student work in Part 2.

3. Student answers will vary. Look for lists of problems related to the design, building, and testing of the seismograph. Also look for explanations of how students solved these problems.

4. Student answers will vary. Look for a list of limiting factors and explanations of how students handled those limitations.

5. Student answers will vary but should make the connection between the functioning of a seismograph and the ability to pinpoint the focus of an earthquake. By learning where an earthquake is centered, scientists can learn the cause of the earthquake. They can provide data that will help predict when an earthquake is likely, which can allow time for people in the area to prepare or evacuate.

Extend the Inquiry

Communicate Student answers will vary, but students should be creative in their advertisements and should explain why their designs are important. Also, the advertisement should describe the evaluation process and the result of the evaluations.

Objectives

After this lesson, students will be able to

F2.4.1 Explain how geologists determine earthquake risk

F2.4.2 Identify the kinds of damage an earthquake can cause

F2.4.3 Provide suggestions to increase earthquake safety and reduce earthquake damage

Target Reading Skill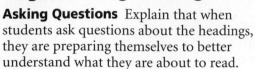

Asking Questions Explain that when students ask questions about the headings, they are preparing themselves to better understand what they are about to read.

Answers

Possible questions are these:

How do earthquakes cause damage? How can you stay safe during an earthquake? What makes a building safe from earthquakes?

All in One Teaching Resources

• Transparency F21

Preteach

Build Background Knowledge   L2

Protection Against Earthquakes

Ask: **What kinds of structures have you seen used to make buildings, bridges, and highway overpasses stronger?** (*Students may mention heavy wooden or steel beams, supporting buttresses, diagonal beams, and the like.*) **Do you think that these structures would help in an earthquake? Why or why not?** (*Accept all reasonable responses. Encourage students to rely on their own direct observations or on what they have seen in news reports and documentary films.*)

Earthquake Safety

Reading Preview

Key Concepts

• How do geologists determine earthquake risk?

• What kinds of damage does an earthquake cause?

• What can be done to increase earthquake safety and reduce earthquake damage?

Key Terms

• liquefaction
• aftershock • tsunami
• base-isolated building

Target Reading Skill

Asking Questions Before you read, preview the red headings and ask a *what, how,* or *where* question for each. As you read, write answers to your questions.

Earthquake Safety

Question	Answer
Where is quake risk highest?	Earthquake risk is highest . . .

Lab zone Discover Activity

Can Bracing Prevent Building Collapse?

1. Tape four straws together to make a square frame. Hold the frame upright on a flat surface.

2. Hold the bottom straw down with one hand while you push the top straw to the left with the other. Push it as far as it will go without breaking the frame.

3. Tape a fifth straw horizontally across the middle of the frame. Repeat Step 2.

Think It Over

Predicting What effect did the fifth straw have? What effect would a piece of cardboard taped to the frame have? Based on your observations, how would an earthquake affect the frame of a house?

Imagine being sound asleep in your bed in the middle of the night. Suddenly, you are jolted wide awake as your home begins to rattle and shake. As objects fall off shelves and walls crack, you crouch under a desk for protection. Around the city, large buildings collapse and fires break out. The quake lasts less than a minute, but leaves behind great devastation. That's what happened in September 1999 when a magnitude 7.6 earthquake hit Taipei, Taiwan. The quake killed more than 2,000 people, and injured thousands more.

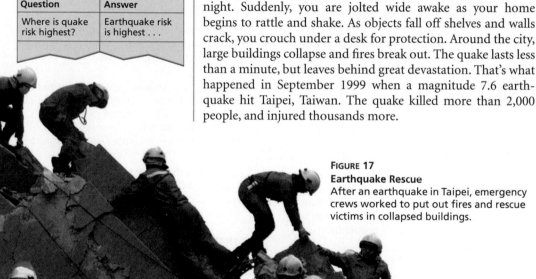

FIGURE 17
Earthquake Rescue
After an earthquake in Taipei, emergency crews worked to put out fires and rescue victims in collapsed buildings.

Lab zone Discover Activity

Skills Focus Predicting

Materials 5 straws, tape

Time 10 minutes

Tips In Step 3, make sure that students tape the fifth straw about halfway up the square.

Expected Outcome In Step 2, the frame will collapse sideways. In Step 3, it will

L1 remain standing for a time but will fall over if more pressure is exerted.

Think It Over The fifth straw provided additional support to the frame. Cardboard would provide even stronger support. Without additional supporting structures, a house's frame would probably collapse in an earthquake.

Earthquake Risk in the United States

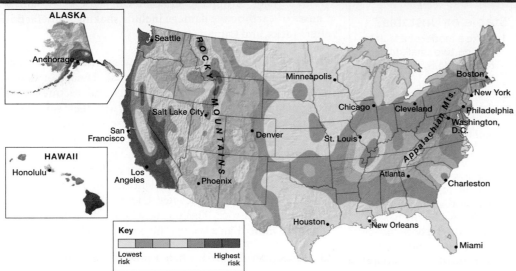

Key

Lowest risk — Highest risk

Earthquake Risk

Geologists know that earthquakes are likely wherever plate movement stores energy in the rock along faults. **Geologists can determine earthquake risk by locating where faults are active and where past earthquakes have occurred.**

Look at Figure 18. In the United States, the risk is highest along the Pacific coast in California, Washington, and Alaska. Plates meet along the Pacific coast, causing many active faults. In California, the Pacific plate and North American plate meet along the San Andreas fault. In Washington, earthquakes result from the subduction of the Juan de Fuca plate beneath the North American plate. In Alaska, subduction of the Pacific plate causes many earthquakes.

The eastern United States generally has a low risk of earthquakes because this region lies far from plate boundaries. But, the East has experienced some of the most powerful quakes in the nation's history. Scientists hypothesize that the continental plate forming most of North America is under stress. This stress could disturb faults that lie hidden beneath thick layers of soil and rock.

Reading Checkpoint What area of the United States has the highest earthquake risk?

FIGURE 18
The map shows areas where serious earthquakes are likely to occur, based on the locations of previous earthquakes.
Interpreting Maps *Where are damaging earthquakes least likely to occur? Most likely to occur?*

Differentiated Instruction

Gifted and Talented **L3**
Locating Earthquakes Encourage students to research the locations and dates (and magnitudes, if known) of notable earthquakes that have occurred in the continental United States, Alaska, and Hawaii during the past 200 years. Suggest that students compile the data chronologically in a class master chart. Let them label a large U.S. map with tags identifying the earthquake locations, dates, and magnitudes. Students could also compare the locations of the earthquakes that occurred in the continental United States with the risk areas shown in Figure 18. **learning modality: visual**

Earthquake Risk

Teach Key Concepts **L2**
Where Earthquakes Occur

Focus Review with students that earthquakes often occur along active fault lines.

Teach Ask: **What happens when plates are pushed together at converging boundaries?** *(A fault forms.)* Have students refer to the map of Earth's lithospheric plates in the section *The Theory of Plate Tectonics.* Ask: **Which plate is close to the United States?** *(The Pacific plate)* **Describe the location of plates relative to the East Coast.** *(They are farther away.)* **Where would you expect earthquake risk to be highest?** *(Along the Pacific Coast)* Have students note the high-risk areas on the map Earthquake Risk in the United States in relation to the map of Earth's lithospheric plates.

Apply Ask: **Which type of landform characterizes an area in which earthquakes are more likely, and why?** *(Mountains, because there is likely to be more fault activity there)* **learning modality: visual**

Independent Practice **L2**

All in One Teaching Resources
• Guided Reading and Study Worksheet: *Earthquake Safety*

 Student Edition on Audio CD

Monitor Progress ———— **L2**

Skills Check Have students locate your state on the map and assess the risk of an earthquake and the reasons for the level of risk.

Answers
Figure 18 *Least likely:* In the Plains states and most areas of the South and Midwest; *most likely:* Along the Pacific Coast, around the Rocky Mountains, and in portions of the Midwest

 Reading Checkpoint The Pacific Coast

How Earthquakes Cause Damage

Teach Key Concepts L2

Earthquake Damage

Focus Remind students that earthquake damage is caused by shaking, liquefaction, aftershocks, and tsunamis.

Teach Ask: **Why does the ground shake during an earthquake?** (*Seismic waves move through the ground.*) **How does this shaking damage buildings and bridges?** (*The structures sway and twist.*) **How does liquefaction damage structures?** (*Support for the structures' foundations is removed.*) **Why are structures even more vulnerable to aftershocks?** (*They might have been weakened by the primary earthquake.*) **How do tsunamis cause damage?** (*A high wave crashes onto shore. This wave can damage areas that are normally well above high tide.*)

Apply Show students photos of areas affected by earthquakes, and ask them to identify what caused the damage. Ask: **What could have been done to help the structures stand up to an earthquake?** (*Accept all reasonable answers. Students might mention construction materials that absorb vibration, reinforcement in concrete, or not building close to ravines or oceans.*) **learning modality: logical/mathematical**

Address Misconceptions L2

Tsunamis

Focus Ask: **What is a tide?** (*An alternate rise and fall in sea level*) **What causes tides?** (*The gravity of the moon and sun*)

Teach Tsunamis often are incorrectly called tidal waves. Ask: **What causes tsunamis?** (*Ground movement associated with earthquakes, volcanic eruptions, or undersea landslides*) **Should tsunamis be called tidal waves?** (*No*) **Why not?** (*They do not form or behave like tides.*)

Apply Ask students to classify the following examples as tide or tsunami: **ocean water gradually rises and falls twice each day** (*Tide*); **a ten-meter-high wave suddenly crashes onto shore** (*Tsunami*) **learning modality: logical/mathematical**

Stable or Unstable?

1. Make a model of a fault by placing two small, folded towels side by side on a flat surface.
2. Pile a stack of books on the fault by placing the light books on the bottom and the heaviest ones on top.
3. Gently pull the towels in opposite directions until the pile topples.
4. Repeat the process, but this time with the heavier books on the bottom.

Relating Cause and Effect Which one of your structures was more stable than the other? Why?

How Earthquakes Cause Damage

When a major earthquake strikes, it can cause great damage. **Causes of earthquake damage include shaking, liquefaction, aftershocks, and tsunamis.**

Shaking The shaking produced by seismic waves can trigger landslides or avalanches. Shaking can also damage or destroy buildings and bridges, topple utility poles, and fracture gas and water mains. S waves and surface waves, with their side-to-side and up-and-down movement, can cause severe damage near the epicenter. As the seismic waves sweep through the ground, they can put enough stress on buildings to tear them apart.

The types of rock and soil determine where and how much the ground shakes. The most violent shaking may occur kilometers away from the epicenter. Loose soil shakes more violently than solid rock. This means a house built on sandy soil will shake more than a house built on solid rock.

Liquefaction In 1964, when a powerful earthquake roared through Anchorage, Alaska, cracks opened in the ground. Some of the cracks were 9 meters wide. The cracks were created by liquefaction. **Liquefaction** (lik wih FAK shun) occurs when an earthquake's violent shaking suddenly turns loose, soft soil into liquid mud. Liquefaction is likely where the soil is full of moisture. As the ground gives way, buildings sink and pull apart.

Aftershocks Sometimes, buildings weakened by an earthquake collapse during an aftershock. An **aftershock** is an earthquake that occurs after a larger earthquake in the same area. Aftershocks may strike hours, days, or even months later.

FIGURE 19
Liquefaction Damage
An earthquake caused the soil beneath this building to liquefy. Liquefaction can change soil to liquid mud.
Posing Questions *What are some questions people might ask before building in a quake-prone area?*

Skills Focus Relating cause and effect L2

Materials 10 books, ranging from light to heavy; 2 dishtowels

Time 10 minutes

Tips Tell students to use paperbacks for the light books and encyclopedias or dictionaries for the heavier ones.

Expected Outcome With the heavier books on top, the stack will topple. With the heavier books at the bottom, the stack will remain intact.

Extend Have students experiment with different types of materials to construct a stable model.

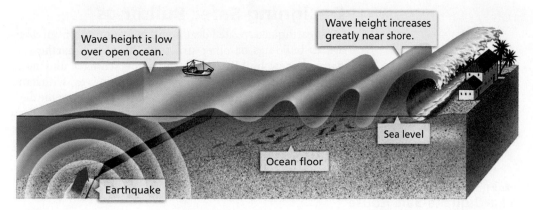

Wave height is low over open ocean.

Wave height increases greatly near shore.

Sea level

Ocean floor

Earthquake

Tsunamis When an earthquake jolts the ocean floor, plate movement causes the ocean floor to rise slightly and push water out of its way. The water displaced by the earthquake may form a large wave called a **tsunami** (tsoo NAH mee), shown in Figure 20. A tsunami spreads out from an earthquake's epicenter and speeds across the ocean. In the open ocean, the height of the wave is low. As a tsunami approaches shallow water, the wave grows into a mountain of water.

Steps to Earthquake Safety

What should you do if an earthquake strikes? The main danger is from falling objects and flying glass. **The best way to protect yourself is to drop, cover, and hold.**

If you are indoors when a quake strikes, crouch beneath a sturdy table or desk and hold on to it. If no desk or table is available, crouch against an inner wall, away from the outside of a building, and cover your head and neck with your arms. Avoid windows, mirrors, wall hangings, and furniture that might topple.

If you are outdoors, move to an open area such as a playground. Avoid vehicles, power lines, trees, and buildings. Sit down to avoid being thrown down.

After a quake, water and power supplies may fail, food stores may be closed, and travel may be difficult. People may have to wait days for these services to be restored. To prepare, an earthquake kit containing canned food, water, and first aid supplies should be stored where it is easy to reach.

 Reading Checkpoint How can furniture be dangerous during a quake? How can it protect you?

FIGURE 20
How a Tsunami Forms
A tsunami begins as a low wave, but turns into a huge wave as it nears the shore. In 2004, a powerful earthquake in the Indian Ocean triggered several tsunamis. The tsunamis caused great loss of life and destruction to coastal areas around the Indian Ocean.

Chapter 2   F ◆ 71

Designing Safer Buildings

Teach Key Concepts

Constructing Earthquake-Safe Structures

Focus Tell students that most earthquake damage and injuries result from collapsing buildings and aboveground structures.

Teach Brainstorm with students about construction methods that might help buildings and other structures withstand earthquakes. (*Some suggestions might include reinforcement, more solid foundations, and shock-absorbing structures.*)

Apply Ask: **How can you make your home more resistant to earthquake damage?** (*Secure gas water heaters or other potential fire hazards, secure large objects that might fall during an earthquake, and place heavy or fragile objects on lower shelves.*) **learning modality: logical/mathematical**

All in One Teaching Resources
- Transparency F22

Making Models of Homes

Materials toothpicks, glue or paste

Time 1 class period; 20 minutes the next day

Focus Review with students about the ground motions that occur during earthquakes.

Teach Challenge students to build an earthquake-safe home with toothpicks and glue or paste. Encourage them to experiment with various designs.

Apply After students' homes are complete, test them for strength and ability to withstand shaking. Ask students to identify designs that are earthquake-safe. **learning modality: kinesthetic**

Go Online
PLANET DIARY
For: More on earthquake risk
Visit: PHSchool.com
Web Code: cfd-1024

Students can review earthquake risks in an online activity.

Designing Safer Buildings

Most earthquake-related deaths and injuries result from damage to buildings or other structures. **To reduce earthquake damage, new buildings must be made stronger and more flexible. Older buildings may be modified to withstand stronger quakes.** People can protect their homes from the dangers of earthquakes. Figure 21 shows some of the steps that can make houses earthquake-safe. Some steps strengthen the house itself. Others may help to keep objects from tipping or falling and causing injury.

FIGURE 21
An Earthquake-Safe House
People can take a variety of steps to make their homes safer in an earthquake.
Predicting *During a quake, what might happen to a house that was not bolted to its foundation?*

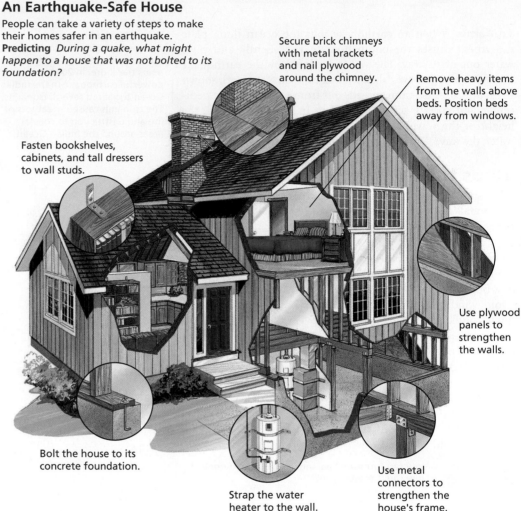

Secure brick chimneys with metal brackets and nail plywood around the chimney.

Remove heavy items from the walls above beds. Position beds away from windows.

Fasten bookshelves, cabinets, and tall dressers to wall studs.

Use plywood panels to strengthen the walls.

Bolt the house to its concrete foundation.

Strap the water heater to the wall.

Use metal connectors to strengthen the house's frame.

Differentiated Instruction

Special Needs
Analyzing Building Safety Refer students to the map of the San Andreas fault in Figure 15. Tell them to compare that map with a political map of California. Ask: **You've just read that people should avoid building near earthquake faults. Have the people in California followed that safety guideline?** (*No; many cities, towns, bridges, highways, and smaller roads are close to the fault.*) **Now that people have already built structures near the San Andreas fault, what could be done to protect those structures from an earthquake?** (*Accept all reasonable responses, such as adding support beams to buildings and rebuilding destroyed highway overpasses so that they are more earthquake-resistant.*) **learning modality: visual**

Protecting Structures The way in which a building is constructed determines whether it can withstand an earthquake. During an earthquake, brick buildings and some wood-frame buildings may collapse if their walls have not been reinforced, or strengthened. To combat damage caused by liquefaction, new homes built on soft ground should be anchored to solid rock below the soil. Bridges and highway overpasses can be built on supports that go through soft soil to firmer ground. To find out more about how buildings can withstand earthquakes, look at *Seismic-Safe Buildings* on the following pages.

A **base-isolated building** is designed to reduce the amount of energy that reaches the building during an earthquake. A base-isolated building rests on shock-absorbing rubber pads or springs. Like the suspension of a car, the pads and springs smooth out a bumpy ride. During a quake, the building moves gently back and forth without any violent shaking.

Making Utilities Safer Earthquakes can cause fire and flooding when gas pipes and water mains break. Flexible joints can be installed in gas and water lines to keep them from breaking. Automatic shut-off valves also can be installed on these lines to cut off gas and water flow.

Go Online
PLANET DIARY
For: More on earthquake risk
Visit: PHSchool.com
Web Code: cfd-1024

Reading Checkpoint How can utilities be protected from earthquake damage?

Section 4 Assessment

Target Reading Skill **Asking Questions** Work with a partner to check the answers in your graphic organizer.

Reviewing Key Concepts
1. **a. Identifying** What factors help geologists determine earthquake risk for a region?
   b. Comparing and Contrasting Why does the risk of quakes vary across the United States?
2. **a. Listing** What are four ways that earthquakes cause damage?
   b. Relating Cause and Effect How does liquefaction cause damage during an earthquake?
   c. Developing Hypotheses How might heavy rain before an earthquake affect the danger of liquefaction?
3. **a. Reviewing** How can you protect yourself during an earthquake?
   b. Describing What will happen to a base-isolated building when seismic waves strike the building during an earthquake?

Lab zone **At-Home Activity**

Quake Safety Plan Work with an adult family member to develop an earthquake safety plan. The plan should tell family members what to do during an earthquake. It should list items your family would need if a quake cut electrical power and water lines. It should also explain where to shut off the gas if your home has a natural gas line. Share your earthquake safety plan with the rest of your family.

Lab zone **Chapter Project**

Keep Students on Track Have each student draw and label a sketch showing three ways to make the model building for the chapter project more earthquake-resistant.

Lab zone **At-Home Activity**

Quake Safety Plan **L2** Have each student make a sketch of the floor plan of his or her home. Students could list steps that can be taken to make each home safer in an earthquake. Ask students to walk through their homes with their parents or guardians and learn where to shut off gas, water, and power lines in case of an emergency.

Monitor Progress _____ **L2**

Answers
Figure 21 It could slip sideways off its foundation and collapse.

Reading Checkpoint Flexible joints and shut-off valves.

Assess

Reviewing Key Concepts

1. a. Location of tectonic plate boundaries, active faults, and the locations of past earthquakes **b.** The location of continental plates and faults varies.

2. a. Shaking, liquefaction, aftershocks, and tsunamis **b.** An earthquake's shaking turns loose, soft, moist soil into liquid mud that gives way, causing buildings to sink and pull apart. **c.** If the soil is very moist, liquefaction can make the ground give way.

3. a. Drop, cover, and hold; students may also cite other precautions described on page 71. **b.** The rubber pads or springs will absorb the shock, and the building will move gently back and forth without any violent shaking.

Reteach **L1**
Have students list the ways that earthquakes cause damage and then list or draw ways to make their own homes safer in the event of an earthquake.

Performance Assessment **L2**
Writing Ask students to suppose that they are planning a housing development in an area where earthquakes are likely to occur. Ask students to describe what types of land they would avoid for development and identify places where it would be safe to build.

All in One Teaching Resources
- Section Summary: *Earthquake Safety*
- Review and Reinforce: *Earthquake Safety*
- Enrich: *Earthquake Safety*

Technology and Society

Seismic-Safe Buildings

Key Concept
Technology can make buildings more resistant to earthquake damage.

Build Background Knowledge

Recalling Effects of Seismic Waves
Help students recall that earthquake energy travels through Earth as seismic waves. Ask: **How does the energy from an earthquake move through rock and soil?** *(It moves as seismic waves.)* **What are the three types of seismic waves?** *(P waves, S waves, and surface waves)* Tell students that most earthquake damage is caused by S waves and surface waves. Ask: **What ground motions occur with S waves and surface waves?** *(S waves produce side-to-side vibrations. Surface waves cause side-to-side vibrations and cause rolling motions in the ground.)* **How do seismic waves damage buildings?** *(The waves cause the buildings to sway and shake.)*

Introduce the Debate
Ask: **How can cities control the way buildings are constructed?** *(Many students will be aware of building codes and inspections.)* **How do cities establish building codes and decide how much money can be spent on seismic-safe construction?** *(Accept all answers at this time. Possible answers: Assess the risk of earthquakes in those cities and the cost of rebuilding particular structures.)*

Facilitate the Debate
- Have students participate in a mock town-hall meeting to discuss how building codes should address seismic-safe construction in a city. Students can role-play city officials, real-estate developers, and emergency planners. Students should consider risk assessment, costs, and priorities.
- After the debate, ask student groups to write building codes for the city. Students also should plan how building codes will be enforced and any new funding that might be required.

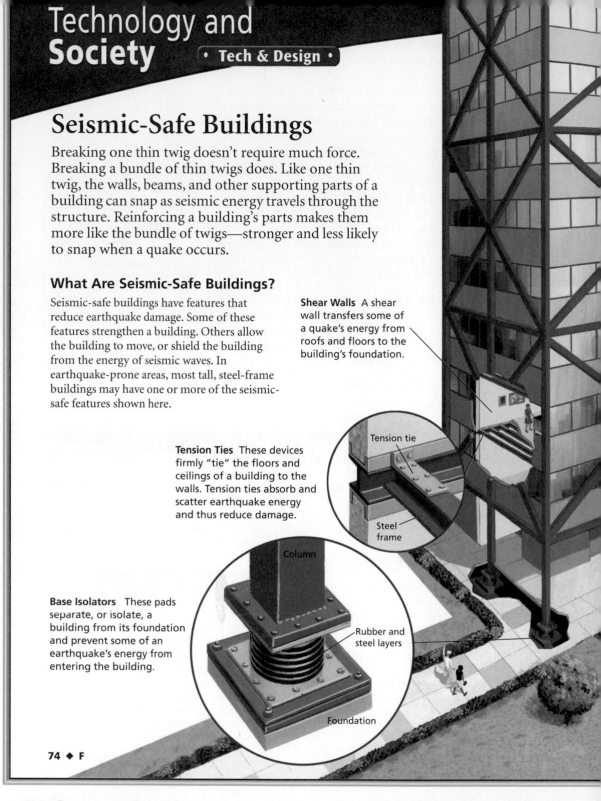

Seismic-Safe Buildings

Breaking one thin twig doesn't require much force. Breaking a bundle of thin twigs does. Like one thin twig, the walls, beams, and other supporting parts of a building can snap as seismic energy travels through the structure. Reinforcing a building's parts makes them more like the bundle of twigs—stronger and less likely to snap when a quake occurs.

What Are Seismic-Safe Buildings?

Seismic-safe buildings have features that reduce earthquake damage. Some of these features strengthen a building. Others allow the building to move, or shield the building from the energy of seismic waves. In earthquake-prone areas, most tall, steel-frame buildings may have one or more of the seismic-safe features shown here.

Shear Walls A shear wall transfers some of a quake's energy from roofs and floors to the building's foundation.

Tension tie

Tension Ties These devices firmly "tie" the floors and ceilings of a building to the walls. Tension ties absorb and scatter earthquake energy and thus reduce damage.

Steel frame

Column

Base Isolators These pads separate, or isolate, a building from its foundation and prevent some of an earthquake's energy from entering the building.

Rubber and steel layers

Foundation

74 ◆ F

Background

History of Science The large earthquake that struck San Francisco in 1906 encouraged research about earthquakes and about building construction. Study of ground movements associated with this earthquake led to an understanding of how energy is stored in rock and then suddenly released as seismic waves during an earthquake. Research also led to the development of construction techniques designed to minimize the hazards associated with earthquakes.

Seismic-Safe, But at What Cost?

Seismic-safe buildings save lives and reduce damage. Despite these benefits, the technologies have drawbacks. Seismic-safe features, such as cross braces, may reduce the amount of usable space in a building. It is also expensive to add seismic-safe features to an existing building. Communities must make trade-offs between the benefits and the costs of seismic-safe buildings.

Even steel-frame buildings need seismic-safe design features.

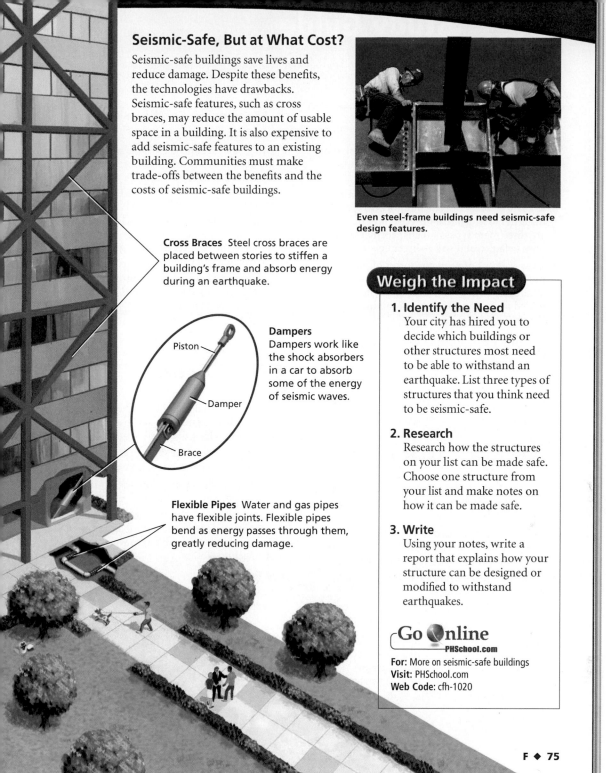

Cross Braces Steel cross braces are placed between stories to stiffen a building's frame and absorb energy during an earthquake.

Piston

Dampers Dampers work like the shock absorbers in a car to absorb some of the energy of seismic waves.

Damper

Brace

Flexible Pipes Water and gas pipes have flexible joints. Flexible pipes bend as energy passes through them, greatly reducing damage.

Weigh the Impact

1. Identify the Need
Your city has hired you to decide which buildings or other structures most need to be able to withstand an earthquake. List three types of structures that you think need to be seismic-safe.

2. Research
Research how the structures on your list can be made safe. Choose one structure from your list and make notes on how it can be made safe.

3. Write
Using your notes, write a report that explains how your structure can be designed or modified to withstand earthquakes.

Go Online
PHSchool.com
For: More on seismic-safe buildings
Visit: PHSchool.com
Web Code: cfh-1020

Weigh the Impact

1. Students might suggest high-rise buildings, schools, hospitals, and fire and police stations, among others.
2. Notes might address reinforcement, energy absorption, or fire prevention.
3. Encourage students to consider the variety of hazards associated with earthquakes and to include in their reports how they have addressed these hazards in their designs.

Go Online
PHSchool.com
For: More on seismic-safe buildings
Visit: PHSchool.com
Web Code: cfh-1020

Students can research this issue online.

Extend

Encourage students to contact city or county building inspectors to find out whether seismic-safe construction techniques are used in your region. Students also might want to include in their reports ask about local building codes.

The BIG Idea

Have students read the answer to the Essential Question. Encourage them to evaluate and revise their own answers as needed.

Help Students Read

Building Vocabulary

Using Context Clues Help students determine the meaning of unfamiliar words. This strategy helps students use clues from the surrounding text to help them infer an unfamiliar word's meaning. Help students review the material in this chapter by looking again at key terms, such as the types of stress described at the beginning of the section *Forces in Earth's Crust*. Have students read the sentences surrounding the key terms *tension, compression,* and *shearing.* Ask: **Even though the term is not specifically defined, what are some clues from the sentences surrounding the term *tension*?** (*Pull, stretching, becomes thinner*) Have students look at other key terms in the chapter and use the same strategy for them.

Paraphrasing Help students define the key terms in their own words. By paraphrasing, students can use words that are already familiar to them to define new terms. Have students write down the key terms *anticline, syncline, plateau, seismograph,* and *seismogram.* Have them read the text associated with the terms. Then have them find the terms in a dictionary or encyclopedia. Have them use the definition they find to help them write another definition in their own words.

Connecting Concepts

Concept Maps Help students develop one way to show how the information in this chapter is related. Forces inside Earth cause rocks to move and to release energy during an earthquake as seismic waves. Have students brainstorm to identify the key concepts, key terms, details, and examples, then write each one on a sticky note and attach it at random on chart paper or on the board.

The **BIG Idea** **Energy Transfer and Earth's Structure** The forces of plate movement deform Earth's crust, forming faults, folds, and mountains. Plate movements also cause earthquakes.

① Forces in Earth's Crust

Key Concepts

- Tension, compression, and shearing work over millions of years to change the shape and volume of rock.
- Faults usually occur along plate boundaries, where the forces of plate motion push or pull the crust so much that the crust breaks. There are three main types of faults: normal faults, reverse faults, and strike-slip faults.
- Over millions of years, the forces of plate movement can change a flat plain into landforms such as anticlines and synclines, folded mountains, fault-block mountains, and plateaus.

Key Terms

stress	footwall
tension	reverse fault
compression	strike-slip fault
shearing	anticline
normal fault	syncline
hanging wall	plateau

② Earthquakes and Seismic Waves

Key Concepts

- Seismic waves carry energy from an earthquake away from the focus, through Earth's interior, and across the surface.
- Three commonly used ways of measuring earthquakes are the Mercalli scale, the Richter scale, and the moment magnitude scale.
- Geologists use seismic waves to locate an earthquake's epicenter.

Key Terms

earthquake	Mercalli scale
focus	magnitude
epicenter	Richter scale
P wave	seismograph
S wave	moment magnitude
surface wave	scale

③ Monitoring Earthquakes

Key Concepts

- During an earthquake, seismic waves cause the seismograph's drum to vibrate. But the suspended weight with the pen attached moves very little. Therefore, the pen stays in place and records the drum's vibrations.
- To monitor faults, geologists have developed instruments to measure changes in elevation, tilting of the land surface, and ground movements along faults.
- Seismographs and fault-monitoring devices provide data used to map faults and detect changes along faults.

Key Terms

seismogram	friction

④ Earthquake Safety

Key Concepts

- Geologists can determine earthquake risk by locating where faults are active and where past earthquakes have occurred.
- Causes of earthquake damage include shaking, liquefaction, aftershocks, and tsunamis.
- The best way to protect yourself is to drop, cover, and hold.
- To reduce earthquake damage, new buildings must be made stronger and more flexible. Older buildings may be modified to withstand stronger quakes.

Key Terms

liquefaction	tsunami
aftershock	base-isolated building

Tell students that this concept map will be organized in hierarchical order and to begin at the top with the key concepts. Ask students these questions to guide them to categorize the information on the stickies: **What are the different types of stress that cause earthquakes, and what kinds of faults result from each? How are seismic waves measured, and what kinds of damage do they cause?**

Prompt students by using connecting words or phrases, such as "break at," "results in," and "measured by," to indicate the basis for the organization of the map. The phrases should form a sentence between or among a set of concepts.

Answer Accept logical presentations by students.

All in One Teaching Resources

- Key Terms Review: *Earthquakes*
- Connecting Concepts: *Earthquakes*

Review and Assessment

Organizing Information

Relating Cause and Effect Fill in the cause-and-effect graphic organizer to show how different stress forces produce different kinds of faults.

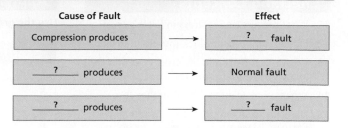

Cause of Fault		Effect
Compression produces	→	_____?_____ fault
_____?_____ produces	→	Normal fault
_____?_____ produces	→	_____?_____ fault

Reviewing Key Terms

Choose the letter of the best answer.

1. The force that causes part of the crust to become shorter and thicker is
   a. tension.
   b. compression.
   c. shearing.
   d. normal force.

2. When the hanging wall of a fault slips down with respect to the footwall, the result is a
   a. reverse fault.
   b. syncline.
   c. normal fault.
   d. strike-slip fault.

3. Which of the following is a rating of earthquake damage at a particular location?
   a. moment magnitude scale
   b. focus scale
   c. Mercalli scale
   d. Richter scale

4. The largest waves on a seismogram are
   a. P waves.
   b. S waves.
   c. surface waves.
   d. tsunamis.

5. In the hours after an earthquake, people should not go inside a building, even if it appears undamaged, because of
   a. aftershocks.
   b. liquefaction.
   c. tsunamis.
   d. deformation.

If the statement is true, write *true*. If it is false, change the underlined word or words to make the statement true.

6. <u>Liquefaction</u> forces squeeze or pull the rock in Earth's crust.

7. Rock uplifted by <u>normal faults</u> creates fault-block mountains.

8. An earthquake's <u>epicenter</u> is located deep underground.

9. As <u>S waves</u> move through the ground, they cause it to compress and then expand.

10. <u>Tsunamis</u> are triggered by earthquakes originating beneath the ocean floor.

Writing in Science

Cause-and-Effect Paragraph Now that you have learned about the awesome power of earthquakes, write a paragraph about how earthquakes cause damage. Discuss both the natural and human-made factors that contribute to an earthquake's destructive power.

DISCOVERY CHANNEL SCHOOL
Earthquakes
Video Preview
Video Field Trip
▶ Video Assessment

Review and Assessment

Organizing Information
1. Compression produces a reverse fault.
2. Tension produces a normal fault.
3. Shearing produces a strike-slip fault.

Reviewing Key Terms
1. b   2. c   3. c   4. c   5. a
6. false; stress
7. true
8. false; focus
9. false; P waves
10. true

Writing in Science

Writing Skill Exposition Cause and Effect

Scoring Rubric
4 includes information about how earthquakes cause damage and the factors that contribute to an earthquake's power; writing is detailed and vivid
3 includes all criteria
2 includes incomplete information and only a brief description
1 includes limited information and inaccuracies

DISCOVERY CHANNEL SCHOOL
Video Assessment

Earthquakes
Show the Video Assessment to review chapter content and as a prompt for the writing assignment. Discussion questions: **How does an earthquake in one place cause damage in another place far away?** (*Seismic waves travel through the ground in all directions.*) **Why did the Marina District of San Francisco sustain more damage than other parts of the city?** (*The homes were built on land dredged from San Francisco Bay, unstable ground even under normal circumstances, but especially dangerous during an earthquake.*)

Go Online
PHSchool.com
For: Self-Assessment
Visit: PHSchool.com
Web Code: cfa-1020

Students can take an online practice test that is automatically scored.

All in One Teaching Resources
- Transparency F23
- Chapter Test
- Performance Assessment Teacher Notes
- Performance Assessment Student Worksheet
- Performance Assessment Scoring Rubric

ExamView® **Computer Test Bank CD-ROM**

Checking Concepts

11. Stress causes changes in the crust's volume or shape through compression, tension, and shearing.

12. Where two plates move away from each other, tension forces may create normal faults. When two normal faults form parallel to each other, a block of rock is left lying between them. As the hanging wall of each normal fault slips downward, the block in between moves upward, forming a fault-block mountain.

13. Compression forms folded mountains. Compression shortens and thickens the crust so that it bends slowly without breaking. If the fold bends upward into an arch, the fold is called an anticline. If the fold bends downward to form a bowl, the fold is called a syncline.

14. A plateau is a large area of flat land that is elevated high above sea level. A plateau may form when vertical faults push up a large, flat block of rock.

15. An earthquake occurs when rock along a fault suddenly breaks at a point beneath the surface called the focus. This break releases the stress stored in the rock as seismic waves. The seismic waves travel outward from the focus in all directions. They reach the surface at the epicenter.

16. An earthquake's magnitude is a number that geologists assign to an earthquake, based on the earthquake's strength. The more energy released, the greater the magnitude.

17. The height of the jagged lines on a seismogram indicates the severity or closeness of an earthquake.

18. New homes and other structures built on soft ground should be anchored to solid rock below the soil.

Review and Assessment

Checking Concepts

11. What process causes stress in Earth's crust?

12. Explain how a fault-block mountain forms.

13. What type of stress in the crust results in the formation of folded mountains? Explain.

14. What are plateaus and how do they form?

15. Describe what happens along a fault beneath Earth's surface when an earthquake occurs.

16. How is the amount of energy released by an earthquake related to its magnitude?

17. What does the height of the jagged lines on a seismogram indicate?

18. How can homes and other structures be protected from liquefaction?

Thinking Critically

19. Classifying Look at the diagram of a fault below. Describe how the hanging wall moves in relation to the footwall. What kind of fault is this?

20. Analyzing Data A geologist has data about an earthquake from two seismographic stations. Is this enough information to determine the location of the epicenter? Why or why not?

21. Predicting A community has just built a street across a strike-slip fault that has frequent earthquakes. How will movement along the fault affect the street?

22. Making Generalizations How can filled land and loose, soft soil affect the amount of damage caused by an earthquake? Explain.

Applying Skills

Use the graph to answer Questions 23–26.

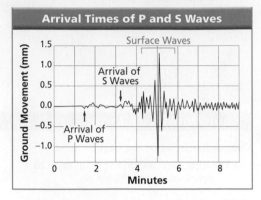

23. Interpreting Diagrams In what order did the seismic waves arrive at the seismograph station?

24. Interpreting Diagrams Which type of seismic wave produced the largest ground movement?

25. Analyzing Data What was the difference in arrival times for the P waves and S waves?

26. Predicting What would the seismogram look like several hours after this earthquake? How would it change if an aftershock occurred?

▶ Lab zone Chapter **Project**

Performance Assessment Before testing how your model withstands an earthquake, explain to your classmates how and why you changed your model. When your model is tested, observe how it withstands the earthquake. How would a real earthquake compare with the method used to test your model? If it were a real building, could your structure withstand an earthquake? How could you improve your model?

Lab zone Chapter **Project** ▪️L3

Performance Assessment Give each student an opportunity to explain any changes made to the model on the basis of the results of previous tests. Then let students test their models for the last time and make final changes before their class presentations. Remind students to note any further improvements they want to make.

Reflect and Record Use the two questions in the student text as the basis for a whole-class discussion. Then let students write in their journals.

Standardized Test Prep

Choose the letter that best answers the question or completes the statement.

1. Stress will build until an earthquake occurs if friction along a fault is
A decreasing.
B high.
C low.
D changed to heat.

2. To estimate the total energy released by an earthquake, a geologist should use the
F Mercalli scale.
G Richter scale.
H epicenter scale.
J moment magnitude scale.

Use the information below and your knowledge of science to answer Questions 3 through 5.

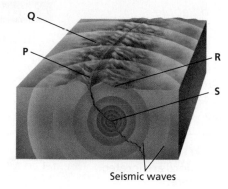

Seismic waves

3. In the diagram, the epicenter is located at point
A Q.
B P.
C R.
D S.

4. When an earthquake occurs, seismic waves travel
F from P in all directions.
G from R to S.
H from S in all directions.
J from Q to P.

5. At point R, seismic waves from an earthquake would be
A weaker than at P.
B likely to cause little damage.
C weaker than at Q.
D likely to cause the most damage.

Constructed Response

6. Explain the process that forms a strike-slip fault and leads to an earthquake along the fault. In your answer, discuss the force that causes stress in Earth's crust, the type of stress that produces a strike-slip fault, the characteristics of a strike-slip fault, and what happens before and during the earthquake.

Thinking Critically

19. The hanging wall moves upward in relation to the footwall. It is a reverse fault.

20. No, this is not enough information, because two circles will show two intersecting points. A third circle is needed to pinpoint one location.

21. The street will break where it crosses the fault, and the two sides will be moved horizontally in opposite directions.

22. In general, filled land and loose, soft soil increase the amount of damage caused by an earthquake. During an earthquake, the loosely packed soil of the filled land shakes more violently than the surrounding rock. Also, an earthquake can cause liquefaction. Liquefaction turns soft soil with a high moisture content into liquid mud.

Applying Skills

23. P waves arrive first, then S waves, and finally surface waves.

24. Surface waves produce the largest ground movement.

25. The difference in arrival times was approximately 1 minute and 50 seconds.

26. The up-and-down spikes of the waves would be much less jagged, perhaps creating an almost straight line. If an aftershock occurred, the spikes would resume.

Standardized Test Prep

1. B **2.** J **3.** C **4.** H **5.** D
6. Strike-slip faults occur at points where plates slide past each other sideways. The movement is caused by stress that builds up in Earth's crust from plate movements. Strike-slip faults are caused by shearing stress that builds up. When enough stress builds up, the rock breaks and the plates slide quickly past each other, causing an earthquake.

Chapter at a Glance

PRENTICE HALL
Teacher EXPRESS™
Plan • Teach • Assess

 Chapter Project   *Volcanoes and People*

Technology

Local Standards

All in One Teaching Resources

- Chapter Project Teacher Notes, pp. 176–177
- Chapter Project Student Overview, pp. 178–179
- Chapter Project Student Worksheets 1–2, pp. 180–181
- Chapter Project Scoring Rubric, p. 182

 **Discovery CHANNEL SCHOOL** Video Preview

 Section 1

Volcanoes and Plate Tectonics

2 periods
1 block

F.3.1.1 Identify where Earth's volcanic regions are located and explain why they are found there.

F.3.1.2 Explain how hot spot volcanoes form.

 **Go Online** PHSchool.com

 Section 2

Properties of Magma

1 period
1/2 block

F.3.2.1 Identify some physical and chemical properties of matter.

F.3.2.2 Explain why some liquids flow more easily than others.

F.3.2.3 Explain what factors determine the viscosity of magma.

 **Go Online** SCLINKS™ NSTA

 Section 3

Volcanic Eruptions

3 periods
1 1/2 blocks

F.3.3.1 Explain what happens when a volcano erupts.

F.3.3.2 Describe the two types of volcanic eruptions.

F.3.3.3 Identify a volcano's stages of activity.

 **Go Online** *active art*

Section 4

Volcanic Landforms

1 period
1 block

F.3.4.1 List the landforms that lava and ash create.

F.3.4.2 Explain how the magma that hardens beneath Earth's surface creates landforms.

F.3.4.3 Identify other distinct features that occur in volcanic areas.

 **Go Online** SCLINKS™ NSTA

 Discovery CHANNEL SCHOOL Video Field Trip

Review and Assessment

Test Preparation

All in One Teaching Resources

- Key Terms Review, p. 219
- Transparency F34
- Performance Assessment Teacher Notes, p. 226
- Performance Assessment Scoring Rubric, p. 227
- Performance Assessment Student Worksheet, p. 228
- Chapter Test, pp. 229–232

 **Go Online** PHSchool.com

 Discovery CHANNEL SCHOOL Video Assessment

Test Preparation Blackline Masters

Lab zone Chapter Activities Planner

For more activities

LAB ZONE
Easy Planner
CD-ROM

Student Edition	Inquiry	Time	Materials	Skills	Resources
Chapter Project, p. 81	Open-ended	2–3 weeks	**All in One** Teaching Resources, p. 176	Classifying, drawing conclusions	**Lab zone Easy Planner**
Section 1					
Discover Activity, p. 82	Guided	10 minutes	None	Developing hypotheses	**Lab zone Easy Planner**
Try This, p. 85	Guided	15–20 minutes	Plastic box, cold water, hot water, red food coloring, small narrow-necked bottle, flat piece of plastic foam	Making models	**Lab zone Easy Planner**
Skills Lab, p. 86	Guided	Prep: 20 minutes Class: 40 minutes	Outline of world map showing longitude and latitude, 4 pencils of different colors	Interpreting data	**Lab zone Easy Planner** **Lab Activity Video** **All in One** Teaching Resources Skills Lab: *Mapping Earthquakes and Volcanoes, pp. 190–192*
Section 2					
Discover Activity, p. 87	Directed	15 minutes	2 small plastic cups, 1 larger cup, oil, honey, stopwatch	Interpreting data	**Lab zone Easy Planner**
Section 3					
Discover Activity, p. 91	Guided	5–10 minutes	Samples of pumice and obsidian, hand lens	Developing hypotheses	**Lab zone Easy Planner**
Try This, p. 94	Directed	10–15 minutes	1- or 2-liter plastic bottle, 10 g baking soda, 65 mL water, 6 raisins, 65 mL vinegar	Making models	**Lab zone Easy Planner**
Section 4					
Discover Activity, p. 99	Guided	10–15 minutes	Tape, balloon, straw, box, damp sand	Making models	**Lab zone Easy Planner**
Skills Lab, pp. 106–107	Guided	Prep: 45 minutes Class: 40 minutes	Plastic cup, tray or shallow pan, aluminum pizza pan with holes punched at 2.5-cm intervals, plastic knife, unflavored gelatin mold in bowl, red food coloring and water, plastic syringe (10 cc), rubber gloves, unlined paper, 3 small cardboard oatmeal boxes	Developing hypotheses, making models, observing	**Lab zone Easy Planner** **Lab Activity Video** **All in One** Teaching Resources Skills Lab: *Gelatin Volcanoes, pp. 217–218*

Section 1 Volcanoes and Plate Tectonics

 *2 periods, 1 block*

Objectives

F.3.1.1 Identify where Earth's volcanic regions are located and explain why they are found there.

F.3.1.2 Explain how hot spot volcanoes form.

Key Terms

• volcano • magma • lava • Ring of Fire • island arc • hot spot

Local Standards

Preteach

Build Background Knowledge

Students share their observations about volcanoes they have seen firsthand or on TV or film.

Lab zone Discover Activity *Where Are Volcanoes Found on Earth's Surface?* **L2**

Targeted Print and Technology Resources

  Teaching Resources

L2 Reading Strategy Transparency F24: Asking Questions

 PresentationExpress™ CD-ROM

Instruct

Volcanoes and Plate Boundaries Use board sketches to review the types of plate boundaries and to help students determine where along the boundaries volcanoes are likely to form.

Hot Spot Volcanoes Guide students to discuss characteristics of volcanoes on Hawaii and predict what will happen when Hawaii moves away from the hot spot.

Lab zone Skills Lab *Mapping Earthquakes and Volcanoes* **L3**

Targeted Print and Technology Resources

Teaching Resources

L2 Guided Reading, pp. 185–187
L2 Transparencies, F25, F26
L2 Skills Lab: *Mapping Earthquakes and Volcanoes*, pp. 190–192

Lab Activity Video/DVD
Skills Lab: *Mapping Earthquakes and Volcanoes*

PHSchool.com Web Code: cfd-1031

Student Edition on Audio CD

Assess

Section Assessment Questions

Have students use their completed graphic organizers with their questions and answers to answer the questions.

Reteach

Students make a chart that compares the differences in how volcanoes form.

Targeted Print and Technology Resources

Teaching Resources

• Section Summary, p. 184
L1 Review and Reinforce, p. 188
L3 Enrich, p. 189

Section 2 **Properties of Magma**

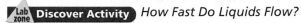 *1 period, 1/2 block*

Objectives

Local Standards

F.3.2.1 Identify some physical and chemical properties of matter.
F.3.2.2 Define viscosity.
F.3.2.3 Explain what factors determine the viscosity of magma.

Key Terms

• element • compound • physical property • chemical property • viscosity
• silica • pahoehoe • aa

Preteach

Build Background Knowledge

Students discuss the differences in eruptions that flow rapidly and slowly in volcanoes that they have observed on TV or on film.

Lab zone **Discover Activity** *How Fast Do Liquids Flow?*   L1

Targeted Print and Technology Resources

 Teaching Resources

L2   Reading Strategy Transparency F27:
Identifying the Main Idea

 PresentationExpress™ CD-ROM

Instruct

Physical and Chemical Properties Lead a discussion of the differences between these types of properties and classify examples.

What Is Viscosity? Help students classify liquids as having high or low viscosity.

Viscosity of Magma Use leading questions to develop an understanding of the factors that affect viscosity.

Targeted Print and Technology Resources

Teaching Resources

L2   Guided Reading, pp. 195–197

www.SciLinks.org Web Code: scn-1032

Student Edition on Audio CD

Assess

Section Assessment Questions

Have students use their completed graphic organizers with main ideas and details to answer the questions.

Reteach

Students suggest examples of liquids that have high viscosity and ones that have low viscosity.

Targeted Print and Technology Resources

Teaching Resources

• Section Summary, p. 194
L1   Review and Reinforce, p. 198
L3   Enrich, p. 199

Section 3 Volcanic Eruptions

3 periods, 1 1/2 blocks

ABILITY LEVELS
L1 Basic to Average
L2 For All Students
L3 Average to Advanced

Objectives

F.3.3.1 Explain what happens when a volcano erupts.

F.3.3.2 Describe the two types of volcanic eruptions.

F.3.3.3 Identify a volcano's stages of activity.

Key Terms

- magma chamber • pipe • vent • lava flow • crater • pyroclastic flow
- dormant • extinct

Local Standards

Preteach

Build Background Knowledge

Students share their observations of what lava looks like as a volcano is erupting and what else comes out of a volcano during an eruption.

Discover Activity *What Are Volcanic Rocks Like?* **L1**

Targeted Print and Technology Resources

All in One Teaching Resources

L2 Reading Strategy Transparency F28: Using Prior Knowledge

○ **PresentationExpress™ CD-ROM**

Instruct

Magma Reaches Earth's Surface Use Figure 10 and the common meanings of the terms "chamber," "pipe," and "vent" to describe the parts of a volcano.

Kinds of Volcanic Eruptions Describe the interaction of gas pressure and viscosity and show how this interaction determines whether an eruption is quiet or explosive.

Stages of Volcanic Activity Use the life-cycle concept to help students understand the stages of a volcano and develop a definition for each stage.

Targeted Print and Technology Resources

All in One Teaching Resources

L2 Guided Reading, pp. 202–206

L2 Transparency F29

PHSchool.com Web Code: cfp-1033

○ **Student Edition on Audio CD**

Assess

Section Assessment Questions

Have students use their graphic organizers that they completed using prior knowledge to answer the questions.

Reteach

Students list characteristics of quiet and explosive eruptions.

Targeted Print and Technology Resources

All in One Teaching Resources

- Section Summary, p. 201
L1 Review and Reinforce, p. 207
L3 Enrich, p. 208

Section 4 Volcanic Landforms

 1 period, 1 block

ABILITY LEVELS
- **L1** Basic to Average
- **L2** For All Students
- **L3** Average to Advanced

Objectives

F.3.4.1 List the landforms that lava and ash create.

F.3.4.2 Explain how the magma that hardens beneath Earth's surface creates landforms.

F.3.4.3 Identify other distinct features that occur in volcanic areas.

Key Terms

- shield volcano • cinder cone • composite volcano • caldera • volcanic neck
- dike • sill • batholith • geothermal activity • geyser

Local Standards

Preteach

Build Background Knowledge

Student volunteers draw on the board what they think volcanoes look like.

 **Discover Activity** *How Can Volcanic Activity Change Earth's Surface?* **L1**

Targeted Print and Technology Resources

 Teaching Resources

L2 Reading Strategy Transparency F30: Outlining

 PresentationExpress™ CD-ROM

Instruct

Landforms From Lava and Ash Use blackboard sketches to show how lava with varying viscosities creates different types of landforms.

Landforms From Magma Show how magma cools and forms rock beneath Earth's surface, and describe the magmatic landforms that ultimately emerge from this process.

Geothermal Activity Ask leading questions to help students compare and contrast hot springs and geysers, and explain how heated groundwater is useful to people.

 Skills Lab *Gelatin Volcanoes* **L2**

Targeted Print and Technology Resources

Teaching Resources

L2 Guided Reading, pp. 211–214
L2 Transparencies F31, F32, F33
L2 Skills Lab: *Gelatin Volcanoes*, pp. 217–218

Lab Activity Video/DVD
Skills Lab: *Gelatin Volcanoes*

www.SciLinks.org Web Code: scn-1034

 Student Edition on Audio CD

Assess

Section Assessment Questions

Have students use their completed outlines to answer the questions.

Reteach

Students list the types of volcanoes and how they form.

Targeted Print and Technology Resources

Teaching Resources

- Section Summary, p. 210
L1 Review and Reinforce, p. 215
L3 Enrich, p. 216

Chapter 3 Content Refresher

Go Online

NSTA–PDLINKS

For: Professional development support
Visit: www.SciLinks.org/PDLinks
Web Code: scf-1030

Professional Development

Section 1 Volcanoes and Plate Tectonics

Krakatau On August 27, 1883, the uninhabited island of Krakatau exploded. Krakatau was a volcanic island located in the Sunda Strait between the islands of Java and Sumatra in Indonesia.

More than 36,000 people were killed as a result of the eruption and 165 villages were destroyed. About 1,000 people in Sumatra were killed by hot ash, pumice, and scalding volcanic gases. The remaining thousands were killed by water. The eruption sent huge waves (tsunamis) outward in all directions. The narrow Sunda Strait funneled the waves up onto land, destroying villages along the shorelines. Waves up to 40 meters high (135 feet) were reported by survivors. Thirty-three hours after the eruption, the tsunamis were detected by a tide gauge at Le Havre, France. Dust from the eruption fell 2,500 kilometers downwind. The sound of the eruption was heard in Australia, the Philippines, Sri Lanka, and Rodriguez Island more than 4,700 kilometers away, across the Indian Ocean.

Krakatau is located along a convergent boundary where the Australian Plate is moving north, colliding with the Asian Plate. Beneath Java, Sumatra, and Krakatau this collision has formed a subduction zone. The region has many active volcanoes and experiences numerous earthquakes.

Address Misconceptions

The terms crater and caldera refer to the same structure. Although the two structures share some similarities, they are two different things. For a strategy for clarifying the difference, see **Address Misconceptions** on page 102.

Section 2 Properties of Magma

Magma Composition and Characteristics The composition of magma depends on the rock that makes it up. In turn, the composition of magma determines the type of volcanic activity associated with it. The most explosive volcanic eruptions occur with rhyolitic magma, which is high in viscosity, gas content, and silica content. Basaltic magma is low in viscosity, gas content, and silica and causes the least explosive eruptions. Andesitic magma's composition is between those of basaltic and rhyolitic magma.

Water also affects magma's properties. Rock that contains water melts at a lower temperature. Basaltic magma, which originates in the upper mantle, contains little water. Most basaltic magma rises to Earth's surface relatively quickly and does not react much with the rocks of the crust.

Rhyolitic magma is formed by the melting of continental crust. The rocks in the crust contain relatively large amounts of water. The average composition of the rocks in the continental crust is also higher in silica than ocean crust or the upper mantle. Both of these factors combine to produce magma that erupts very explosively.

Andesitic magma forms from melted ocean crust and ocean sediments carried downward into subduction zones along continental margins. Ocean crust contains less water than continental crust. However, the ocean sediments contain relatively large amounts of water.

Help Students Read

Previewing Visuals

Identify Similarities and Differences

Strategy Help students read and understand material that discusses two or more related topics or concepts. This strategy helps students identify similarities and differences, thus enabling them to link prior knowledge with new information. Before students begin, assign a section in this chapter for them to read.

Example

1. Have students compare two or more topics or concepts under a section heading. Tell them that, when they compare, they should focus on both similarities and differences. Remind them to look for these signal words:
- Similarities: similar, similarly, also, just as, like, likewise, in the same way
- Differences: but, however, although, whereas, on the other hand, different, unlike

2. Have students contrast two or more topics or concepts. Remind students that, when they contrast, they should focus only on differences.

3. Have students create a chart or diagram comparing or contrasting two or more topics or concepts they read about in the section. Suggest that they make either a compare/contrast table or a Venn diagram to present their information.

Section 3 Volcanic Eruptions

Dangers of Monitoring Volcanoes Geologists measure seismic activity, temperature, gas emissions, and ground elevations and movements, as well as collect rock and ash samples inside volcanoes.

Studying active volcanoes sometimes means descending into a volcano's crater. In 1993, six geologists and three tourists were killed during a small eruption of Galeras in Colombia. They were all in or near the crater at the time. Since 1975, more than 30 geologists have been killed while studying volcanoes.

The United States has several dozen volcanoes that have been active within the last few thousand years. Of these, 10 are in Hawaii and do not erupt explosively. Alaska has 52 volcanoes, but most are in remote, unpopulated areas. The most dangerous volcanoes are the 15 in western states. In addition to Mount Saint Helens, two of these are of particular concern—Mammoth Mountain and Mount Rainier. Mammoth Mountain, in the Sierra Nevadas in California, is a popular ski resort east of Yosemite National Park. An eruption would cause dangerous mudflows as the snow melted. Mount Rainier, about 120 kilometers (75 miles) from Seattle,

Washington, last erupted in 1825. Rainier has not erupted explosively in the past, but the glaciers and snow on its peak could form dangerous mudflows, even during a minor eruption. Geologists at the Cascades Volcanic Observatory in Vancouver, Washington, keep a watchful eye on all the volcanoes in the western United States.

Section 4 Volcanic Landforms

Other Volcanic Landforms The diagram below shows some of the major volcanic landforms. The most prominent landform of course is a volcano. Batholiths form one of the largest volcanic landforms. Most other features form beneath Earth's surface and can be exposed by later erosion or uplift.

Three important landforms are dikes, sills, and volcanic necks. A dike is formed when magma cools and solidifies inside Earth in a tabular feature that cuts across other rock layers. A sill is a tabular feature that forms parallel to other rock layers. A volcanic neck forms when the hardened magma in a volcanic pipe or vent is exposed by erosion. The surrounding, less resistant rock is stripped away, leaving the interior volcanic pipe exposed. A famous example of a volcanic neck is Shiprock in New Mexico.

Active Volcanoes in the American West

Bellingham • ▲ Mount Baker
▲ Glacier Peak
• Seattle • Spokane • Great Falls
Mount Rainier ▲
Washington
Mount St. Helens ▲
• Portland
45°N ▲ Mount Hood Montana • Billings
Eugene • ▲ **Three Sisters**
▲ • Bend Idaho
Newberry Crater ▲ • Boise
Oregon • Pocatello Wyoming
Pacific Ocean
Mount Shasta ▲ ▲ **Medicine Lake**
Lassen Peak ▲ • Salt Lake City
40°N Nevada
California • Reno Utah Colorado
N W E S • Sacramento
• San Francisco ▲ **Long Valley Caldera (Mammoth Mountain)**
0   200 mi
0   200 km

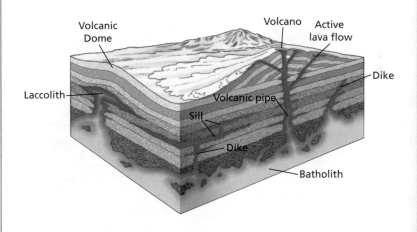

Volcanic Dome — Volcano — Active lava flow — Dike — Volcanic pipe — Laccolith — Sill — Dike — Batholith

The BIG Idea

The Big Idea is the major scientific concept of the chapter. It is followed by the Essential Question. Read aloud the question to students. As students study the chapter, tell them to think about the Essential Question. Explain that they will discover the answer to the question as they read. The chapter Study Guide provides a sample answer.

Chapter Project

L3

Objectives

This project will give students an opportunity to investigate the variety of ways in which people have been affected by volcanoes. Students will communicate their findings in a multimedia, documentary presentation. After this Chapter Project, students will be able to

- classify types of volcanoes
- draw conclusions about the volcano's effects on people living near it
- communicate how the volcano has affected the people living in a volcanic region

Skills Focus

classifying, drawing conclusions, communicating

Project Time Line 2 to 3 weeks

All in One Teaching Resources

- Chapter Project Teacher Notes
- Chapter Project Overview
- Chapter Project Worksheet 1
- Chapter Project Worksheet 2
- Chapter Project Scoring Rubric

Developing a Plan

Each group should study a map showing volcanic regions, choose one region, and investigate one aspect of how that region affects people in the area. After choosing the topic, group members should research information about that topic and take relevant, well-organized notes. Have students create a storyboard showing each step in the presentation, including the media materials that will be used.

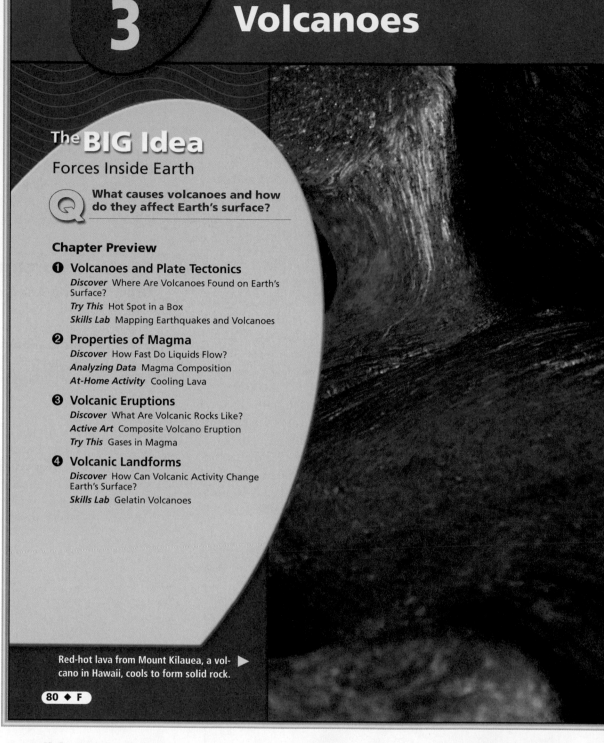

Chapter 3

Volcanoes

The BIG Idea
Forces Inside Earth

Q **What causes volcanoes and how do they affect Earth's surface?**

Chapter Preview

❶ **Volcanoes and Plate Tectonics**
Discover Where Are Volcanoes Found on Earth's Surface?
Try This Hot Spot in a Box
Skills Lab Mapping Earthquakes and Volcanoes

❷ **Properties of Magma**
Discover How Fast Do Liquids Flow?
Analyzing Data Magma Composition
At-Home Activity Cooling Lava

❸ **Volcanic Eruptions**
Discover What Are Volcanic Rocks Like?
Active Art Composite Volcano Eruption
Try This Gases in Magma

❹ **Volcanic Landforms**
Discover How Can Volcanic Activity Change Earth's Surface?
Skills Lab Gelatin Volcanoes

Red-hot lava from Mount Kilauea, a volcano in Hawaii, cools to form solid rock. ▶

Possible Materials

- Provide a wide variety of age-appropriate source materials for students to use in their research, including encyclopedias, nonfiction library books, magazine articles, films on videocassette and CD-ROM, and the Internet.
- Students could use index cards for taking notes and self-stick removable tags for flagging appropriate information in the books.
- When students are ready to prepare their multimedia materials, provide a variety of materials and devices: poster paper, art supplies, acetate sheets for making overhead transparencies, videocameras, and tape recorders for taping songs, background music, or sound effects.

Lab zone™ **Chapter Project**

Volcanoes and People

The eruptions of a volcano can be dangerous. Yet volcanoes and people have been closely connected throughout history. People often live near volcanoes because of the benefits they offer, from rich soil, to minerals, to hot springs. In this chapter project, you will investigate how volcanoes have affected the people living in a volcanic region.

Your Goal To make a documentary about life in a volcanic region

Your documentary must

• describe the type of volcano you chose and give its history

• focus on one topic, such as how people have benefited from living near the volcano or how people show the volcano in their art and stories

• use a variety of media

Plan It! Brainstorm with a group of other students which geographic area you would like to learn about. Your teacher may suggest some volcanic regions for you to check out. Decide what research resources you will need and what media you want to use. For media, you might consider video, computer art, overhead transparencies, a skit, or a mural. Be creative! When your documentary is finished, rehearse your presentation. Then present your documentary to your class.

Chapter 3 F ◆ 81

Discovery CHANNEL SCHOOL Video Preview

Volcanoes

Show the Video Preview to introduce the Chapter Project and overview the chapter content. Discussion question: **What forces do you think are responsible for volcanoes?** *(Accept student responses that show some connection to plate boundaries that are pushing apart or pulling together.)*

Performance Assessment

The Chapter Project Scoring Rubric will help you evaluate how well students complete the Chapter Project. You may want to share the scoring rubric with your students so that they are clear about what will be expected of them. Students will be assessed on

• their ability to identify the type of volcano they have chosen and summarize its history

• how well they have focused both their research and their presentation on a single topic related to the volcano's effect on people living in the area

• their creativity in making use of a variety of media to support the narrative part of their presentation

• how well they present their documentary to the rest of the class

Portfolio

Launching the Project

To introduce the project, ask: **What are some ways that people have been affected by volcanoes?** *(Accept all responses at this time, and encourage creative thinking. Possible answer: by the destruction of homes and buildings and by being forced to relocate)* Allow time for students to read the project description. Encourage discussion of the different topics students could focus on and the types of source materials they could use

for their research. Also answer any initial questions that students may have.

Emphasize that although they may divide responsibilities so that only some group members will prepare the visuals, *all* members of the group should take part in planning the visuals and be prepared to answer questions about them.

Objectives

After completing the lesson, students will be able to

F.3.1.1 Identify where Earth's volcanic regions are located and explain why they are found in these areas

F.3.1.2 Explain how hot spot volcanoes form

Target Reading Skill

Asking Questions Explain that changing a head into a question helps students anticipate the ideas, facts, and events that they are about to read.

Answer

Possible questions: Where are volcanoes found? What are hot spots? Possible answers: Most volcanoes are found along plate boundaries. A hot spot is an area where material from deep within the mantle rises and then melts, forming magma.

All in One Teaching Resources

• Transparency F24

Preteach

Build Background Knowledge **L1**

Volcanic Eruptions

Ask students: **Have you ever seen a volcano? Were you on the scene, or did you see it on TV or in film? Was it erupting? What was happening? What effects did you see? How were people affected?** *(Answers will vary, depending on students' experience. Encourage students to share their observations and describe details.)*

Go Online
PLANET DIARY

For: More on volcanoes
Visit: PHSchool.com
Web Code: cfd-1031

Students can review volcanoes in an online interactivity.

Section
1
Volcanoes and Plate Tectonics

Reading Preview

Key Concepts
• Where are most of Earth's volcanoes found?
• How do hot spot volcanoes form?

Key Terms
• volcano • magma • lava
• Ring of Fire • island arc
• hot spot

Target Reading Skill

Asking Questions Before you read, preview the red headings. In a graphic organizer like the one below, ask a *where, what,* or *how* question for each heading. As you read, write the answers to your questions.

Volcanoes and Plate Tectonics

Question	Answer
Where are volcanoes found?	Most volcanoes are found along plate boundaries.

Lab zone Discover **Activity**

Where Are Volcanoes Found on Earth's Surface?

1. Look at the map of Earth's Active Volcanoes in Figure 2. What symbols are used to represent volcanoes? What other symbols are shown on the map?

2. Do the locations of the volcanoes form a pattern? Do the volcanoes seem related to any other features on Earth's surface?

Think About It
Developing Hypotheses Develop a hypothesis to explain where Earth's volcanoes are located.

In 2002, Mount Etna erupted in glowing fountains and rivers of molten rock. Located on the island of Sicily in the Mediterranean Sea, Mount Etna is Europe's largest volcano. Over the last 2,500 years, it has erupted often. The ancient Greeks believed that Mount Etna was one home of Hephaestus, the Greek god of fire. Beneath the volcano was the forge where Hephaestus made beautiful metal objects for the other Greek gods.

The eruption of a volcano is among the most awe-inspiring events on Earth. A **volcano** is a weak spot in the crust where molten material, or magma, comes to the surface. **Magma** is a molten mixture of rock-forming substances, gases, and water from the mantle. When magma reaches the surface, it is called **lava.** After lava has cooled, it forms solid rock. Lava released during volcanic activity builds up Earth's surface.

FIGURE 1
Lava Flow on Mount Etna
A lava flow from Mount Etna in Sicily almost buried this small building.

82 ◆ F

Lab zone Discover **Activity**

Skills Focus Developing hypotheses **L2**

Time 10 minutes

Tips Direct students' attention to the map's key to answer the questions in Step 1.

Expected Outcome **1.** Triangles symbolize active volcanoes; solid lines symbolize plate boundaries.

2. Yes, there is a pattern: volcanoes seem to be related to plate boundaries.

Think It Over Volcanoes are concentrated along plate boundaries. *Exceptions:* A few volcanoes occur within plates.

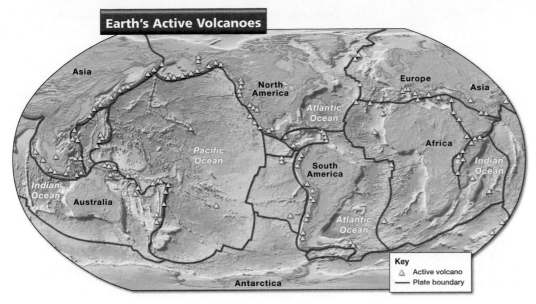

Earth's Active Volcanoes

Asia

North America

Atlantic Ocean

Europe

Asia

Africa

Indian Ocean

Pacific Ocean

South America

Indian Ocean

Australia

Atlantic Ocean

Antarctica

Key
△ Active volcano
— Plate boundary

Volcanoes and Plate Boundaries

There are about 600 active volcanoes on land. Many more lie beneath the sea, where it is difficult for scientists to observe and map them. Figure 2 shows the location of some of Earth's major volcanoes. Notice how volcanoes occur in belts that extend across continents and oceans. One major volcanic belt is the **Ring of Fire,** formed by the many volcanoes that rim the Pacific Ocean.

Volcanic belts form along the boundaries of Earth's plates. At plate boundaries, huge pieces of the crust diverge (pull apart) or converge (push together). As a result, the crust often fractures, allowing magma to reach the surface. Most volcanoes form along diverging plate boundaries such as mid-ocean ridges and along converging plate boundaries where subduction takes place. For example, Mount Etna formed near the boundary of the Eurasian and African plates.

Diverging Boundaries Volcanoes form along the mid-ocean ridges, which mark diverging plate boundaries. Recall that ridges are long, underwater mountain ranges that sometimes have a rift valley down their center. Along the rift valley, lava pours out of cracks in the ocean floor, gradually building new mountains. Volcanoes also form along diverging plate boundaries on land. For example, there are several large volcanoes along the Great Rift Valley in East Africa.

FIGURE 2
Many of Earth's volcanoes are located along the boundaries of tectonic plates. The Ring of Fire is a belt of volcanoes that circles the Pacific Ocean. **Observing** *What other regions have a large number of volcanoes?*

Go Online
PLANET DIARY

For: More on volcanoes
Visit: PHSchool.com
Web Code: cfd-1031

Instruct

Volcanoes and Plate Boundaries

Teach Key Concepts L2

Plate Tectonic Setting of Volcanoes

Focus Review the types of plate boundaries, and make sketches on the board.

Teach Ask: **Where should volcanoes and magma chambers be included?** (*Fill in sketches: Volcanoes and magma chambers should occur at diverging boundaries and at two types of converging boundaries: ocean-ocean and ocean-continent. They are less likely to occur at transform or continent-continent converging boundaries.*)

Apply Ask: **Why don't volcanoes occur along the San Andreas Fault in California?** (*It is a transform boundary.*) **Would you expect volcanoes to occur along the Mid-Atlantic Ridge?** (*Yes, this is a diverging boundary.*) **learning modality: visual**

Independent Practice L2

All in One Teaching Resources

• Guided Reading and Study Worksheet: *Volcanoes and Plate Boundaries*

 Student Edition on Audio CD

Use Visuals: Figure 2 L2

Volcanic Regions

Focus Remind students that the volcanoes in the Ring of Fire occur at converging boundaries.

Teach Ask: **What other volcanic belts do you see on the map?** (*Possible answers: in southern Europe, within Africa at the Great Rift Valley, between Africa and Arabia, in the eastern Caribbean*)

Apply Ask students why volcanism might occur in the Mediterranean Sea. (*Possible answer: A plate boundary runs through it.*) **learning modality: visual**

All in One Teaching Resources

• Transparencies F25 and F26

Monitor Progress L2

Oral Presentation Call on students to explain what causes the Ring of Fire.

Answer
Figure 2 The Mediterranean area, East Africa, and the Middle East

---

Differentiated Instruction

English Learners/Beginning L1
Vocabulary: Science Glossary
Pronounce and define aloud key terms for students. Suggest that they start a personal glossary, with each term and its definition in English on one side of an index card and in the student's primary language on the other side. They also might draw and label diagrams. **learning modality: verbal**

English Learners/Intermediate L2
Vocabulary: Science Glossary Students can expand on the activity described in *Beginning* by adding other scientific terms in this section: *diverge, converge, subduction.* Have students write sentences that use each of these words. Give students an opportunity to practice pronunciation by calling on individuals to read their sentences aloud. **learning modality: verbal**

Teacher Demo

Interpreting Maps   L2

Materials large world map

Time 10 minutes

Focus Refer students to the text paragraphs that list some island arcs and continent-margin volcanic regions.

Teach Ask students to locate each of the six island arcs mentioned: Japan, New Zealand, Indonesia, the Caribbean islands, the Philippines, and the Aleutians. Also ask them to locate the two regions of subduction-related volcanism on continent margins: Andes Mountains, and the Pacific Northwest.

Apply Ask students to compare these regions with the plate boundaries shown in Figure 2. **learning modality: visual**

Hot Spot Volcanoes

Teach Key Concepts   L2

Hot Spots

Focus Ask: **How would you describe the volcanoes on Hawaii?** (*Broad, tall volcanoes; lava fountains and flows; lava might reach ocean and cool*)

Teach Ask: **What would happen if volcanic eruptions continued to occur on the sea floor?** (*Islands would form.*) **Is the island of Hawaii getting larger today?** (*Yes, every time Kilauea erupts and lava pours into the sea.*) **Why do geysers occur at Yellowstone?** (*Groundwater is heated in hot rock near shallow magma bodies.*)

Apply Ask students to predict what will happen after the Pacific plate moves Hawaii away from the hot spot. (*Volcanism will stop on Hawaii; a new island will form away from Hawaii.*) **learning modality: logical/mathematical**

Converging Boundaries Many volcanoes form near converging plate boundaries where oceanic plates return to the mantle. Volcanoes may form where two oceanic plates collide or where an oceanic plate collides with a continental plate. Figure 3 shows how converging plates produce volcanoes.

Many volcanoes occur near boundaries where two oceanic plates collide. Through subduction, the older, denser plate sinks beneath a deep-ocean trench into the mantle. Some of the rock above the subducting plate melts and forms magma. Because the magma is less dense than the surrounding rock, it rises toward the surface. Eventually, the magma breaks through the ocean floor, creating volcanoes.

The resulting volcanoes create a string of islands called an **island arc.** The curve of an island arc echoes the curve of its deep-ocean trench. Major island arcs include Japan, New Zealand, Indonesia, the Philippines, the Aleutians, and the Caribbean islands.

Volcanoes also occur where an oceanic plate is subducted beneath a continental plate. Collisions of this type produced the volcanoes of the Andes Mountains in South America and the volcanoes of the Pacific Northwest in the United States.

Reading Checkpoint How did the volcanoes in the Andes Mountains form?

FIGURE 3
Volcanoes at Converging Boundaries
Volcanoes often form where two oceanic plates collide or where an oceanic plate collides with a continental plate. In both situations, an oceanic plate sinks beneath a trench. Rock above the plate melts to form magma, which then erupts to the surface as lava.

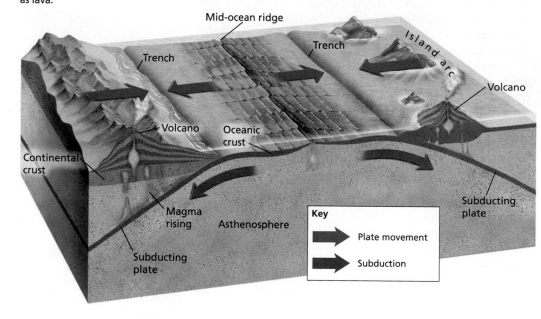

Key
→ Plate movement
→ Subduction

Try This Activity

Skills Focus Making models   L1

Materials plastic box, cold water, hot water, red food coloring, small narrow-necked bottle, flat piece of plastic foam

Time 15–20 minutes

Tips Tell students to make sure that the water in the box is deeper than the height of the bottle.

Expected Outcome The "magma" rises out of the bottle and to the water's surface, where it hits the "tectonic plate" in a spot directly above the bottle. When the plate is moved in one direction, the magma hits it in a spot behind the original spot. If the plate continued to move in the same direction, magma would hit it in a series of

spots, with the newer volcanoes closer to the "hot spot" and the older volcanoes farther away from it.

Extend Suggest that students continue the plate movement and number the volcanoes to show the sequence in which the volcanoes form. **learning modality: kinesthetic**

FIGURE 4
Hot Spot Volcanoes
Eventually, the Pacific plate's movement will carry the island of Hawaii away from the hot spot.
Inferring *Which island on the map formed first?*

Hot Spot Volcanoes

Some volcanoes result from "hot spots" in Earth's mantle. A **hot spot** is an area where material from deep within the mantle rises and then melts, forming magma. **A volcano forms above a hot spot when magma erupts through the crust and reaches the surface.** Some hot spot volcanoes lie in the middle of plates far from any plate boundaries. Other hot spots occur on or near plate boundaries.

A hot spot in the ocean floor can gradually form a series of volcanic mountains. For example, the Hawaiian Islands formed one by one over millions of years as the Pacific plate drifted over a hot spot. Hot spots can also form under the continents. Yellowstone National Park in Wyoming marks a hot spot under the North American plate.

Lab zone Try This **Activity**

Hot Spot in a Box

1. Fill a plastic box half full of cold water. This represents the mantle.
2. Mix red food coloring with hot water in a small, narrow-necked bottle to represent magma.
3. Hold your finger over the mouth of the bottle as you place the bottle in the center of the box. The mouth of the bottle must be under water.
4. Float a flat piece of plastic foam on the water above the bottle to model a tectonic plate.
5. Take your finger off the bottle and observe what happens to the "magma."

Making Models Move the plastic foam slowly along. Where does the magma touch the "plate"? How does this model a hot spot volcano?

Section ❶ Assessment

🅞 **Target Reading Skill Asking Questions** Work with a partner to check the answers in your graphic organizer.

Reviewing Key Concepts

1. **a. Defining** What is a volcano?
   b. Reviewing Where are most volcanoes located?
   c. Relating Cause and Effect What causes volcanoes to form at a diverging plate boundary?
2. **a. Defining** What is a hot spot?
   b. Summarizing How does a hot spot volcano form?
   c. Predicting What features form as an oceanic plate moves across a hot spot?

Writing in Science

Travel Brochure As a travel agent, you are planning a Pacific Ocean cruise that will visit volcanoes in the Ring of Fire and Hawaii. Write a travel brochure describing the types of volcanoes the group will see and explaining why the volcanoes formed where they did.

Chapter 3 F ◆ 85

Lab zone Chapter **Project**

Keep Students on Track See that students have selected the region that they will study. Possible topics for their research include myths and legends, the importance of volcanic soils, mineral resources, tourism, and geothermal power. Ask students to begin their research and start taking notes. To avoid duplication, check the regions and topics that student groups select.

Writing in Science

Writing Skill Explanation
Scoring Rubric
4 includes complete description of the types of volcanoes and how they form, and is written in a friendly, engaging tone
3 includes all criteria
2 includes description of one volcanic belt; other description is incomplete
1 includes incomplete or inaccurate descriptions of volcanic belts

Lab zone Skills Lab

Mapping Earthquakes and Volcanoes L3

Prepare for Inquiry

Key Concept
Earthquakes and volcanoes are concentrated together in belts.

Skills Objectives
Students will be able to
- interpret data to plot the locations of earthquakes and volcanoes on a world map
- interpret data to observe areas in which earthquakes and volcanoes are concentrated
- infer that earthquakes and volcanoes occur together in certain areas.

Prep Time 20 minutes
Class Time 40 minutes

All in One Teaching Resources
Skills Lab: *Mapping Earthquakes and Volcanoes*

Advance Planning
Photocopy an outline world map for each student.

Safety
 Students should exercise caution in using scissors. Review Safety Guidelines in Appendix A.

Guide Inquiry

Invitation
Remind students of the locations of recent earthquakes and volcanic eruptions.

Introduce the Procedure
Review the terms *longitude* and *latitude* and how to use those lines on the map to determine precise locations. Make sure that students know how to determine longitudes and latitudes that fall between lines.

Troubleshooting the Experiment
When students have plotted all locations, display a copy of the map that you have marked so students can check their work.

Expected Outcome
The marked map should indicate belts in which *both* volcanoes *and* earthquakes occur.

Lab zone Skills Lab

Mapping Earthquakes and Volcanoes

Problem
Is there a pattern in the locations of earthquakes and volcanoes?

Skills Focus
interpreting data

Materials
- outline world map showing longitude and latitude
- 4 pencils of different colors

Procedure
1. Use the information in the table to mark the location of each earthquake on the world map. Use a colored pencil to draw a letter E inside a circle at each earthquake location.

2. Use a pencil of a second color to mark the volcanoes on the world map. Indicate each volcano with the letter V inside a circle.

3. Use a third pencil to lightly shade the areas in which earthquakes are found.

4. Use a fourth colored pencil to lightly shade the areas in which volcanoes are found.

Analyze and Conclude
1. **Interpreting Data** How are earthquakes distributed on the map? Are they scattered evenly or concentrated in zones?

2. **Interpreting Data** How are volcanoes distributed? Are they scattered evenly or concentrated in zones?

3. **Inferring** From your data, what can you infer about the relationship between earthquakes and volcanoes?

4. **Communicating** Suppose you added the locations of additional earthquakes and volcanoes to your map. Would the overall pattern of earthquakes and volcanoes change? Explain in writing why you think the pattern would or would not change.

Earthquakes and Volcanoes			
Earthquakes		Volcanoes	
Longitude	Latitude	Longitude	Latitude
120° W	40° N	150° W	60° N
110° E	5° S	70° W	35° S
77° W	4° S	120° W	45° N
88° E	23° N	61° W	15° N
121° E	14° S	105° W	20° N
34° E	7° N	75° W	0°
74° W	44° N	122° W	40° N
70° W	30° S	30° E	40° N
10° E	45° N	60° E	30° N
85° W	13° N	160° E	55° N
125° E	23° N	37° E	3° S
30° E	35° N	145° E	40° N
140° E	35° N	120° E	10° S
12° E	46° N	14° E	41° N
75° E	28° N	105° E	5° S
150° W	61° N	35° E	15° N
68° W	47° S	70° W	30° S
175° E	41° S	175° E	39° S
121° E	17° N	123° E	38° N

More to Explore
On a map of the United States, locate active volcanoes and areas of earthquake activity. Determine the distance from your home to the nearest active volcano.

Analyze and Conclude
1., 2. Both earthquakes and volcanoes are concentrated in definite zones.
3. Earthquakes and volcanoes often occur in the same areas.
4. The pattern would not change very much. Additional data would be added to already apparent zones.

Extend Inquiry
More to Explore Provide copies of a U.S. map that includes insets for Alaska and Hawaii, and have students research and plot active volcanoes and recent earthquakes in the United States.

Reading Preview

Key Concepts
- Why is it helpful to know the physical and chemical properties of a substance?
- What causes some liquids to flow more easily than others?
- What factors determine the viscosity of magma?

Key Terms
- element
- compound
- physical property
- chemical property
- viscosity
- silica
- pahoehoe
- aa

Target Reading Skill
Identifying Main Ideas
As you read Viscosity of Magma, write the main idea in a graphic organizer like the one below. Then write three supporting details that further explain the main idea.

Main Idea

Magma's viscosity depends on . . .

Detail	Detail	Detail

Lab zone Discover Activity

How Fast Do Liquids Flow?

1. Fill one third of a small plastic cup with honey. Fill one third of another cup with cooking oil.
2. Hold the cup containing honey over a third cup and tip it until the liquid begins to flow out of the cup. Time how long it takes from the time the cup was tipped until all the liquid drains out of the cup. Record the time.
3. Repeat Step 2 with the cup filled with oil.

Think About It
Forming Operational Definitions The tendency of a fluid to resist flowing is called viscosity. How did you measure the viscosity of honey and cooking oil? Which had a greater viscosity?

Measured from the bottom of the Pacific Ocean, the Big Island of Hawaii is the largest mountain on Earth. The island is made up of massive volcanoes. One of these volcanoes, Mount Kilauea (kee loo AY uh) erupts frequently and produces huge amounts of lava.

At a temperature of around 1,000°C, lava from Mount Kilauea is very dangerous. Yet most of the time, the lava moves slower than a person can walk—about 1 kilometer per hour. Some types of lava move much more slowly—less than the length of a football field in an entire day. How fast lava flows depends on the properties of the magma from which it formed.

Physical and Chemical Properties

Like all substances, magma and lava are made up of elements and compounds. An **element** is a substance that cannot be broken down into other substances. Carbon, hydrogen, and oxygen are examples of elements. A **compound** is a substance made of two or more elements that have been chemically combined. Water, carbon dioxide, and table salt are familiar compounds. **Each substance has a particular set of physical and chemical properties. These properties can be used to identify a substance or to predict how it will behave.**

Chapter 3 F ◆ 87

Lab zone Discover Activity

Skills Focus Forming operational definitions [L1]

Materials 2 small plastic cups, 1 larger cup, oil, honey, stopwatch

Prep Time 5 minutes

Class Time 15 minutes

Tips If the honey is chilled before the activity, it will drain even more slowly.

Expected Outcome It should take longer for the honey to drain out of the cup than for the cooking oil to drain.

Think It Over Students determined viscosity by timing how long it took for two different liquids to drain from the same type of cup. The honey has a greater viscosity.

Section 2
Properties of Magma

Objectives
After completing the lesson, students will be able to
F.3.2.1 Identify some physical and chemical properties of matter
F.3.2.2 Explain why some fluids flow more easily than others
F.3.2.3 Explain what factors determine the viscosity of magma

Target Reading Skill

Identifying Main Ideas Explain that identifying main ideas and details helps students sort the facts from the material into groups. Each group can have a main topic, subtopics, and details.

Answers
Main Idea: Magma's viscosity depends on its physical and chemical properties.

Details: **1.** Magma is made of elements and of compounds, among them silica.

2. Viscosity is a property of magma.

3. Viscosity depends on silica content and temperature.

All in One Teaching Resources
- Transparency F27

Preteach

Build Background Knowledge [L1]
Lava Flows

Remind students about film clips of flowing lava that they have observed. Ask: **Has anyone seen lava flowing rapidly?** *(Some will say yes; this sometimes occurs in Hawaii when lava races through a channel or tube.)* **Has anyone seen lava flow very slowly?** *(This is the most common case. Flows can creep along, or domes of sticky lava can accumulate at the top of a volcano.)* Tell students that this stickiness is called viscosity.

Physical and Chemical Properties

Teach Key Concepts `L2`

How Do Properties Differ?

Focus Write some simple chemical formulae on the board, and identify each symbol: Si, H, and O are elements, and SiO$_2$ and H$_2$O are compounds.

Teach Ask: **Which properties can be observed while the chemical composition remains the same?** *(Physical)* **Which properties cause compounds to form or break apart?** *(Chemical)*

Apply Ask students to identify the following as a physical or a chemical property: **color of your shoes** *(Physical)*, **boiling water** *(Physical)*, **formation of rust** *(Chemical)*, **minerals forming from magma** *(Chemical)*. **learning modality: logical/mathematical**

Independent Practice `L2`

 Teaching Resources

• Guided Reading and Study Worksheet: *Properties of Magma*

 **Student Edition on Audio CD**

What Is Viscosity?

Teach Key Concepts `L2`

Viscosity Is a Physical Property

Focus Remind students that liquids have the ability to flow.

Teach Ask: **If a liquid flows slowly or hardly at all, is its viscosity high or low?** *(High)* **If a liquid flows easily, is its viscosity high or low?** *(Low)*

Apply Ask: **What are some liquids that have high viscosity?** *(Examples include maple syrup, hand lotion, shampoo, and liquid detergent.)* **What are liquids that have low viscosity?** *(Examples include water, milk, and juice.)* **learning modality: logical/ mathematical**

Go Online
SciLINKS NSTA

For: Links on volcanic eruptions
Visit: www.SciLinks.org
Web Code: scn-1032

Download a worksheet to guide students' review of Internet resources on volcanic eruptions.

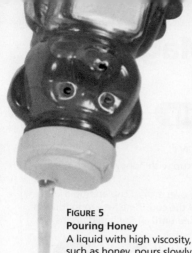

FIGURE 5
Pouring Honey
A liquid with high viscosity, such as honey, pours slowly from its container.
Predicting *If you poured water out of a similar container, how would its behavior differ from the honey? Explain your answer.*

Go Online
SciLINKS NSTA

For: Links on volcanic eruptions
Visit: www.SciLinks.org
Web Code: scn-1032

Physical Properties A **physical property** is any characteristic of a substance that can be observed or measured without changing the composition of the substance. Examples of physical properties include density, hardness, melting point, boiling point, and whether a substance is magnetic. A substance always has the same physical properties under particular conditions. Under normal conditions at sea level, for example, water's freezing point is 0°C and its boiling point is 100°C. Between its freezing and boiling points, water is a liquid.

Chemical Properties A **chemical property** is any property that produces a change in the composition of matter. Examples of chemical properties include a substance's ability to burn and its ability to combine, or react, with other substances. You can often tell that one substance has reacted with another if it changes color, produces a gas, or forms a new, solid substance. For example, a piece of silver jewelry darkens when exposed to air. This change indicates that silver has reacted with oxygen to form tarnish. The ability to react with oxygen is a chemical property of silver.

✓ **Reading Checkpoint** Is the boiling point of a substance a physical property or a chemical property?

What Is Viscosity?

When you pour yourself a glass of milk, you are making use of a familiar physical property of liquids. Because particles in a liquid are free to move around one another, a liquid can flow from place to place. The physical property of liquids called **viscosity** (vis KAHS uh tee) is the resistance of a liquid to flowing. **Because liquids differ in viscosity, some liquids flow more easily than others.**

The greater the viscosity of a liquid, the slower it flows. For example, honey is a thick, sticky liquid with high viscosity. Honey flows slowly. The lower the viscosity, the more easily a liquid flows. Water, rubbing alcohol, and vinegar are thin, runny liquids with low viscosities.

Why do different liquids have different viscosities? The answer lies in the movement of the particles that make up each type of liquid. In some liquids, there is a greater degree of friction among the liquid's particles. These liquids have higher viscosity.

✓ **Reading Checkpoint** Why do liquids differ in viscosity?

Magma Composition

Magma varies in composition and is classified according to the amount of silica it contains. The graphs show the average composition of two types of magma. Use the graphs to answer the questions.

1. **Reading Graphs** Study both graphs. What materials make up both types of magma?
2. **Reading Graphs** Which type of magma has more silica? About how much silica does this type of magma contain?
3. **Estimating** A third type of magma has a silica content that is halfway between that of the other two types. About how much silica does this magma contain?

4. **Predicting** What type of magma would have a higher viscosity? Explain.

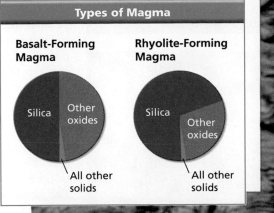

Types of Magma

Basalt-Forming Magma — Silica, Other oxides, All other solids

Rhyolite-Forming Magma — Silica, Other oxides, All other solids

Viscosity of Magma

At the extremely high temperatures and pressures inside Earth, mantle rock sometimes melts to form magma. Surprisingly, the properties of magma can vary. For example, not all types of magma have the same viscosity. **The viscosity of magma depends upon its silica content and temperature.**

Silica Content Magma is a complex mixture, but its major ingredient is silica. The compound **silica** is made up of particles of the elements oxygen and silicon. Silica is one of the most abundant materials in Earth's crust. The silica content of magma ranges from about 50 percent to 70 percent.

The amount of silica in magma helps to determine its viscosity. The more silica magma contains, the higher its viscosity. Magma that is high in silica produces light-colored lava that is too sticky to flow very far. When this type of lava cools, it forms the rock rhyolite, which has the same composition as granite.

The less silica magma contains, the lower its viscosity. Low-silica magma flows readily and produces dark-colored lava. When this kind of lava cools, it forms rocks like basalt.

FIGURE 6
Sampling Magma
A geologist samples magma from a lava flow in Hawaii.

Differentiated Instruction

Special Needs L1
Determining Viscosity Have students "race" a variety of liquids down an inclined surface. Students might use corn syrup, honey, and water. After the race, ask students to rank each liquid according to its viscosity. **learning modality: kinesthetic**

Gifted and Talented L3
Ordering Viscosity Challenge students to find out which SI unit is used to measure viscosity. *(Coefficient of viscosity, which is* $N \times s/m^2$*)* Then have them research and make a table showing the viscosities of common substances. Have students include in their tables the substances used in the race. **learning modality: logical/mathematical**

Math ▶ Analyzing Data

Math Skill Making and Interpreting Graphs

Focus Remind students that circle graphs are often used to show portions of a whole.

Teach Ask: **If the entire circle represents 100 percent, what does half the circle represent?** *(50 percent)* **Why do you think showing two circle graphs together like this might be a good idea?** *(Answers should explain that it is easy to see the differences in proportion when the graphs appear together.)*

Answers

1. silica, other oxides, and other solids
2. rhyolite-forming magma; about 70 percent
3. about 60 percent
4. The rhyolite forming magma would have higher viscosity because it contains more silica.

Viscosity of Magma

Teach Key Concepts L1
Factors That Affect Lava Viscosity

Focus Remind students that some lava flows rapidly, but that most lava flows slowly.

Teach Ask: **Which flows faster: warm syrup or cold syrup?** *(Warm syrup)* **Which flows faster: hot lava or cold lava?** *(Hot lava)* Ask: **What else might affect the viscosity of lava?** *(Some students might suggest chemical composition.)*

Apply Ask: **Why might lava flow more slowly as it moves farther away from a volcano's vent?** *(The lava progressively cools.)* **Which magma will flow faster, one that has 55 percent silica or one that has 65 percent silica?** *(55 percent)* **learning modality: logical/mathematical**

Monitor Progress L2

Skills Check Have students make a table to compare and contrast high-viscosity lava and low-viscosity lava.

Answers
Figure 5 The water would pour faster because it has a lower viscosity.

✓ **Reading Checkpoint** Different liquids have different degrees of friction among their particles. The greater the friction, the higher the viscosity.

Answers

Figure 7 Pahoehoe

Reading Checkpoint The temperature of magma and lava can range from about 750°C to 1,175°C.

Assess

Reviewing Key Concepts

1. a. Any characteristic of a substance that can be observed or measured without changing the composition of the substance **b.** Any property that produces a change in the composition of matter **c.** Physical properties are "hot" and "liquid."
2. a. The resistance of a liquid to flowing **b.** slow-flowing liquid **c.** The particles have a low degree of friction.
3. a. Silica content and temperature **b.** The lava flow would change from pahoehoe to aa as the lava cooled, giving the surface a rough, jagged look.

Reteach **L1**

Have students suggest liquids that have high viscosity and liquids that have low viscosity. Write suggestions on the board as they are offered.

All in One Teaching Resources

- Section Summary: *Properties of Magma*
- Review and Reinforce: *Properties of Magma*
- Enrich: *Properties of Magma*

FIGURE 7
Pahoehoe and Aa
Both pahoehoe and aa can come from the same volcano. Pahoehoe flows easily and hardens into a rippled surface. Aa hardens into rough chunks. **Inferring** *Which type of lava has lower viscosity?*

Temperature How does temperature affect viscosity? Viscosity increases as temperature decreases. On a hot day, honey pours easily. But if you put the honey in the refrigerator, its viscosity increases. The cold honey flows very slowly.

The temperature of magma and lava can range from about 750°C to 1,175°C. The hotter the magma is, the lower its viscosity and the more rapidly it flows. Cooler types of magma have high viscosity and flow very slowly.

In Figure 7, you can see how temperature differences produce two different types of lava: pahoehoe and aa. **Pahoehoe** (pah HOH ee hoh ee) is fast-moving, hot lava that has low viscosity. The surface of a lava flow formed from pahoehoe looks like a solid mass of wrinkles, billows, and ropelike coils. Lava that is cooler and slower-moving is called **aa** (AH ah). Aa has higher viscosity than pahoehoe. When aa hardens, it forms a rough surface consisting of jagged lava chunks.

Reading Checkpoint How hot are magma and lava?

Section 2 Assessment

Target Reading Skill Identifying Main Ideas Use your graphic organizer to help you answer Question 3 below.

Reviewing Key Concepts

1. a. Defining What is a physical property?
  b. Defining What is a chemical property?
  c. Classifying Magma is a hot, liquid mixture that changes to solid rock when it cools and hardens. Which of these characteristics are physical properties?
2. a. Identifying What is viscosity?
  b. Applying Concepts Which has a higher viscosity, a fast-flowing liquid or a slow-flowing liquid?
  c. Inferring What can you infer about the amount of friction among the particles of a liquid that has low viscosity?

3. a. Reviewing What two main factors affect magma's viscosity?
  b. Predicting A lava flow cools as it moves away from the vent. How would this affect the surface appearance of the lava flow?

Lab zone At-Home Activity

Cooling Lava Place cold water in one cup and hot tap water in another. Ask members of your family to predict what will happen when melted candle wax drops into each cup of water. Have an adult family member drip melted wax from a candle into each cup. **CAUTION:** *Handle the lit candle carefully.* Explain how this models what happens when lava cools quickly or slowly.

90 ◆ F

Lab zone At-Home Activity

Cooling Lava **L2** You may want to let students do this activity in class before they present it at home. (**CAUTION:** Handle the lighted candle yourself; do not let students do so.) The wax in cold water will solidify more quickly and form a more rounded shape than the wax in hot water, with a greater temperature difference between the two cups producing more dramatic results. The model shows that lava that cools quickly forms distinct "lumps," whereas lava that cools slowly continues to spread out and forms a flatter mass.

Reading Preview

Key Concepts
- What happens when a volcano erupts?
- What are the two types of volcanic eruptions?
- What are a volcano's stages of activity?

Key Terms
- magma chamber • pipe
- vent • lava flow • crater
- pyroclastic flow • dormant
- extinct

Target Reading Skill

Using Prior Knowledge Before you read, look at the section headings to see what the section is about. Then write what you know about how a volcano erupts in a graphic organizer like the one below. As you read, write what you learn.

What You Know
1. Lava flows out of a volcano.
2.

What You Learned
1.
2.

Lab zone — Discover **Activity**

What Are Volcanic Rocks Like?
Volcanoes produce lava, which hardens into rock. Two of these rocks are pumice and obsidian.

1. Observe samples of pumice and obsidian with a hand lens.
2. How would you describe the texture of the pumice? What could have caused this texture?
3. Observe the surface of the obsidian. How does the surface of the obsidian differ from pumice?

Think It Over
Developing Hypotheses What could have produced the difference in texture between the two rocks? Explain your answer.

Pumice

Obsidian

In Hawaii, there are many myths about Pele (PAY lay), the fire goddess of volcanoes. Pele lives in the depths of Hawaii's erupting volcanoes. According to legend, when Pele is angry, she causes a volcanic eruption. One result of an eruption is "Pele's hair," a fine, threadlike rock formed by lava. Pele's hair forms when lava sprays out of the ground like water from a fountain. As it cools, the lava stretches and hardens into thin strands, as shown in Figure 8.

Where does this lava come from? Lava begins as magma, which usually forms in the asthenosphere. The materials of the asthenosphere are under great pressure. Liquid magma is less dense than the solid material around it. Therefore, magma flows upward into any cracks in the rock above. As magma rises, it sometimes becomes trapped beneath layers of rock. But if an opening in weak rock allows the magma to reach the surface, a volcano forms.

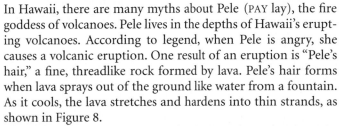

FIGURE 8
Pele's Hair
Pele's hair is a type of rock formed from lava. Each strand is as fine as spun glass.

Chapter 3   F ◆ 91

Objectives
After completing the lesson, students will be able to
F.3.3.1 Explain what happens when a volcano erupts
F.3.3.2 Describe the two types of volcanic eruptions
F.3.3.3 Identify a volcano's stages of activity

Target Reading Skill

Using Prior Knowledge Explain that using prior knowledge helps students connect what they already know to what they are about to read.

Answers
Possible answers: Know: Lava flows out of a volcano. Magma reaches the surface at volcanoes. Eruptions are not all the same. Some volcanoes are dormant. Learned: Magma rises toward Earth's surface through a pipe that leads to a vent. Differences in gas and silica content cause some eruptions to be explosive and others to be quiet. Dormant volcanoes can become active at any time.

All in One Teaching Resources
- Transparency F28

Preteach

Build Background Knowledge   **L1**

Volcanic Eruptions

Ask: **What does lava look like when it comes out of a volcano?** (*Judging by photographs or videos they have seen, students may describe lava as red-hot and thick or gooey.*) **What else comes out of a volcano when it erupts?** (*Students may mention steam and dark clouds of volcanic dust. Accept all responses without comment at this time.*)

Lab zone — Discover **Activity**

Skills Focus Developing hypotheses **L1**

Materials samples of pumice and obsidian, hand lens

Time 5–10 minutes

Tips Help students with the correct pronunciations of *pumice* (PUHM is) and *obsidian* (ob SID ee uhn).

Expected Outcome The obsidian is smooth and glassy, whereas the pumice is rough and porous. (**CAUTION:** Advise students to handle the obsidian with care because it sometimes has sharp edges.)

Think It Over The lava that produced the pumice had more gas in it than did the lava that produced the obsidian. Obsidian formed when lava cooled very quickly.

Magma Reaches Earth's Surface

Teach Key Concepts   L2

Exploring a Volcano

Focus Ask students to provide common definitions for the words *chamber (A cavity or enclosed space)*, *pipe (A cylinder through which liquid or gas moves)*, and *vent (An opening that serves as an outlet)*.

Teach Refer students to Figure 10. Call out each label in the figure, and have student volunteers define these terms.

Apply Ask: **What might happen if more magma is injected into the chamber from below?** *(This could trigger a new eruption.)* **learning modality: visual**

Independent Practice   L2

  **Teaching Resources**

- Guided Reading and Study Worksheet: *Volcanic Eruptions*

⊙ **Student Edition on Audio CD**

Lab zone **Build Inquiry**   L1

Observing Gas Bubbles

Materials 2 clear, capped plastic bottles of soda water

Time 10 minutes

Focus Remind students that the amount of gas that can dissolve in a liquid depends on the pressure.

Teach Provide each pair of students with the materials. One student should closely watch a bottle while the other student slowly uncaps it. Students then can switch places and repeat. Ask: **What did you see in the bottle as the cap was removed?** *(Bubbles formed.)* **Why did that happen?** *(Pressure was released, allowing carbon dioxide gas to come out of solution and form bubbles.)*

Apply Ask: **What releases the pressure on gases trapped in magma?** *(As magma rises, there is less rock above and therefore less pressure on the magma.)* **learning modality: visual**

Magma Reaches Earth's Surface

A volcano is more than a large, cone-shaped mountain. Inside a volcano is a system of passageways through which magma moves.

Inside a Volcano All volcanoes have a pocket of magma beneath the surface and one or more cracks through which the magma forces its way. Beneath a volcano, magma collects in a pocket called a **magma chamber.** The magma moves upward through a **pipe,** a long tube in the ground that connects the magma chamber to Earth's surface. You can see these features in Figure 10.

Molten rock and gas leave the volcano through an opening called a **vent.** Often, there is one central vent at the top of a volcano. However, many volcanoes also have other vents that open on the volcano's sides. A **lava flow** is the area covered by lava as it pours out of a vent. A **crater** is a bowl-shaped area that may form at the top of a volcano around the central vent.

A Volcanic Eruption What pushes magma to the surface? The explosion of a volcano is similar to the soda water bubbling out of a warm bottle of soda pop. You cannot see the carbon dioxide gas in a bottle of soda pop because it is dissolved in the liquid. But when you open the bottle, the pressure is released. The carbon dioxide expands and forms bubbles, which rush to the surface. Like the carbon dioxide in soda pop, dissolved gases are trapped in magma. These dissolved gases are under tremendous pressure.

FIGURE 9
Lava Burp
During an eruption on Mount Kilauea, the force of a bursting gas bubble pushes up a sheet of red-hot lava.

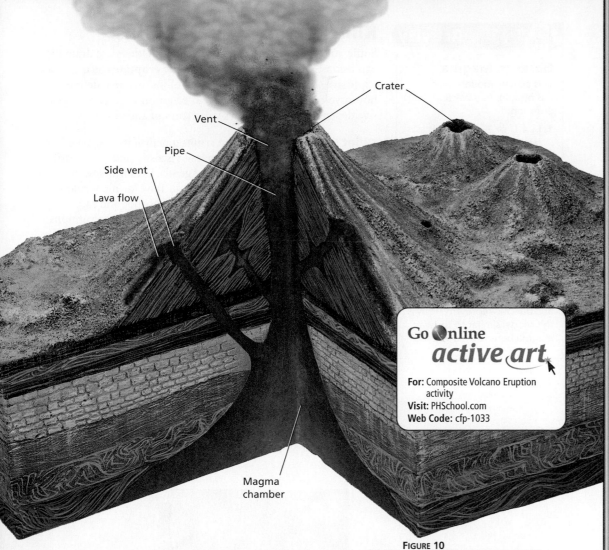

Crater

Vent

Pipe

Side vent

Lava flow

Go Online
active art

For: Composite Volcano Eruption activity
Visit: PHSchool.com
Web Code: cfp-1033

Magma chamber

As magma rises toward the surface, the pressure of the surrounding rock on the magma decreases. The dissolved gases begin to expand, forming bubbles. As pressure falls within the magma, the size of the gas bubbles increases greatly. These expanding gases exert an enormous force. **When a volcano erupts, the force of the expanding gases pushes magma from the magma chamber through the pipe until it flows or explodes out of the vent.** Once magma escapes from the volcano and becomes lava, the remaining gases bubble out.

Reading Checkpoint What happens to the pressure in magma as the magma rises toward the surface?

FIGURE 10
A Volcano Erupts
A volcano forms where magma breaks through Earth's crust and lava flows over the surface.
Interpreting Diagrams *What part of a volcano connects the vent with the magma chamber?*

Differentiated Instruction

Less Proficient Readers [L1]
Answering Questions Select a passage from the text, such as *A Volcanic Eruption.* Read the passage aloud as students follow along in their books. After reading, ask some questions about the passage. If students cannot provide the answers, challenge them to find the information in the passage. **learning modality: verbal**

Gifted and Talented [L3]
Researching Gases Have students research the different types and relative abundances of gases that occur in magma and then orally summarize what they have learned. (*Abundant gases are water, carbon dioxide, and sulfur dioxide. Less abundant gases are hydrogen, carbon monoxide, sulfur, hydrogen sulfide, hydrogen chloride, nitrogen, and fluorine.*) **learning modality: verbal**

Use Visuals: Figure 10 [L1]
How Magma Moves
Focus Review the parts of a volcano.

Teach Call on students to explain how magma flows through each part. Then have a volunteer explain the entire sequence while the other students use their pencil erasers to trace the movement in their texts. Make sure students notice the side vent as well. Ask: **Why would magma flow to a side vent?** *(A crack in the rock layers might offer less resistance to the magma's flow than the magma-filled main pipe.)*

Apply Ask: **When is an eruption over?** *(When the pressure eases after the gases bubble out of the magma)* **What happens when the volcano stops erupting?** *(The lava at the surface will have turned to rock, magma will have solidified in the vent and pipe, and some magma might remain in the chamber.)* **learning modality: visual**

All in One Teaching Resources
• Transparency F29

Go Online
active art

For: Composite Volcano Eruption activity
Visit: PHSchool.com
Web Code: cfp-1033

Students interact with the art of a composite volcano eruption online.

Monitor Progress [L2]

Drawing Have each student, without referring to the diagram on this page, draw a simple cross-sectional diagram of a volcano and label the magma chamber, pipe, vent, crater, and lava. Have students place their drawings in their portfolios.

Answers
Figure 10 The pipe

Reading Checkpoint Presssure decreases, allowing gas to come out of the magma.

Kinds of Volcanic Eruptions

Teach Key Concepts L2

Quiet and Explosive Eruptions

Focus Ask: **Is it harder to blow air through a straw into a glass of water or a thick milkshake?** *(A milkshake)* **Why?** *(The milkshake has higher viscosity, so gas cannot move through it as easily.)*

Teach Ask: **Why might gas pressure build up in high-silica lava?** *(It is thicker, so gas cannot escape easily.)* **What would happen if the gas pressure became higher than the pressure of the surrounding material?** *(The magma would burst to the surface as an explosive eruption.)* **Why does low-silica magma often erupt quietly?** *(Gas can escape without building too much pressure.)*

Apply Have students classify the following as high-silica lava or low-silica lava: **a lava river flowing away from a volcano** *(Low-silica)*, **a plug of lava covering a volcano's vent** *(High-silica)*, **small pieces of lava being blasted high into the air** *(High-silica)*.
learning modality: logical/mathematical

Help Students Read L1

Compare and Contrast You can find guidelines for comparing and contrasting in the Content Refresher section of this chapter.

Ask students to construct a compare/contrast table. Have them skim the sections on the kinds of volcanic eruptions. Then ask students to describe similarities and differences of quiet and explosive eruptions.

Lab zone Try This **Activity**

Gases in Magma

This activity models the gas bubbles in a volcanic eruption.

1. In a 1- or 2-liter plastic bottle, mix 10 g of baking soda into 65 mL of water.
2. Put about six raisins in the water.
3. While swirling the water and raisins, add 65 mL of vinegar and stir vigorously.
4. Once the liquid stops moving, observe the raisins.

Making Models What happens after you add the vinegar? What do the raisins and bubbles represent? How is this model similar to the way magma behaves in a volcano?

Kinds of Volcanic Eruptions

Some volcanic eruptions occur gradually. Others are dramatic explosions. **Geologists classify volcanic eruptions as quiet or explosive.** The physical properties of its magma determine how a volcano erupts. Whether an eruption is quiet or explosive depends on the magma's silica content and viscosity.

Quiet Eruptions A volcano erupts quietly if its magma is low in silica. Low-silica magma has low viscosity and flows easily. The gases in the magma bubble out gently. Lava with low viscosity oozes quietly from the vent and can flow for many kilometers. Quiet eruptions can produce both pahoehoe and aa.

The Hawaiian Islands were formed from quiet eruptions. On the Big Island of Hawaii, lava pours out of the crater near the top of Mount Kilauea. But lava also flows out of long cracks on the volcano's sides. Quiet eruptions have built up the Big Island over hundreds of thousands of years.

Explosive Eruptions A volcano erupts explosively if its magma is high in silica. High-silica magma has high viscosity, making it thick and sticky. The high-viscosity magma does not always flow out of the crater. Instead, it builds up in the volcano's pipe, plugging it like a cork in a bottle. Dissolved gases, including water vapor, cannot escape from the thick magma. The trapped gases build up pressure until they explode. The erupting gases and steam push the magma out of the volcano with incredible force. That's what happened during the eruption of Mount St. Helens, shown in Figure 11.

Before Eruption

During Eruption

94 ◆ F

Lab zone Try This **Activity**

Skills Focus Making models L2

Materials 1- or 2-liter plastic bottle, 10 g baking soda, 65 mL water, 6 raisins, 65 mL vinegar

Time 10–15 minutes

Tips You may want to supply funnels for pouring the materials into the bottle.

Expected Outcome The vinegar reacts with the baking soda solution to produce carbon dioxide gas. Bubbles of gas adhere to the raisins, causing the raisins to rise to the surface, where the bubbles pop. The raisins sink again, and the cycle repeats. The raisins represent magma; the bubbles represent gases trapped in the magma. In this model, the raisins and gas bubbles are

not under great pressure, as magma and gases are in a real volcano. Also, magma, unlike raisins, doesn't go up and down in a volcano, but rather goes up and out.

Extend Students could repeat this activity using raisins and clear carbonated soda.
learning modality: kinesthetic

An explosive eruption breaks lava into fragments that quickly cool and harden into pieces of different sizes. The smallest pieces are volcanic ash—fine, rocky particles as small as a speck of dust. Pebble-sized particles are called cinders. Larger pieces, called bombs, may range from the size of a base-ball to the size of a car. A **pyroclastic flow** (py roh KLAS tik) occurs when an explosive eruption hurls out a mixture of hot gases, ash, cinders, and bombs.

Pumice and obsidian, which you observed if you did the Discover Activity, form from high-silica lava. Obsidian forms when lava cools very quickly, giving it a smooth, glossy surface like glass. Pumice forms when gas bubbles are trapped in fast-cooling lava, leaving spaces in the rock.

 Reading Checkpoint   What is a pyroclastic flow?

FIGURE 11
An Explosive Eruption
Mount St. Helens in Washington State erupted at 8:30 A.M. on May 18, 1980. The explosion blew off the top of the mountain, leaving a huge crater and causing great destruction.

After Eruption

F ◆ 95

F ● 95

Build Inquiry

L2

Inferring Why Volcanic Ash Is Hazardous

Materials Sealed, clear bags containing volcanic ash (volcanic ash can be purchased from Earth science suppliers at reasonable prices), hand lens

Time 10 minutes

Focus Before passing around the samples, ask students to draw circles that predict the sizes of volcanic ash particles.

Teach Have students examine the samples, without opening the bags and with and without a hand lens. Tell them to note the varying sizes of the particles, particularly the extremely small size of the finest ash. Have students compare what they see with their drawings.

Apply Ask: **Why would something as tiny as these smallest ash particles be hazardous?** (*People and animals can breathe them in; plants covered with ash die; ash can clog engines and other machinery.*) **learning modality: visual**

Science and History

Focus Remind students that all of these eruptions happened in just 150 years. Tell them that although eruptions from many volcanoes are rare, eruptions are fairly common worldwide.

Teach Focus students' attention on the introductory statement that volcanic eruptions "have greatly affected the land and people around them." Ask: **How do you think each of these eruptions affected the people in the area?** (*Some eruptions killed people, people lost homes and possessions, they might have had to evacuate an area, and crops were destroyed.*)

Writing in Science

Writing Mode Research
Scoring Rubric

4 includes a complete and accurate description of the eruption; written from first-person point of view and reflects emotional responses
3 includes all criteria
2 includes only brief but accurate description
1 includes inaccurate description

Volcano Hazards Although quiet eruptions and explosive eruptions produce different hazards, both types of eruption can cause damage far from the crater's rim.

During a quiet eruption, lava flows from vents, setting fire to, and then burying, everything in its path. A quiet eruption can cover large areas with a thick layer of lava.

During an explosive eruption, a volcano can belch out hot clouds of deadly gases as well as ash, cinders, and bombs. Volcanic ash can bury entire towns. If it becomes wet, the heavy ash can cause roofs to collapse. If a jet plane sucks ash into its engine, the engine may stall. Eruptions can cause landslides and avalanches of mud, melted snow, and rock. The Science and History timeline shows the effects of several explosive eruptions.

 Reading Checkpoint How does volcanic ash cause damage?

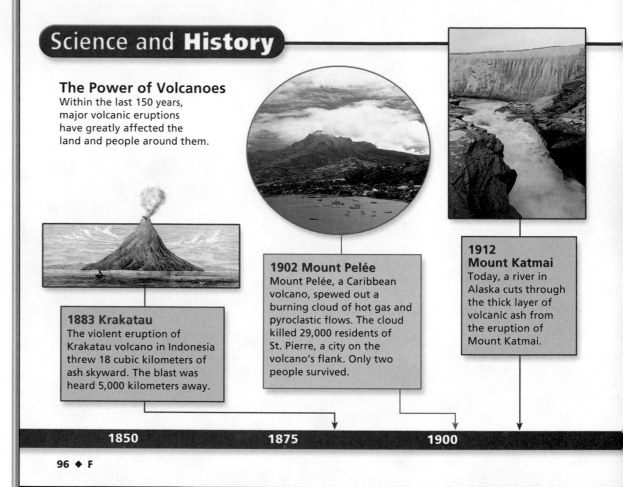

Science and History

The Power of Volcanoes
Within the last 150 years, major volcanic eruptions have greatly affected the land and people around them.

1883 Krakatau
The violent eruption of Krakatau volcano in Indonesia threw 18 cubic kilometers of ash skyward. The blast was heard 5,000 kilometers away.

1902 Mount Pelée
Mount Pelée, a Caribbean volcano, spewed out a burning cloud of hot gas and pyroclastic flows. The cloud killed 29,000 residents of St. Pierre, a city on the volcano's flank. Only two people survived.

1912 Mount Katmai
Today, a river in Alaska cuts through the thick layer of volcanic ash from the eruption of Mount Katmai.

1850	1875	1900

96 ◆ F

Background

Facts and Figures Of the six volcanic eruptions presented in the time line on these pages, two—Krakatau in 1883 and Mount Pelée in 1902—are among the five most destructive volcanic eruptions since 1700. The remaining three are Unzen, Japan, in 1792; Mt. Tambora, Indonesia, in 1815; and Nevada del Ruiz, Colombia, in 1985.

As evidence of a volcano's varying hazards, 80,000 of the 92,000 people killed as a result of the 1815 Mt. Tambora eruption died not from the volcanic activity itself but from starvation afterward. Ninety percent of Krakatau's 36,000 victims were killed by a tsunami. Pyroclastic flows claimed about 30,000 lives in the Mount Pelée eruption. Mudflows killed about 25,000 people in the Nevada del Ruiz eruption. Clearly, lava flows and collapsing cones are not the only volcanic hazards.

Stages of Volcanic Activity

The activity of a volcano may last from less than a decade to more than 10 million years. Most long-lived volcanoes, however, do not erupt continuously. Geologists try to determine a volcano's past and whether the volcano will erupt again.

Life Cycle of a Volcano Geologists often use the terms *active, dormant,* or *extinct* to describe a volcano's stage of activity. An active, or live, volcano is one that is erupting or has shown signs that it may erupt in the near future. A dormant, or sleeping, volcano is like a sleeping bear. Scientists expect a **dormant** volcano to awaken in the future and become active. An **extinct,** or dead, volcano is unlikely to erupt again.

The time between volcanic eruptions may span hundreds to many thousands of years. People living near a dormant volcano may be unaware of the danger. But a dormant volcano can become active at any time.

Writing in Science

Research and Write People have written eyewitness accounts of famous volcanic eruptions. Research one of the eruptions in the timeline. Then write a letter describing what someone observing the eruption might have seen.

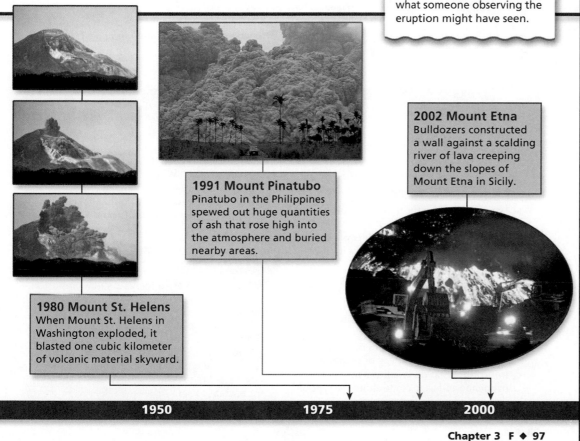

1980 Mount St. Helens
When Mount St. Helens in Washington exploded, it blasted one cubic kilometer of volcanic material skyward.

1991 Mount Pinatubo
Pinatubo in the Philippines spewed out huge quantities of ash that rose high into the atmosphere and buried nearby areas.

2002 Mount Etna
Bulldozers constructed a wall against a scalding river of lava creeping down the slopes of Mount Etna in Sicily.

1950   1975   2000

Stages of Volcanic Activity

Teach Key Concepts L2
Life Cycle of a Volcano

Focus Help students understand that volcanoes progress through a cycle that is similar to the life cycles of organisms (birth, activity, death). Volcanoes come into existence with an eruption, are sometimes active, and eventually cease to erupt.

Teach To help students understand the terms *active, dormant,* and *extinct,* remind them that some animals, such as bears, are active during summer and dormant during winter, and that a species can become extinct. Ask: **What is a volcano like when it's active?** *(Eruptions are occurring, or subsurface activity indicates that an eruption is possible.)* **A dormant volcano?** *(No activity is observed, but the volcano is likely to erupt again.)* **An extinct volcano?** *(The volcano will not erupt again.)*

Apply Tell students that by using historical records and by monitoring volcanoes, geologists can determine which stage a volcano is in. **learning modality: logical/mathematical**

Help Students Read L1

Cause and Effect Have students list cause-and-effect relationships as they read about volcano hazards. Then have students compare their lists. **learning modality: verbal**

Monitor Progress L2

Writing Ask students to list some signs that a volcano may be about to become active.

Answer

✓ **Reading Checkpoint** Volcanic ash can bury towns, cause roofs to collapse when they are wet, and stall engines of jet planes if it is sucked in.

Differentiated Instruction

**English Learners/Beginning L1
Compression: Modified Cloze**
Write some simple sentences on the board that require the terms *active, dormant,* and *extinct.* For example: When you are moving around, you are _____. In winter, _____ trees do not make food but are still alive. Complete one or two sentences as a model, and then fill in the blanks together.
learning modality: verbal

**English Learners/Intermediate L2
Compression: Modified Cloze**
Use the same sentences described for *Beginning,* but fill in incorrect terms. Have students work in pairs to determine the correct answers. **learning modality: verbal**

Monitor Progress ___ L2

Answer

✓ **Reading Checkpoint** Geologists use instruments to detect surface changes caused by magma moving underground, gases escaping from the volcano, temperature increases in underground water, and small earthquakes that occur before an eruption.

Assess

Reviewing Key Concepts

1. a. Magma chamber, pipe, vent, and crater **b.** Magma collects in the magma chamber, moves upward through the pipe, and leaves the volcano through the vent. **c.** The force of the expanding gases
2. a. Quiet and explosive **b.** Silica content and viscosity **c.** The eruption was quiet.
3. a. Active, dormant, extinct **b.** A volcano that erupts frequently is more likely to erupt again in the near future, so it is more dangerous. However, if a dormant volcano were to erupt, people might be unprepared and many lives could be lost.

Reteach L1

List *Quiet Eruptions* and *Explosive Eruptions* on the board, and have students work in pairs to list characteristics of each type and how it forms.

Performance Assessment L2

Drawing Have students draw and label a sketch to identify the parts of a volcano and describe what happens underground to cause an eruption.

All in One Teaching Resources

- Section Summary: *Volcanic Eruptions*
- Review and Reinforce: *Volcanic Eruptions*
- Enrich: *Volcanic Eruptions*

FIGURE 12
Volcano Watch
Near Mount Kilauea in Hawaii, these geologists are testing instruments to monitor temperatures in and around a crater.

Monitoring Volcanoes Geologists have been more successful in predicting volcanic eruptions than in predicting earthquakes. Geologists use instruments to detect changes in and around a volcano. These changes may give warning a short time before a volcano erupts. But geologists cannot be certain about the type of eruption or how powerful it will be.

Geologists use tiltmeters and other instruments to detect slight surface changes in elevation and tilt caused by magma moving underground. They monitor any gases escaping from the volcano. A temperature increase in underground water may be a sign that magma is nearing the surface. Geologists also monitor the many small earthquakes that occur around a volcano before an eruption. The upward movement of magma triggers these quakes.

✓ **Reading Checkpoint** How do geologists monitor volcanoes?

Section 3 Assessment

⟳ **Target Reading Skill** Using Prior Knowledge Review your graphic organizer and revise it based on what you just learned in the section.

Reviewing Key Concepts

1. a. Listing What are the main parts of a volcano?
   b. Sequencing Describe the order of parts through which magma travels as it moves to the surface.
   c. Relating Cause and Effect As a volcano erupts, what force pushes magma out of a volcano onto the surface?
2. a. Identifying What are the two main kinds of volcanic eruptions?
   b. Explaining What properties of magma help to determine the type of eruption?
   c. Inferring What do lava flows made of pahoehoe and aa indicate about the type of volcanic eruption that occurred?

3. a. Naming What are the three stages of volcanic activity?
   b. Predicting Which is more likely to be dangerous—a volcano that erupts frequently or a volcano that has been inactive for a hundred years? Why?

Writing in Science

Interview You are a television news reporter who will be interviewing a geologist. The geologist has just returned from studying a nearby volcano that may soon erupt. Write the questions that you would ask. Be sure to ask about the evidence that an eruption is coming, the type of eruption expected, and any hazards that will result. Write an answer for each question.

98 ◆ F

Writing in Science

Writing Mode Explanation
Scoring Rubric
4 Includes questions and answers that address all requested information
3 Includes all criteria
2 Includes only one or two criteria
1 Includes very brief descriptions or many inaccuracies

Lab zone Chapter Project

Consult with each group to determine whether students were able to find the information they wanted to include. Suggest or provide additional source materials if needed. Help students start preparing their storyboards as a class. Suggest that students sketch each major step on a separate sheet of paper and decide who will present each step. Review the storyboards for the required elements.

Reading Preview

Key Concepts
- What landforms do lava and ash create?
- How does magma that hardens beneath the surface create landforms?
- What other distinctive features occur in volcanic areas?

Key Terms
- shield volcano • cinder cone
- composite volcano • caldera
- volcanic neck • dike
- sill • batholith
- geothermal activity • geyser

Target Reading Skill
Outlining As you read, make an outline about volcanic landforms that you can use for review. Use the red headings for main topics and the blue headings for subtopics.

Volcanic Landforms
I. Landforms From Lava and Ash
A. Shield Volcanoes
B.
C.
D.
E.
II. Landforms From Magma

FIGURE 13
Mount Fuji
The almost perfect volcanic cone of Mount Fuji in Japan has long been a favorite subject for artists.

Lab zone Discover Activity

How Can Volcanic Activity Change Earth's Surface?

1. Use tape to secure the neck of a balloon over one end of a straw.
2. Place the balloon in the center of a box with the straw protruding.
3. Partially inflate the balloon.
4. Put damp sand on top of the balloon until it is covered.
5. Slowly inflate the balloon more. Observe what happens to the surface of the sand.

Think It Over
Making Models This activity models one of the ways in which volcanic activity can cause a mountain to form. What do you think the sand represents? What does the balloon represent?

Volcanoes have created some of Earth's most spectacular landforms. The perfect cone of Mount Fuji in Japan, shown in Figure 13, is famous around the world.

For much of Earth's history, volcanic activity on and beneath the surface has built up Earth's land areas. Volcanic activity also formed the rock of the ocean floor. Some volcanic landforms arise when lava flows build up mountains and plateaus on Earth's surface. Other volcanic landforms are the result of the buildup of magma beneath the surface.

F ◆ 99

Lab zone Discover Activity

Skills Focus Making models

Materials tape, balloon, straw, box, damp sand

Time 10–15 minutes

Tips Make sure that the box is large enough fully inflated to accommodate the balloon. Tell students to inflate the balloon slowly in Step 5.

L1

Expected Outcome As the balloon is inflated, a dome will form in the sand.

Think It Over The sand represents Earth's crust. The balloon represents a filling magma chamber.

Objectives
After completing this lesson, students will be able to

F.3.4.1 List the landforms that lava and ash create

F.3.4.2 Explain how the magma that hardens beneath Earth's surface creates landforms

F.3.4.3 Identify other distinct features that occur in volcanic areas

Target Reading Skill

Outlining Explain that using an outline format helps organize information by main topic, subtopic, and details.

Answers
Students' outlines should have Roman numerals followed by major headings and capital letters followed by minor headings.

Volcanic Landforms
I. Landforms from Lava and Ash
   A. Shield volcanoes
   B. Cinder cone volcanoes
   C. Composite volcanoes
   D. Lava plateaus
   E. Calderas
   F. Soils from lava and ash
II. Landforms from Magma
   A. Volcanic necks, dikes, and sills
   B. Dikes and sills
   C. Batholiths
   D. Dome mountains
III. Geothermal Activity
   A. Hot springs
   B. Geysers
   C. Geothermal energy

All in One Teaching Resources
- Transparency F30

Preteach

Build Background Knowledge
L1

Shapes of Volcanoes

Ask: **What shape is a volcano?** Choose several volunteers to come to the board and draw what they think a volcano looks like. *(Students are likely to draw cone-shaped mountains.)* **Are all volcanoes shaped like this?** *(Accept all responses without comment at this time.)*

Landforms From Lava and Ash

Teach Key Concepts L2

Shapes of Volcanic Landforms

Focus Remind students that lava can have varying viscosity.

Teach Make a labeled sketch of each landform on the board. Ask: **If runny, thin lava flowed out from a small area, would it form steep sides or gentle sides?** *(Gentle)* **Which type of volcano would this be?** *(Shield)* **What if this same lava erupted from long cracks?** *(A plateau might form.)* **Which landform could form when thick, sticky lava is blown apart and falls as ash and cinders?** *(Cinder cone)* **Why would it have steep sides?** *(The ash piles up around the vent at steep angles.)* **Which landform do you think would form from flows of thick lava and some ash?** *(Composite)*

Apply Ask: **How would you describe each of these landforms?** *(Lava plateau: an extensive, fairly flat area; shield volcano: a huge, broad mountain; composite volcano: a steep, tall mountain; cinder cone: a hill with cinder slopes that are hard to walk on)*
learning modality: visual

Independent Practice

All in One Teaching Resources

- Guided Reading and Study Worksheet: *Volcanic Landforms*
- Transparency F31

 Student Edition on Audio CD

Use Visuals: Figure 14 L1

Comparing and Contrasting Volcanoes

Focus Point out that the interior of each type of volcano is shown.

Teach Ask: **Which type of volcano consists entirely of layers of cooled lava flows?** *(Shield)* **Layers of cooled lava flows and layers of ash?** *(Composite)* **Only of layers of ash?** *(Cinder cone)*

Apply Have students infer the relative sizes of these three types of volcanoes. *(Largest to smallest: shield, composite, cinder cone)*
learning modality: visual

Landforms From Lava and Ash

Volcanic eruptions create landforms made of lava, ash, and other materials. These landforms include shield volcanoes, cinder cone volcanoes, composite volcanoes, and lava plateaus. Look at Figure 14 to see these features. Another landform results from the collapse of a volcanic mountain.

Shield Volcanoes At some places on Earth's surface, thin layers of lava pour out of a vent and harden on top of previous layers. Such lava flows gradually build a wide, gently sloping mountain called a **shield volcano.** Shield volcanoes rising from a hot spot on the ocean floor created the Hawaiian Islands.

Cinder Cone Volcanoes If a volcano's lava has high viscosity, it may produce ash, cinders, and bombs. These materials build up around the vent in a steep, cone-shaped hill or small mountain called a **cinder cone.** For example, Paricutín in Mexico erupted in 1943 in a farmer's cornfield. The volcano built up a cinder cone about 400 meters high.

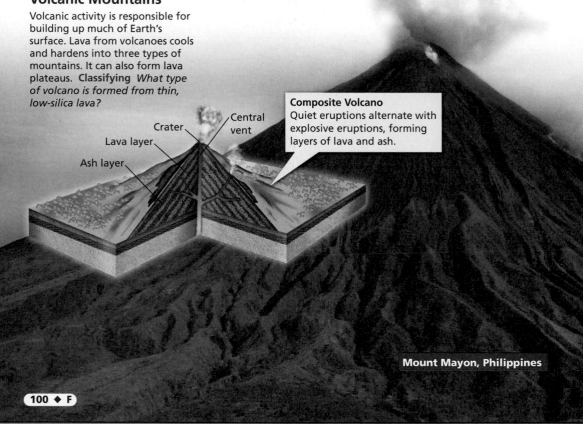

FIGURE 14
Volcanic Mountains
Volcanic activity is responsible for building up much of Earth's surface. Lava from volcanoes cools and hardens into three types of mountains. It can also form lava plateaus. *Classifying What type of volcano is formed from thin, low-silica lava?*

Crater
Lava layer
Ash layer
Central vent

Composite Volcano
Quiet eruptions alternate with explosive eruptions, forming layers of lava and ash.

Mount Mayon, Philippines

Composite Volcanoes Sometimes, lava flows alternate with explosive eruptions of ash, cinder, and bombs. The result is a composite volcano. **Composite volcanoes** are tall, cone-shaped mountains in which layers of lava alternate with layers of ash. Examples of composite volcanoes include Mount Fuji in Japan and Mount St. Helens in Washington State.

Lava Plateaus Instead of forming mountains, some eruptions of lava form high, level areas called lava plateaus. First, lava flows out of several long cracks in an area. The thin, runny lava travels far before cooling and solidifying. Again and again, floods of lava flow on top of earlier floods. After millions of years, these layers of lava can form high plateaus. One example is the Columbia Plateau, which covers parts of the states of Washington, Oregon, and Idaho.

Volcanoes

Video Preview
▶ Video Field Trip
Video Assessment

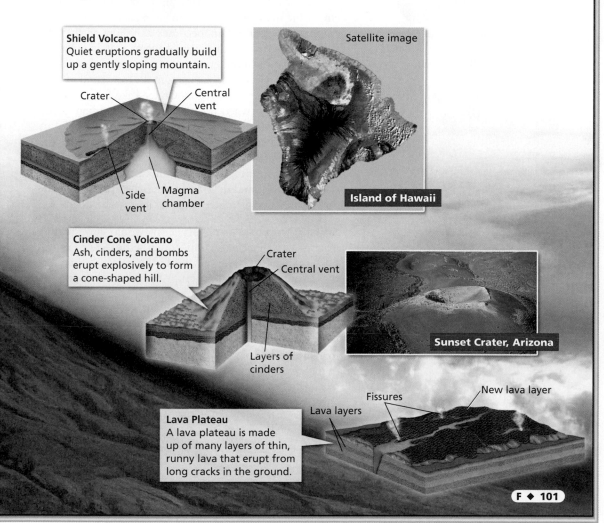

Shield Volcano
Quiet eruptions gradually build up a gently sloping mountain.

Crater
Central vent
Side vent
Magma chamber

Satellite image

Island of Hawaii

Cinder Cone Volcano
Ash, cinders, and bombs erupt explosively to form a cone-shaped hill.

Crater
Central vent

Layers of cinders

Sunset Crater, Arizona

Fissures
Lava layers
New lava layer

Lava Plateau
A lava plateau is made up of many layers of thin, runny lava that erupt from long cracks in the ground.

F ◆ 101

Differentiated Instruction

Special Needs L1
Classifying Volcanoes Have students title three pieces of poster board *Shield Volcanoes, Composite Volcanoes,* and *Cinder Cones* and then collect photographs of volcanoes and mount them. Have students include the volcano's name, a short caption, and labels with each photo and then assemble the boards into a tripartite display. **learning modality: visual**

Gifted and Talented L3
Creating Displays Have students make a poster-board display about lava plateaus, including the following: the Columbia Plateau, the Deccan Traps, the Siberian Traps, and the Karroo Lavas. (*Columbia Plateau, U.S.A., 220,000 km²; Deccan Traps, India, 500,000 km²; Siberian Traps, Siberia, 2,500,000 km²; and the Karroo Lavas, South Africa, 2,000,000 km²*) **learning modality: visual**

Making Models of Composite Volcanoes

Materials fine sand, coarse sand, small pebbles, plaster of Paris or wheat paste

Time 30 minutes on each of three separate days

Focus Remind students that composite volcanoes consist of layers of pyroclastic material and lava flows.

Teach Have small groups of students design models that show how composite volcanoes build up through time. Then allow groups to build the models with materials you provide or materials of their own choice. (*Beginning with a small hill made of plaster of Paris or wheat paste as a "core," students could add a layer of mixed fine sand, coarse sand, and pebbles to represent ash, cinders, and bombs, then pour plaster of Paris or wheat paste over it to represent lava and let it harden, and repeat these layers alternately to build up a composite cone.*)

Apply Have students create a scale for the model composite volcano. **learning modality: kinesthetic**

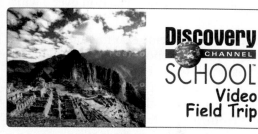

Video Field Trip

Volcanoes

Show the Video Field Trip to let students experience volcanoes and help them understand the dangers of volcanoes. Discussion question: **Why do you think a dormant volcano could still be dangerous?** (*A volcano can have a life span of over a million years. Unpredictable, it can lie dormant for hundreds of years, explode, sleep for another few hundred years, and then erupt again.*)

Monitor Progress _____ L2

Drawing Have each student draw a cross-sectional view of the three volcano types, label each with its name, and add a brief explanation of how it formed. Students can place their drawings in their portfolios.

Portfolio

Answer
Figure 14 Shield volcano or lava plateau

Crater or Caldera

Focus Students might think that the terms *crater* and *caldera* are used interchangeably to refer to the same structure.

Teach Ask: **What is a crater?** *(A bowl-shaped area around a volcano's vent)* If students cannot recall this information, refer them to Figure 14. **What happens to change a crater into a caldera?** *(The vent and magma chamber empty during an eruption, and the top of the volcano collapses.)*

Apply Ask: **What does a caldera look like?** *(It looks like a large depression at the top of a volcano. Many are filled with water to form lakes, such as Crater Lake.)* **learning modality: logical/mathematical**

Lab zone Build Inquiry

Observing Succession

Materials photographs of Mount St. Helens soon after the 1980 eruption and at intervals through the years afterward

Time 30 minutes

Focus Remind students that the eruption of this volcano killed all vegetation over a wide area.

Teach Have students examine the photo series to find evidence of plant regrowth—first of small, scattered "settler" plants, then of wider areas of larger plants and saplings. Ask: **Where do you think the new plants came from?** *(Accept all reasonable answers. Examples: Seeds blew in from other, undamaged areas. Seeds were carried in by animals.)*

Apply Ask: **How will the ash from the eruption contribute to plant growth?** *(The ash will form fertile soil.)*

All in One Teaching Resources

• Transparencies F32 and F33

FIGURE 15
How a Caldera Forms
Today, Crater Lake (right) fills an almost circular caldera. A caldera forms when a volcano's magma chamber empties and the roof of the chamber collapses.

Crater Lake

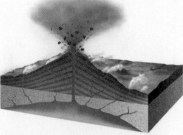

1 The top of a composite volcano explodes. Lava flows partially empty the magma chamber.

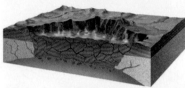

2 The roof of the magma chamber collapses, forming a caldera.

3 Later, a small cinder cone forms in the caldera, which partly fills with water.

Calderas The huge hole left by the collapse of a volcanic mountain is called a **caldera** (kal DAIR uh). The hole is filled with the pieces of the volcano that have fallen inward, as well as some lava and ash.

How does a caldera form? Enormous eruptions may empty the main vent and the magma chamber beneath a volcano. The mountain becomes a hollow shell. With nothing to support it, the top of the mountain collapses inward, forming a caldera.

In Figure 15 you can see steps in the formation of Crater Lake, a caldera in Oregon. Crater Lake formed about 7,700 years ago when a huge explosive eruption partly emptied the magma chamber of a volcano called Mount Mazama. When the volcano exploded, the top of the mountain was blasted into the atmosphere. The caldera that formed eventually filled with water from rain and snow. Wizard Island in Crater Lake is a small cinder cone that formed during a later eruption inside the caldera.

Soils From Lava and Ash Why would anyone live near an active volcano? People often settle close to volcanoes to take advantage of the fertile volcanic soil. The lava, ash, and cinders that erupt from a volcano are initially barren. Over time, however, the hard surface of the lava breaks down to form soil. When volcanic ash breaks down, it releases potassium, phosphorus, and other substances that plants need. As soil develops, plants are able to grow. Some volcanic soils are among the richest soils in the world. Saying that soil is rich means that it's fertile, or able to support plant growth.

Reading Checkpoint How are volcanic soils important?

Landforms From Magma

Sometimes magma forces its way through cracks in the upper crust, but fails to reach the surface. There the magma cools and hardens into rock. Over time, the forces that wear away Earth's surface—such as flowing water, ice, or wind—may strip away the layers above the hardened magma and finally expose it. **Features formed by magma include volcanic necks, dikes, and sills, as well as batholiths and dome mountains.**

Volcanic Necks A volcanic neck looks like a giant tooth stuck in the ground. A **volcanic neck** forms when magma hardens in a volcano's pipe. The softer rock around the pipe wears away, exposing the hard rock of the volcanic neck. Ship Rock in New Mexico, shown in Figure 16, is a volcanic neck formed from a volcano that erupted about 30 million years ago.

Dikes and Sills Magma that forces itself across rock layers hardens into a **dike.** Sometimes, a dike can be seen slanting through bedrock along a highway cut.

When magma squeezes between horizontal layers of rock, it forms a **sill.** One famous example of a sill is the Palisades in New York State and New Jersey. The Palisades form a series of long, dark cliffs. These cliffs stretch for about 30 kilometers along the west bank of the Hudson River.

Go Online
SciLINKS NSTA
For: Links on volcanic effects
Visit: www.SciLinks.org
Web Code: scn-1034

FIGURE 16
Volcanic Necks, Dikes, and Sills Magma that hardens beneath the surface may form volcanic necks, dikes, and sills. A dike extends outward from Ship Rock, a volcanic neck in New Mexico. *Comparing and Contrasting What is the difference between a dike and a sill?*

Volcanic neck
Dike
Sill

Landforms From Magma

Teach Key Concepts L2
Classifying Magmatic Landforms

Focus Remind students about photos they have seen of lava cooling to form rock at Earth's surface. Point out that magma also can cool and form rock beneath Earth's surface.

Teach Ask: **Why might magma turn to rock before reaching the surface?** *(It might get trapped beneath rock layers, or it might cool below its melting temperature before it can reach the surface.)* **How are landforms from magma classified?** *(They are classified according to their size and shape.)*

Apply Have students preview Figures 16 and 17. Then ask: **Which features are shaped like the top of a table?** *(Dikes and sills)* **Which feature used to be a volcano's pipe?** *(Volcanic neck)* **Which feature is very large and has an irregular shape?** *(Batholith)* **learning modality: visual**

Go Online
SciLINKS NSTA
For: Links on volcanic effects
Visit: www.SciLinks.org
Web Code: scn-1034

Download a worksheet to guide students' review of Internet resources on volcanic effects.

Help Students Read L1

Sequencing The formation of volcanic landforms involves a sequence. Have students describe the formation of Crater Lake or volcanic soil as a sequence of events. *The sequence may resemble the following: 1) Eruption empties main vent and magma chamber. 2) Top of mountain is blasted away. 3) Caldera fills with rainwater.*

Monitor Progress ____ L2

Oral Presentation Call on individual students to name one of the landforms and explain how it forms.

Answers
Figure 16 A dike cuts across rock layers. A sill is parallel to them.

Reading Checkpoint Volcanic soils are very fertile. They are rich in potassium, phosphorus, and other materials that plants need.

Differentiated Instruction

Less Proficient Readers L1
Labeling a Diagram Make a cross-sectional sketch into Earth's crust that includes dikes, sills, batholiths, volcanic necks, and dome mountains. Provide each student with a copy of this sketch. Ask students to label each feature with a term from the textbook. **learning modality: visual**

Gifted and Talented L3
Illustrating Laccoliths Have students do research to learn about one additional landform from magma—a laccolith then—and draw a cross section illustrating its features. *(Laccoliths are igneous intrusions that have a mushroom shape.)* **learning modality: visual**

Geothermal Activity

Teach Key Concepts

Hot Springs and Geysers

Focus Ask students whether they or anyone they know has ever visited a hot spring.

Teach Ask: **How could water beneath Earth's surface be heated?** *(In volcanic regions, shallow magma bodies or cooling hot rock can provide the heat to warm groundwater. Groundwater that flows deep in Earth also is heated.)* **Where might this warm water reach Earth's surface?** *(Hot springs, geysers)* **How are these two things different?** *(Hot springs occur at points where hot water rises to the surface and flows out. Geysers occur when steam and hot water are rapidly forced upward through a fracture in rock.)*

Apply Ask: **How can heated groundwater be useful to people?** *(Steam can be used to produce electricity; people could use it to heat homes or as a source of hot water.)* **learning modality: logical/mathematical**

Integrating Technology

Invite students to consider the problems and benefits involved in tapping steam and hot underground water. Ask: **Why are the steam and water sometimes difficult to access?** *(They may be far underground, so deep wells must be drilled.)* **What dangers are involved?** *(Steam could rupture pipes and injure workers.)* **What are the advantages of geothermal energy?** *(It is clean, with no dangerous wastes or fumes; it is a renewable energy source.)* **What are some disadvantages?** *(Accessible hot groundwater does not occur everywhere.)* **learning modality: logical/mathematical**

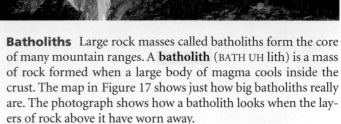

FIGURE 17
Batholiths
Several large batholiths form the core of mountain ranges in western North America. Half Dome in Yosemite National Park, California is part of the Sierra Nevada batholith.

Batholiths Large rock masses called batholiths form the core of many mountain ranges. A **batholith** (BATH UH lith) is a mass of rock formed when a large body of magma cools inside the crust. The map in Figure 17 shows just how big batholiths really are. The photograph shows how a batholith looks when the layers of rock above it have worn away.

Dome Mountains Other, smaller bodies of hardened magma can create dome mountains. A dome mountain forms when uplift pushes a batholith or smaller body of hardened magma toward the surface. The hardened magma forces the layers of rock to bend upward into a dome shape. Eventually, the rock above the dome mountain wears away, leaving it exposed. This process formed the Black Hills in South Dakota.

Geothermal Activity

The word *geothermal* comes from the Greek *geo* meaning "Earth" and *therme* meaning "heat." In **geothermal activity,** magma a few kilometers beneath Earth's surface heats underground water. A variety of geothermal features occur in volcanic areas. **Hot springs and geysers are types of geothermal activity that are often found in areas of present or past volcanic activity.**

Hot Springs A hot spring forms when groundwater is heated by a nearby body of magma or by hot rock deep underground. The hot water rises to the surface and collects in a natural pool. (Groundwater is water that has seeped into the spaces among rocks deep beneath Earth's surface.) Water from hot springs may contain dissolved gases and other substances from deep within Earth.

Geysers Sometimes, rising hot water and steam become trapped underground in a narrow crack. Pressure builds until the mixture suddenly sprays above the surface as a geyser. A **geyser** (GY zur) is a fountain of water and steam that erupts from the ground. Figure 18 shows one of Earth's most famous geysers.

Geothermal Energy In some volcanic areas, water heated by magma can provide an energy source called geothermal energy. The people of Reykjavik, Iceland, pipe this hot water into homes for warmth. Geothermal energy can also be used as a source of electricity. Steam from underground is piped into turbines. Inside a turbine, the steam spins a wheel in the same way that blowing on a pinwheel makes the pinwheel turn. The moving wheel in the turbine turns a generator that changes the energy of motion into electrical energy. Geothermal energy provides some electrical power in California and New Zealand.

 Reading Checkpoint How can geothermal energy be used to generate electricity?

FIGURE 18
A Geyser Erupts
Old Faithful, a geyser in Yellowstone National Park, erupts about every 33 to 93 minutes. That's how long it takes for the pressure to build up again after each eruption.

Section 4 Assessment

Target Reading Skill Outlining Use the information in your outline about volcanic landforms to help you answer the questions below.

Reviewing Key Concepts

1. a. **Identifying** What are the three main types of volcanoes?
   b. **Comparing and Contrasting** Compare the three types of volcanic mountains in terms of shape, type of eruption, and the materials that make up the volcano.
2. a. **Listing** What features form as a result of magma hardening beneath Earth's surface?
   b. **Explaining** What are two ways in which mountains can form as a result of magma hardening beneath Earth's surface?
   c. **Predicting** After millions of years, what landform forms from hardened magma in the pipe of an extinct volcano?

3. a. **Listing** What are some features found in areas of geothermal activity?
   b. **Relating Cause and Effect** What causes a geyser to erupt?

Writing in Science

Explaining a Process Write an explanation of the process that formed Crater Lake. In your answer, include the type of volcanic mountain and eruption involved, as well as the steps in the process. (*Hint:* Look at the diagram in Figure 15 before you write.)

Answer

 Reading Checkpoint Steam is used to turn a turbine, which turns a generator to produce electricity.

Assess

Reviewing Key Concepts
1. **a.** Shield, cinder cones, composite
b. Shield: broad with low slope, low viscosity lava flows, consists of lava flows; cinder: small volcano with steep sides, pyroclastic eruptions, consists of ash and cinders; composite: steep sides, lava flows and ash falls and flows, consists of layers of both ash and lava flows
2. **a.** Volcanic necks, dikes, sills, batholiths, dome mountains **b.** Batholiths are large rock masses that form the core of many mountain ranges. Dome mountains form when uplift forces hardened magma to bend rock upward. Then the rock above the hardened magma wears away, leaving it exposed. **c.** Volcanic neck
3. **a.** Hot springs and geysers **b.** Pressure builds up in a narrow crack until water and steam erupt from it.

Reteach L1
As a class, list the types of volcanoes and how they form.

Performance Assessment L2
Skills Check Ask students to create sketches that illustrate how a cinder cone volcano forms. Sketches should include at least three stages of growth.

All in One Teaching Resources
- Section Summary: *Volcanic Landforms*
- Review and Reinforce: *Volcanic Landforms*
- Enrich: *Volcanic Landforms*

Writing in Science

Writing Mode Explanation

Scoring Rubric

4 includes steps clearly and logically explained with strong, detailed description of the type of mountain and eruption
3 includes all criteria, but not as detailed
2 includes two criteria
1 includes some details, but steps are missing or inaccurate

Lab zone Chapter Project

Keep Students on Track Each student group should have planned its documentary and decided on materials to use. Ask students to finalize their presentations by finishing visual aids or refining their scripts. Provide tape recorders, transparency film, or video cameras as desired.

Lab zone Skills Lab

Gelatin Volcanoes L2

Prepare for Inquiry

Key Concept
Magma inside a volcano generally flows vertically to form dikes.

Skills Objectives
Students will be able to
- develop a hypothesis about how magma flows inside a volcano
- make a model volcano to test their hypothesis
- observe how "magma" flows inside their model

Prep Time 45 minutes
Class Time 40 minutes

Safety
Ensure that students wear lab aprons to protect their clothing from food coloring. Caution them to be careful using the knives. Review the safety guidelines in Appendix A.

All in One Teaching Resources
- Skills Lab: *Gelatin Volcanoes*

Advance Planning
Gelatin molds: At least five hours before students will do this lab, make a gelatin mold for each student group. You can use bowls ranging from 2 1/2 cups to 2 quarts in capacity. For a 2 1/2 cup bowl, mix one 7-oz envelope of unflavored gelatin with 1/2 cup of room-temperature water. Add 1 1/2 cups of boiling water, and stir until the gelatin is completely dissolved. Add 1/3 cup of cold water. Refrigerate the mold for 3–5 hours or until set. Also make a test mold in a smaller container. After 3 hours, check the firmness of the test mold by removing it from its container. If it is not completely set, refrigerate the large molds for at least another 2 hours.

Pizza pan: Use an aluminum pizza pan with holes punched in it with a nail at 2.5-cm intervals. Drive the nail *downward* through the tray so that the upper surface stays ~~th and the gelatin mold will not snag~~ ~~les' edges.~~
~~leas~~ plastic bird-feeding syringes, ~~through the holes in the~~
~~06 ● F~~ce the gelatin by at

Lab zone Skills Lab

Gelatin Volcanoes

Problem
How does magma move inside a volcano?

Skills Focus
developing hypotheses, making models, observing

Materials
- plastic cup
- tray or shallow pan
- aluminum pizza pan with holes punched at 2.5-cm intervals
- plastic knife
- unflavored gelatin mold in bowl
- red food coloring and water
- plastic syringe, 10 cc
- rubber gloves
- unlined paper
- 3 small cardboard oatmeal boxes

106 ◆ F

Procedure
1. Before magma erupts as lava, how does it travel up from underground magma chambers? Record your hypothesis.
2. Remove the gelatin from the refrigerator. Loosen the gelatin from its container by briefly placing the container of gelatin in a larger bowl of hot water.
3. Place the pizza pan over the gelatin so the mold is near the center of the pizza pan. While holding the pizza pan against the top of the mold, carefully turn the mold and the pizza pan upside down.
4. Carefully lift the bowl off the gelatin mold to create a gelatin volcano.
5. Place the pizza pan with the gelatin mold on top of the oatmeal boxes as shown below.
6. Mix the red food coloring and water in the plastic cup. Then fill the syringe with "magma" (the red water). Remove air bubbles from the syringe by holding it upright and squirting out a small amount of water.
7. Insert the tip of the syringe through a hole in the pizza pan near the center of the gelatin volcano. Inject the magma into the gelatin very slowly. Observe what happens to the magma.
8. Repeat steps 6 and 7 as many times as possible. Observe the movement of the magma each time. Note any differences in the direction the magma takes when the syringe is inserted into different parts of the gelatin volcano. Record your observations.

Layered volcano (Design an Experiment): Fill a bowl only halfway with gelatin solution, and set aside the rest at room temperature. Add the second layer to the bowl after the first layer has been refrigerated for 2 hours.

Data Table

Test	Initial Location of Magma	Position and Shape of Magma Bodies	Other Observations
1.			
2.			
3.			
4.			

9. Look down on your gelatin volcano from above. Make a sketch of the positions and shapes of the magma bodies. Label your drawing "Top View."

10. Carefully use a knife to cut your volcano in half. Separate the pieces and examine the cut surfaces for traces of the magma bodies.

11. Sketch the positions and shapes of the magma bodies on one of the cut faces. Label your drawing "Cross Section."

Analyze and Conclude

1. **Observing** Describe how the magma moved through your model. Did the magma move straight up through the center of your model volcano or did it branch off in places? Explain why you think the magma moved in this way.

2. **Developing Hypotheses** What knowledge or experience did you use to develop your hypothesis? How did the actual movement compare with your hypothesis?

3. **Inferring** How would you explain any differences in the direction the magma flowed when the syringe was inserted in different parts of the gelatin volcano?

4. **Making Models** How does what you observed in your model compare to the way magma moves through real volcanoes? How could you change your model to be more like a real volcano?

5. **Communicating** Prepare your model as a display to teach other students about volcanoes. Make a list of the volcanic features in your model. For each feature, write a description of how the feature would form in a real volcano.

More to Explore

Plan to repeat the investigation using a mold made of two layers of gelatin. Before injecting the magma, predict what effect the layering will have on the movement of magma. Record your observations to determine if your hypothesis was correct. What volcanic feature is produced by this version of the model? Can you think of other volcanic features that you could model using gelatin layers? *Obtain your teacher's permission before carrying out your investigation.*

An eruption of
Mount Kilauea, Hawaii

F ◆ 107

Extend Inquiry

More to Explore Horizontal sills will form along the contact between the layers. Students might also be able to model dome mountains or batholiths.

Guide Inquiry

Invitation
Ask: **What are dikes and sills made of?** (*Hardened magma*) **What is the major difference between a dike and a sill?** (*Dikes cut across rock layers; sills are parallel to them.*)

Troubleshooting the Experiment
- Demonstrate the mold-removal process described in steps 2–5.
- Have students wear rubber or vinyl gloves in steps 6–8 to keep the food coloring from staining their hands.
- In Step 6, have students lightly tap the syringe before they squirt water out.
- Before students begin injecting colored water in Step 7, make sure that they have put a tray under the pizza pan to catch any water that drains out of the mold.
- If colored water dribbles down the syringe in steps 7 and 8, students can wrap a folded paper towel around the syringe.
- In Step 10, make sure that students cut the volcano in half *from top to bottom*, not across its diameter.

Expected Outcome
With a slow, steady injection rate, the colored water will create thin, vertical dikes inside the gelatin.

Analyze and Conclude
1. The magma spread vertically from the point of injection into a fan-shaped dike that gradually grew until it broke the surface. The magma moved this way because it was injected under pressure.
2. Answers should be based on what students have already learned about how magma flows through a volcano and how dikes are formed in a vertical or near-vertical plane.
3. When injected near the center, magma flowed radially outward in any direction. When injected near the edge, magma flowed to the closest surface point, following the path of least resistance.
4. The colored water flowed vertically in the direction of least resistance, much like a flow of magma in an actual volcano.
5. Provide art materials. Encourage students to prepare clear, logical descriptions.

The BIG Idea

Have students read the answer to the Essential Question. Encourage them to evaluate and revise their own answers as needed.

Help Students Read

Developing Vocabulary

Word Forms Ask students to use a dictionary to write definitions for *shield* and *composite* in their own words. Then, have students explain how these definitions relate to the terms *shield volcano* and *composite volcano*.

Words in Context Select key terms from the chapter. Have students write a sentence for each term that places the term in a correct context. Provide them with one example before they begin: *viscosity: High-silica magma has a higher viscosity than low-silica magma.*

Connecting Concepts

Concept Maps Help students develop one way to show how the information in this chapter is related. Forces inside Earth cause magma to heat, move, and push through the crust to erupt as volcanoes that pose hazards and form land features. Have students brainstorm to identify key concepts, key terms, details, and examples. Then write each item on a self-stick note and attach it at random to chart paper or to the board.

Tell students that this concept map will be organized in hierarchical order and to begin at the top with the key concepts. Ask students these questions to guide them to categorize the information on the self-stick notes: **How does magma flow through a volcano and what landforms can result? What are the physical and chemical properties of the different types of volcanic eruptions?**

Prompt students by using connecting words or phrases, such as "leads to" and "results in," to indicate the basis for the organization of the map. The phrases should

---

Chapter 3 Study Guide

The BIG Idea **Forces Inside Earth** Most volcanoes form where Earth's plates collide or move apart, allowing magma to reach the surface. Lava forms landforms such as volcanic mountains or lava plateaus.

① Volcanoes and Plate Tectonics

Key Concepts

- Volcanic belts form along the boundaries of Earth's plates.
- A volcano forms above a hot spot when magma erupts through the crust and reaches the surface.

Key Terms
- volcano • magma • lava • Ring of Fire
- island arc • hot spot

② Properties of Magma

Key Concepts

- Each substance has a particular set of physical and chemical properties. These properties can be used to identify a substance or to predict how it will behave.
- Because liquids differ in viscosity, some liquids flow more easily than others.
- The viscosity of magma depends upon its silica content and temperature.

Key Terms

element	viscosity
compound	silica
physical property	pahoehoe
chemical property	aa

③ Volcanic Eruptions

Key Concepts

- When a volcano erupts, the force of the expanding gases pushes magma from the magma chamber through the pipe until it flows or explodes out of the vent.
- Geologists classify volcanic eruptions as quiet or explosive.
- Geologists often use the terms *active, dormant,* or *extinct* to describe a volcano's stage of activity.

Key Terms
- magma chamber • pipe • vent • lava flow
- crater • pyroclastic flow • dormant
- extinct

④ Volcanic Landforms

Key Concepts

- Volcanic eruptions create landforms made of lava, ash, and other materials. These landforms include shield volcanoes, cinder cone volcanoes, composite volcanoes, and lava plateaus.
- Features formed by magma include volcanic necks, dikes, and sills, as well as batholiths and dome mountains.
- Hot springs and geysers are types of geothermal activity that are often found in areas of present or past volcanic activity.

Key Terms

shield volcano
cinder cone
composite volcano
caldera
volcanic neck
dike
sill
batholith
geothermal activity
geyser

---

form a sentence between or among a set of concepts.

Answer Accept logical presentations by students.

All in One Teaching Resources
- Key Terms Review: *Volcanoes*
- Connecting Concepts: *Volcanoes*

Review and Assessment

Organizing Information

Concept Mapping Fill in the concept map to show the characteristics of the different types of volcanic mountains.

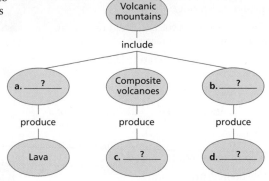

Reviewing Key Terms

Choose the letter of the best answer.

1. Volcanoes found where two oceanic plates collide form a(n)
   a. cinder cone.
   b. island arc.
   c. hot spot.
   d. Ring of Fire.

2. Magma becomes lava when it reaches a volcano's
   a. geyser.
   b. magma chamber.
   c. pipe.
   d. vent.

3. Lava that forms smooth, ropelike coils when it hardens is called
   a. aa.
   b. silica.
   c. pahoehoe.
   d. pyroclastic flow.

4. A volcanic mountain made up of volcanic ash, cinders, and bombs is called a
   a. shield volcano.
   b. cinder cone.
   c. composite volcano.
   d. caldera.

5. The collapse of a volcano's magma chamber may produce a(n)
   a. crater.
   b. island arc.
   c. caldera.
   d. batholith.

6. Lava that cuts across rock layers hardens to form a feature called a
   a. dike.
   b. caldera.
   c. volcanic neck.
   d. sill.

7. When magma heats underground water, the result may be a
   a. lava flow.
   b. vent.
   c. hot spot.
   d. hot spring.

Writing in Science

Comparison Write a comparison of the three different kinds of volcanoes. Discuss the ways in which all three are similar and the ways in which they are different. Use the correct terms to describe each type of volcano.

Discovery CHANNEL SCHOOL
Volcanoes
Video Preview
Video Field Trip
▶ Video Assessment

Go Online
PHSchool.com
For: Self-assessment
Visit: PHSchool.com
Web Code: cfa-1030

Students can take a practice test online that is automatically scored.

All in One Teaching Resources
- Transparency F34: *Concept Map*
- Chapter Test
- Performance Assessment Teacher Notes
- Performance Assessment Student Worksheet
- Performance Assessment Scoring Rubric

 *ExamView®* Computer Test Bank CD-ROM

Review and Assessment

Organizing Information
a. shield volcanoes
b. cinder cones
c. lava and ash
d. ash, cinders, and bombs

Reviewing Key Terms
1. b **2.** d **3.** c **4.** b **5.** c **6.** a **7.** d

Writing in Science

Writing Mode Comparison

Scoring Rubric
4 includes complete, accurate comparison of volcano types and provides details on magma composition
3 includes all criteria but not many details
2 includes accurate but brief comparison; some significant points are omitted
1 includes brief comparison that fails to demonstrate comparison among types

Discovery CHANNEL SCHOOL Video Assessment

Volcanoes

Show the video assessment to review chapter content and as a prompt for the writing assignment. Discussion questions: **What type of eruption destroyed Pompeii?** *(Explosive)* **Where on Earth's surface are volcanoes most likely to form?** *(Near the boundaries of Earth's tectonic plates, occupying a weak spot that lets magma from the mantle rise to the surface. They also can form near hot spots.)*

Checking Concepts

8. The Ring of Fire is a volcanic belt formed by volcanoes that rim the Pacific Ocean.

9. The mid-ocean ridge marks a diverging plate boundary, and lava erupts from cracks in the ocean floor.

10. An oceanic plate can sink beneath another oceanic plate, or an oceanic plate can sink beneath a continental plate.

11. As temperature increases, the viscosity of magma decreases, so the magma flows more easily.

12. A shield volcano forms when lava repeatedly flows out of a fissure and cools to form layers. A gently sloping mountain forms gradually.

13. An active volcano is one that has erupted in the recent past and that is likely to erupt in the near future. A dormant volcano is one that is currently inactive but may someday become active again. An extinct, or dead, volcano is unlikely to erupt again.

14. Many small earthquakes can occur in the area around a volcano before it erupts. These quakes are triggered by movement of magma into the magma chamber and through the pipe.

15. Hot springs form when water heated by magma or hot rock rises to the surface. A geyser forms when hot water and steam suddenly erupt from a fracture in rock.

Checking Concepts

8. What is the Ring of Fire?

9. What process causes volcanoes to form along the mid-ocean ridge?

10. What are two ways volcanoes can form near converging plate boundaries?

11. What effect does temperature have on the characteristics of magma?

12. How does a shield volcano form?

13. Describe the three stages in the "life cycle" of a volcano.

14. Why can earthquakes be a warning sign that an eruption is about to happen?

15. How do hot springs form?

Thinking Critically

16. Predicting Is a volcanic eruption likely to occur on the East Coast of the United States? Explain your answer.

17. Comparing and Contrasting Compare the way in which an island arc forms with the way in which a hot spot volcano forms.

18. Making Generalizations How might a volcanic eruption affect the area around a volcano, including its plant and animal life?

19. Relating Cause and Effect Look at the diagram of a lava plateau below. Why doesn't the type of eruption that produces a lava plateau produce a volcanic mountain instead?

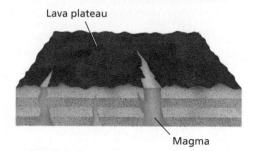

Lava plateau

Magma

20. Predicting In a particular volcanic region, many small faults fracture the rocks of the crust. What features are likely to form beneath the surface? Explain your answer.

Applying Skills

Refer to the diagram to answer Questions 21–24.

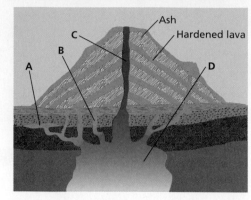

Ash
Hardened lava
C
B
A
D

21. Classifying What is this volcano made of? How do geologists classify a volcano made of these materials?

22. Developing Hypotheses What is the feature labeled A in the diagram? What is the feature labeled B? How do these features form?

23. Predicting What is the feature labeled C in the diagram? If this feature becomes plugged with hardened magma, what could happen to the volcano? Explain.

24. Inferring What is the feature labeled D in the diagram? What can you infer about this feature if the volcano becomes dormant?

Lab zone Chapter **Project**

Performance Assessment Present your documentary about a volcanic region to your class. Evaluate how well your documentary presented the information you collected. As you watched the other documentaries, did you see any similarities between how people in different regions live with volcanoes?

Lab zone Chapter **Project** L3

Performance Assessment You may want to provide time for groups to practice their presentations. Inform students how much time each group will have for its presentation. Point out that if their practice presentation runs too long, they should find ways to cut its length without jeopardizing its content or flow.

Reflect and Record Ask students to evaluate how well their documentary presented the information they collected. Give students time to record their thoughts individually, and then encourage them to discuss their ideas with the other members of their group.

Standardized Test Prep

Choose the letter that best answers the question or completes the statement.

1. A composite volcano is most likely to form
   A above a hot spot.
   B where an oceanic plate collides with a continental plate.
   C along the mid-ocean ridge.
   D along a rift valley.

2. As the temperature of magma increases, its viscosity
   F affects the magma's silica content.
   G increases.
   H stays the same.
   J decreases.

3. Which step in a volcanic eruption occurs just before the volcano erupts?
   A Magma collects in the magma chamber.
   B Lava hardens to form volcanic rock.
   C Expanding gases push magma through the pipe.
   D The roof of the empty magma chamber collapses.

4. Magma that hardens between layers of rock forms a
   F volcanic neck.
   G dike.
   H batholith.
   J sill.

5. The diagram below shows the formation of what volcanic feature?
   A caldera
   B island arc volcano
   C hot spot
   D mid-ocean ridge

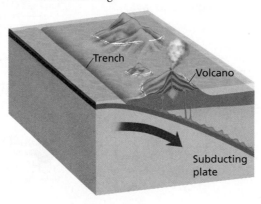

Trench

Volcano

Subducting plate

Constructed Response

6. A geologist was observing the area around a dormant volcano. She decided that this volcano must have had an explosive eruption. Describe the evidence geologists would use to make this decision. In your answer, discuss the properties of the magma and the types of rock that would result from an explosive eruption.

Thinking Critically

16. A volcanic eruption is not likely to occur on the East Coast of the United States because that region does not have any active volcanoes. Students might recall that this part of the North American plate is far from any plate boundary. Volcanoes commonly occur along converging plate boundaries.

17. An island arc forms at a converging plate boundary where one oceanic plate sinks beneath another oceanic plate. A hot spot volcano forms in continental or oceanic crust where magma from the mantle erupts. Hot spot volcanoes often are far from plate boundaries.

18. Accept all reasonable responses. Possible answers: Plants and animals could be killed by lava flows, pyroclastic flows, toxic gases, mudflows, or avalanches; the land surface would change, and new landforms would be created; nutrient-rich lava, ash, and cinders would in time form fertile soil.

19. Lava plateaus form where thin, runny lava flows out of long cracks in the ground. Because the lava is fluid and erupts from a wide area, it spreads out rather than forming steep sides.

20. Dikes are likely to form beneath the surface because magma could move along the faults and some might cool there.

Applying Skills

21. This volcano is made of ash and lava. Geologists classify it as a composite volcano.

22. A is a sill. B is a dike. A sill forms when magma moves between rock layers and cools. A dike forms when magma forces its way across rock layers and cools.

23. C is a volcanic pipe. If additional magma enters the volcano, an explosive eruption might occur.

24. D is a magma chamber. If the volcano becomes dormant, the magma chamber must be empty.

Standardized Test Prep

1. B **2.** J **3.** C **4.** J **5.** B

6. Sample answer: The geologist might find volcanic ash, cinders, and bombs. These eruption products indicate that an explosive eruption occurred. They could also be evidence of a pyroclastic flow. The rock formed from the magma produced by this eruption would be high in silica content, probably rhyolite.

Chapter 4 Minerals

Chapter at a Glance

Chapter Project *Growing a Crystal Garden*

Teaching Resources
- Chapter Project Teacher Notes, pp. 242–243
- Chapter Project Student Overview, pp. 244–245
- Chapter Project Student Worksheets 1–2, pp. 246–247
- Chapter Project Scoring Rubric, p. 248

Technology

Local Standards

Video Preview

Section 1 Properties of Minerals
2 periods
1 block

F.4.1.1 Define a mineral.
F.4.1.2 Explain how minerals are identified.

active.art.

Section 2 How Minerals Form
2 periods
1 block

F.4.2.1 Explain how minerals form from magma and lava.
F.4.2.2 Explain how minerals form from water solutions.

PHSchool.com

Section 3 Using Mineral Resources
2 periods
1 block

F.4.3.1 Describe how minerals are used.
F.4.3.2 Explain how ores are processed to obtain metals.

SciLINKS NSTA

Video Field Trip

Review and Assessment

Teaching Resources
- Key Terms Review, p. 277
- Transparency F41
- Performance Assessment Teacher Notes, p. 284
- Performance Assessment Scoring Rubric, p. 285
- Performance Assessment Student Worksheet, p. 286
- Chapter Test, pp. 287–290

Video Assessment

PHSchool.com

Test Preparation

Test Preparation Blackline Masters

Chapter Activities Planner

For more activities

 LAB ZONE
Easy Planner
CD-ROM

Student Edition	Inquiry	Time	Materials	Skills	Resources
Chapter Project, p. 113	Open-Ended	2 weeks	All in One Teaching Resources, p. 242	Measuring, observing	Lab zone Easy Planner
Section 1					
Discover Activity, p. 114	Directed	15 minutes	Samples of black hematite and magnetite, porcelain or ceramic tile, paper towel	Observing	Lab zone Easy Planner
Skills Activity, p. 120	Directed	10 minutes	Penny; samples of talc, calcite, and quartz	Classifying	Lab zone Easy Planner
Skills Lab, p. 123	Guided	Prep: 20 minutes Class: 40 minutes	Graduated cylinder, 100 mL; 3 mineral samples: pyrite, quartz, and galena; water; balance	Measuring, drawing conclusions	All in One Teaching Resources Skills Lab: *Finding the Density of Minerals, p. 257*
Section 2					
Discover Activity, p. 124	Directed	15 minutes	Salol, plastic spoon, 2 microscope slides, tongs, candle, matches, ice cube, hand lens	Forming hypotheses	Lab zone Easy Planner
Try This, p. 125	Directed	10 minutes, then 1 day to dry	Table salt solution, Epsom salt solution, 2 shallow pans, large sheet of black construction paper	Observing	Lab zone Easy Planner
Section 3					
Discover Activity, p. 130	Guided	10 minutes	Samples of bauxite and graphite, aluminum can, pencil	Posing questions	Lab zone Easy Planner
At Home Activity, p. 135	Directed	Home	3 iron nails, petroleum jelly, clear nail polish, water, vinegar, clear drinking glass	Communicating	Lab zone Easy Planner
Consumer Lab, pp. 136–137	Guided	Prep: 25 minutes Class: 40 minutes	Samples of 3 different types of toothpaste, worn-out toothbrushes, tap water, a ceramic tile stained on the unglazed side with a felt-tip marker or pen	Observing, controlling variables	All in One Teaching Resources Consumer Lab: *A Mouthful of Minerals, pp. 275–276*

Section 1 Properties of Minerals

 *2 periods, 1 block*

Objectives

F.4.1.1 Define a mineral.
F.4.1.2 Explain how minerals are identified.

Key Terms

- mineral • inorganic • crystal • streak • luster • Mohs hardness scale
- cleavage • fracture

Local Standards

Preteach

Build Background Knowledge

Students share their knowledge about the definition of minerals and where they can find minerals in nature.

 Discover Activity *What Is the True Color of a Mineral?* **L1**

Targeted Print and Technology Resources

 Teaching Resources
L2 Reading Strategy Transparency F35: Outlining

 PresentationExpress™ CD-ROM

Instruct

What Is a Mineral? Use objects and samples to demonstrate the differences between rocks and minerals on the basis of the definition of a mineral.

Identifying Minerals Bring students together for a discussion of the physical properties of minerals and to examine a mineral identification table.

 Skills Lab *Finding the Density of Minerals* **L3**

Targeted Print and Technology Resources

Teaching Resources
L2 Guided Reading, pp. 251–254
L2 Transparency F36
L2 Skills Lab: *Finding the Density of Minerals*, p. 257

Lab Activity Video/DVD
Skills Lab: *Finding the Density of Minerals*

PHSchool.com Web Code: cfd-1041
PHSchool.com Web Code: cfp-1041

Student Edition on Audio CD

Assess

Section Assessment Questions

Have students use their completed graphic organizers with their outlines to answer the questions.

Reteach

Students create a concept map that includes the definition of a mineral and mineral properties.

Targeted Print and Technology Resources

Teaching Resources
- Section Summary, p. 250
L1 Review and Reinforce, p. 255
L3 Enrich, p. 256

Section 2 How Minerals Form

 *2 periods, 1 block*

ABILITY LEVELS
L1 Basic to Average
L2 For All Students
L3 Average to Advanced

Objectives

F.4.2.1 Explain how minerals form from magma and lava.
F.4.2.2 Explain how minerals form from water solutions.

Key Terms

• geode • crystallization • solution • vein

Local Standards

Preteach

Build Background Knowledge

Students are provided an analogy between how cotton candy is made and how crystals form.

 **Discover Activity** *How Does the Rate of Cooling Affect Crystals?* **L3**

Targeted Print and Technology Resources

 Teaching Resources

L2 Reading Strategy Transparency F37: Asking Questions

 PresentationExpress™ CD-ROM

Instruct

Minerals From Magma and Lava Explain that the size of crystals in minerals depends on the location of molten rock as it cools. Discuss these differences and guide students to hypothesize how fast volcanic glass cools.

Minerals From Solutions Use Figure 10 to help explain how some minerals crystallize from hot water solutions underground.

Targeted Print and Technology Resources

Teaching Resources

L2 Guided Reading, pp. 262–264
L2 Transparency F38

PHSchool.com Web Code: cfd-1042
PHSchool.com Web Code: cfh-1040

Student Edition on Audio CD

Assess

Section Assessment Questions

Have students use their completed graphic organizers with their questions and answers to answer the questions.

Reteach

Students list examples of minerals from magma or lava and minerals from solutions.

Targeted Print and Technology Resources

Teaching Resources
• Section Summary, p. 261
L1 Review and Reinforce, p. 265
L3 Enrich, p. 266

Section 3 Using Mineral Resources

 2 periods, 1 block

Objectives

F.4.3.1 Describe how minerals are used.

F.4.3.2 Explain how ores are processed to obtain metals.

Key Terms

• gemstone • ore • smelting • alloy

ABILITY LEVELS

L1 Basic to Average

L2 For All Students

L3 Average to Advanced

Local Standards

Preteach

Build Background Knowledge

Students name items they use every day that are made from minerals and recall that steel mills smelt ore in furnaces.

Lab zone Discover Activity *How Are Minerals Processed Before They Are Used?* **L1**

Targeted Print and Technology Resources

All in One Teaching Resources

L2 Reading Strategy Transparency F39: Using Prior Knowledge

⊙ **PresentationExpress™ CD-ROM**

Instruct

The Uses of Minerals Challenge students to name items that are not made from rock or minerals to help them understand the importance of minerals. Guide a discussion on how the use of minerals has affected the development of society.

Producing Metals From Minerals Work with students as a class to create a concept map that shows how people prospect for, mine, and process ore. Given the fictional scenario of an iron shortage, guide them to apply their knowledge to develop a plan to increase iron supplies.

Lab zone Consumer Lab *A Mouthful of Minerals* **L2**

Targeted Print and Technology Resources

All in One Teaching Resources

L2 Guided Reading, pp. 269–272

L2 Transparency F40

L2 Consumer Lab: *A Mouthful of Minerals*, pp. 275–276

📼 **Lab Activity Video/DVD**
Consumer Lab: *A Mouthful of Minerals*

www.SciLinks.org Web Code: scn-1043

⊙ **Student Edition on Audio CD**

Assess

Section Assessment Questions

↻ Have students use the graphic organizers that they completed using prior knowledge to answer the questions.

Reteach

Students make a table of minerals and their uses.

Targeted Print and Technology Resources

All in One Teaching Resources

• Section Summary, p. 268

L1 Review and Reinforce, p. 273

L3 Enrich, p. 274

Go Online

NSTA-PD*Links*

For: Professional development support
Visit: www.SciLinks.org/PDLinks
Web Code: scf-1040

Professional Development

Section 1 **Properties of Minerals**

Other Special Properties To identify most minerals, a combination of several tests or the use of multiple properties is required. But some minerals have special properties that are very distinctive and make identification relatively easy. An example is calcite. Calcite is found in a variety of colors but is usually white or clear. It can resemble several common minerals, including dolomite, fluorite, quartz, and halite. A series of tests to determine hardness, cleavage, and density can be used to distinguish calcite from these other minerals. But calcite has one unique property that allows it to be quickly and easily identified—the acid test. Calcite will fizz when a drop of dilute hydrochloric acid is applied. No mineral besides calcite will react to the acid in this way.

Other minerals can be identified by distinctive taste, smell, or feel. For example, halite has a salty taste. (Do not allow students to taste any mineral.) Talc has a very distinctive feel. It feels soapy or greasy.

Section 2 **How Minerals Form**

Diamond Formation Diamonds are one of the most precious minerals on Earth. They have been found on every continent; however, mines in Southern Africa produce 45 percent (by value) of the world's total diamonds. But how do they form?

The formation of diamonds occurs under tremendous temperatures and pressures deep inside Earth. Diamonds are formed in the mantle at depths of more than 300 km. The diamonds are brought toward the surface by magma in explosive eruptions. These eruptions form narrow carrot-shaped pipes called kimberlites. Kimberlites are named for the town of Kimberley, South Africa, where they were first described. Diamonds are either mined directly from the kimberlites or from deposits that form from the erosion of the pipes.

Address Misconceptions

Students may think that crystal faces must be present for a mineral to have a crystal structure. This misconception is addressed in the section Properties of Minerals.

Section 3 **Using Mineral Resources**

Nonmetallic Mineral Resources When you think of mineral resources, you probably think about either metallic minerals such as gold or gems such as diamonds. But other minerals are valuable and useful resources. Most diamonds (90 percent), for example, are not gem-quality, but are used as industrial abrasives.

Many other common minerals have industrial uses. Feldspar is used in ceramics. Quartz sand is used to make glass. Halite or rock salt is used in food, as a de-icer on roads, and to manufacture sodium hydroxide and chlorine gas. Fluorite is used in the chemical industry to manufacture hydrofluoric acid. It is also used to make glass, fiberglass, pottery, and enamel. You probably use a mineral to write with. The "lead" in pencils is not lead at all but the mineral graphite.

Help Students Read

Relating Text and Visuals
Using Graphic Elements to Clarify and Extend

Strategy Help students relate visuals to text in order to clarify difficult concepts in the text or to understand information beyond that stated in the text. This strategy enables students to learn to actively make use of photos and illustrations as tools to support comprehension. Before students begin, choose something from a section in the chapter.

Example
1. Have students keep their books closed as you read a few paragraphs aloud, including text that refers to a figure. You may want to think aloud as you read, saying, for example, "I wonder what that would look like?"
2. Then have the students open their books to the passage that you have read. Tell them to reread it and then study the figure and its caption carefully. Ask what parts of the passage make more sense when students look at the figure.
3. Point out that visuals also sometimes communicate information that is not in the text. Have students identify any new information that can be learned from the figure.
4. Have students work in pairs, with one reading aloud the next reference to a figure, and then both working together to discuss how the figure helps them understand the passage or provides additional information.

The BIG Idea

The Big Idea is the major scientific concept of the chapter. It is followed by the Essential Question. Read aloud the question to students. As students study the chapter, tell them to think about the Essential Question. Explain that they will discover the answer to the question as they read. The chapter Study Guide provides a sample answer.

 **Chapter Project** L3

Objectives

Students will design and create a crystal garden using at least two different crystal-growth solutions. After this Chapter Project, students will be able to

- measure and prepare a chemical solution
- observe and sketch various types of crystals
- compare and contrast different kinds of crystals
- create a data table to record crystal growth rates
- communicate results to the class

Skills Focus

Measuring, observing, comparing and contrasting, creating data tables, communicating

Project Time Line 2 weeks

All in One Teaching Resources

- Chapter Project Teacher Notes
- Chapter Project Overview
- Chapter Project Worksheet 1
- Chapter Project Worksheet 2
- Chapter Project Scoring Rubric

Developing a Plan

Students can individually make crystal gardens or work in small groups. Students should first design and create a garden scene. Students then prepare a solution with which to begin crystal growth in their garden scenes. They also use additional teacher-made solutions to add to their crystal gardens. Students sketch the crystals in their gardens and present their gardens to the class.

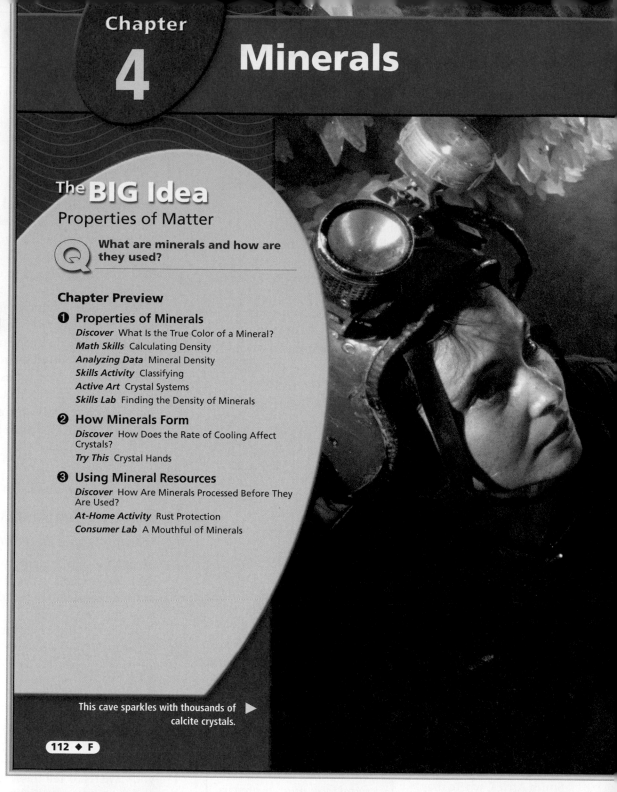

Chapter

4 Minerals

The BIG Idea
Properties of Matter

Q What are minerals and how are they used?

This cave sparkles with thousands of calcite crystals. ▶

112 ◆ F

Possible Materials

Possibly the best type of container in which to grow a crystal garden is a plastic shoe box, although students may find other containers that will work as well. Base materials in the garden include charcoal, brick pieces, porous rocks (such as sandstone), plastic foam of various shapes, pipe cleaners, cotton swabs, and small kitchen sponges. Various chemicals can be used to create different crystalline structures, including salt (sodium chloride), sugar (sucrose), Epsom salts, alum (aluminum potassium sulfate), and magnesium sulfate. You may need to order some of these chemicals from a pharmacy in advance of the start of the project. To vary the color of crystals, use dye powder, liquid bluing, or food coloring. Students will also need a hand lens to observe the crystals.

Lab zone™ Chapter **Project**

Growing a Crystal Garden

Minerals occur in an amazing variety of colors and shapes—from clear, tiny cubes of halite (table salt), to the masses of calcite crystals in the photograph, to precious rubies and sapphires. In this project, you will grow crystals to see how different types of chemicals form different crystal shapes.

Your Goal To design and grow a crystal garden

To complete this project successfully, you must

● create a three-dimensional garden scene as a base on which to grow crystals
● prepare at least two different crystal-growth solutions
● observe and record the shapes and growth rates of your crystals
● follow the safety guidelines in Appendix A

Plan It! Begin by deciding what materials you will use to create your garden scene. Your teacher will suggest a variety of materials and also describe the types of crystal-growth solutions that you can use. Then, design and build a setting for your crystal garden and add the solutions. Observe and record the growth of the crystals. Finally, display your finished crystal garden to your class. Be prepared to describe your procedure, observations, and conclusions.

Discovery CHANNEL SCHOOL Video Preview

Minerals

Show the Video Preview to introduce the Chapter Project and overview the chapter content. Discussion question: **Why are some minerals considered more valuable than others?** (*When a mineral is more difficult to find, it is more valuable.*)

Performance Assessment

The Chapter Project Scoring Rubric will help you evaluate how well students complete the Chapter Project. You may want to share the rubric with your students so that they will know what is expected. Students will be assessed on

● how well they create a three-dimensional crystal garden
● how well they observe and record the growth of crystals in the crystal garden
● how effectively they present the crystal garden and growth data to the class
● how well they participate in their groups

Portfolio

Possible Shortcuts

● You can make this project shorter by having individual students grow one kind of crystal on a simple base, such as a sponge in a clear glass.
● For a class project, have students design and create one elaborate garden scene in an aquarium tank or similar container. Then have small groups grow different kinds of crystals at different places in the garden.

Launching the Project

To introduce this project, show students pictures of mineral crystals from geology books. Then explain that they will be growing similar crystals in garden scenes that they will build and design. Ask: **What are some materials you could use to build such a garden scene?** (*Practically any porous material could serve as a substrate for crystal growth.*)

Objectives

After this lesson, students will be able to
F.4.1.1 Define a mineral
F.4.1.2 Explain how minerals are identified

Target Reading Skill

Outlining Explain that using an outline format helps students organize information by main topic, subtopic, and detail.

Answers

Properties of Minerals
I. What Is a Mineral?
  A. Naturally Occurring
  B. Inorganic
  C. Solid
  D. Crystal Structure
  E. Definite Chemical Composition
II. Identifying Minerals
  A. Color
  B. Streak
  C. Luster
  D. Density
  E. Hardness
  F. Crystal Systems
  G. Cleavage and Fracture
  H. Special Properties

All in One Teaching Resources

• Transparency F35

Preteach

Build Background Knowledge   L2

Experience With Minerals
Ask: **What are minerals?** (*Some students may know that minerals are the crystalline solids that make up rocks, but many students probably will mention dietary minerals, such as iron and calcium.*) **Where could you find minerals in nature?** (*A few students may know that some minerals, such as gold and diamond, occur in deposits and are mined. Students may suggest that minerals occur in rocks.*)

Reading Focus

Key Concepts
• What is a mineral?
• How are minerals identified?

Key Terms
• mineral • inorganic
• crystal • streak • luster
• Mohs hardness scale
• cleavage • fracture

Target Reading Skill

Outlining An outline shows the relationship between major ideas and supporting ideas. As you read, make an outline about the properties of minerals. Use the red headings for the main topics and the blue headings for the subtopics.

Properties of Minerals
I. What is a mineral?
A. Naturally occurring
B. Inorganic
C.
D.
E.
II. Identifying minerals

Lab zone Discover **Activity**

What Is the True Color of a Mineral?

1. Examine samples of magnetite and black hematite. Both minerals contain iron. Describe the color and appearance of the two minerals. Are they similar or different?
2. Rub the black hematite across the back of a porcelain or ceramic tile. Observe the color of the streak on the tile.
3. Wipe the tile clean before you test the next sample.
4. Rub the magnetite across the back of the tile. Observe the color of the streak.

Think It Over
Observing Does the color of each mineral match the color of its streak? How could this streak test be helpful in identifying them as two different minerals?

Look at the two different substances in Figure 1. On the left are beautiful quartz crystals. On the right is a handful of coal. Both are solid materials that form beneath Earth's surface. But only one is a mineral. To determine which of the two is a mineral, you need to become familiar with the characteristics of minerals. Then you can decide what's a mineral and what's not!

What Is a Mineral?

A mineral is a naturally occurring, inorganic solid that has a crystal structure and a definite chemical composition. For a substance to be a **mineral**, it must have all five of these characteristics.

Naturally Occurring To be classified as a mineral, a substance must be formed by processes that occur in the natural world. The mineral quartz forms naturally as magma cools and hardens deep beneath Earth's surface. Materials made by people, such as plastic, brick, glass, and steel, are not minerals.

Lab zone Discover **Activity**

Skills Focus Observing   L1

Materials black hematite, magnetite, porcelain or ceramic tile, paper towel

Time 15 minutes

Tip Use black hematite, not red.

Expected Outcome Hematite (Fe_2O_3) and magnetite (Fe_3O_4) are types of iron ore; both are dark and similar in appearance. Hematite leaves a reddish-brown streak; magnetite leaves a black streak.

Think It Over The streak of magnetite matches its color, but the streak of black hematite does not. Because the streak colors are different, this streak test can be helpful in identifying these samples as two different minerals.

Inorganic A mineral must also be **inorganic.** This means that the mineral cannot form from materials that were once part of a living thing. For example, coal forms naturally in the crust. But geologists do not classify coal as a mineral because it comes from the remains of plants that lived millions of years ago.

Solid A mineral is always a solid, with a definite volume and shape. The particles that make up a solid are packed together very tightly, so they cannot move like the particles that make up a liquid.

Crystal Structure The particles of a mineral line up in a pattern that repeats over and over again. The repeating pattern of a mineral's particles forms a solid called a **crystal.** A crystal has flat sides, called faces, that meet at sharp edges and corners. The quartz in Figure 1 has a crystal structure. In contrast, most coal lacks a crystal structure.

Definite Chemical Composition A mineral has a definite chemical composition or range of compositions. This means that a mineral always contains certain elements in definite proportions.

Almost all minerals are compounds. For example, a crystal of the mineral quartz has one atom of silicon for every two atoms of oxygen. Each compound has its own properties, or characteristics, which usually differ greatly from the properties of the elements that form it.

Some elements occur in nature in a pure form, and not as part of a compound with other elements. Elements such as copper, silver, and gold are also minerals. Almost all pure, solid elements are metals.

> **Reading Checkpoint** What does the phrase "definite chemical composition" mean?

FIGURE 1
Quartz and Coal
Quartz (below) has all the characteristics of a mineral. But coal (above) is formed from the remains of plants, lacks a crystal structure, and has no definite chemical composition.

Mineral Characteristics	Quartz	Coal
Naturally occurring	✓	✓
Inorganic	✓	No
Solid	✓	✓
Crystal structure	✓	No
Definite chemical composition	✓	No

F ◆ 115

Differentiated Instruction

Gifted and Talented `L3`
Interpreting Data Minerals have definite, but not fixed, chemical compositions. There may be some substitution of atoms. Have students research forsterite and fayalite, two varieties of olivine, and describe how the chemical formula changes. **learning modality: logical/ mathematical**

Less Proficient Readers `L1`
Communicating Ask students to create a display using the five conditions for being a mineral. Under each condition, students include examples that satisfy the condition and examples that fail to satisfy it. Ask students to determine whether any of their examples are minerals. **learning modality: kinesthetic**

F ● 115

Identifying Minerals

Teach Key Concepts L2

Properties of Minerals

Focus Tell students that minerals can be identified by their physical properties.

Teach To identify minerals, students must understand the various physical properties that are used for this purpose. Bring students together for a round-table discussion. Introduce the concepts of mineral color, streak, luster, density, hardness, crystal systems, cleavage and fracture, and special properties.

Apply Show students a mineral identification table, and have them identify the properties of several minerals. **learning modality: visual**

Teaching Resources

- Transparency F36

L2

Comparing and Contrasting Minerals

Materials mineral samples, hand lens

Time 10 minutes

Focus Remind students that each mineral has a unique set of properties.

Teach Invite students to examine several mineral samples. Then have each student list properties that could be used to distinguish between types of minerals.

Apply Ask: **Are the properties that you listed similar to those discussed in this chapter?** *(Most students will list at least a few of the properties discussed in the chapter.)* **learning modality: visual**

Identifying Minerals

Geologists have identified about 3,800 minerals. Because there are so many different kinds of minerals, telling them apart can often be a challenge. **Each mineral has characteristic properties that can be used to identify it.** When you have learned to recognize the properties of minerals, you will be able to identify many common minerals around you.

You can see some of the properties of a mineral just by looking at a sample. To observe other properties, however, you need to conduct tests on that sample. As you read about the properties of minerals, think about how you could use them to identify a mineral.

Color The color of a mineral is an easily observed physical property. But the color of a mineral alone often provides too little information to make an identification. All three minerals in Figure 2 are the color gold, yet only one is the real thing. Color can be used to identify only those few minerals that always have their own characteristic color. The mineral malachite is always green. The mineral azurite is always blue. No other minerals look quite the same as these.

FIGURE 2
Color of Minerals
These women in India are searching for bits of gold in river sand. Just because a mineral is gold in color doesn't mean it really is gold. Chalcopyrite and pyrite, also known as "fool's gold," are similar in color to real gold.

Gold   Pyrite   Chalcopyrite

FIGURE 3
Streak

A mineral's streak can be the same as or quite different from its color. **Observing** *How do the streaks of these minerals compare with their colors?*

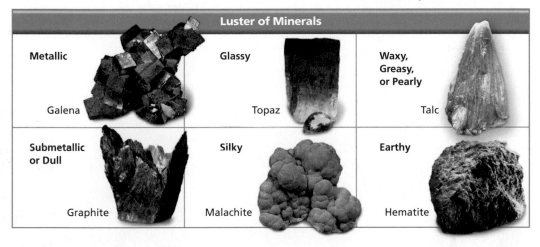

Malachite ►

Hematite ►

▲ Galena

Streak A streak test can provide a clue to a mineral's identity. The **streak** of a mineral is the color of its powder. You can observe a streak by rubbing a mineral against a piece of unglazed porcelain tile, as shown in Figure 3. Even though the color of the mineral may vary, its streak does not. Surprisingly, the streak color and the mineral color are often different. For example, although pyrite has a gold color, it always produces a greenish black streak. Real gold, on the other hand, produces a golden yellow streak.

Luster Another simple test to identify a mineral is to check its luster. **Luster** is the term used to describe how light is reflected from a mineral's surface. Minerals containing metals are often shiny. For example, galena is an ore of lead that has a bright, metallic luster. Quartz has a glassy luster. Some of the other terms used to describe luster include earthy, waxy, and pearly. Figure 4 shows the luster of several minerals.

 Reading Checkpoint What characteristic of minerals does the term *luster* describe?

FIGURE 4

Geologists use many different terms to describe the luster of minerals. **Interpreting Tables** *Which mineral has an earthy luster?*

Luster of Minerals

Metallic	Glassy	Waxy, Greasy, or Pearly
Galena	Topaz	Talc
Submetallic or Dull	Silky	Earthy
Graphite	Malachite	Hematite

Differentiated Instruction

Special Needs L1
Classifying and Communicating

Organize students in groups of three or four. Have each group make a poster that illustrates various mineral lusters. Photographs of minerals can be used for this purpose. Student groups should divide lusters into metallic and nonmetallic types.

Nonmetallic lusters can be further divided into several additional types: vitreous (glassy), adamantine (brilliant, like diamond), silky (fibrous minerals), pearly (iridescent luster), and greasy (appears to have an oily surface). Display the posters in the classroom. **learning modality: visual**

Lab zone **Build Inquiry** L2

Observing Mineral Streak

Materials hand lens, unglazed porcelain tile, numbered samples of various minerals

Time 10 minutes

Focus Ask: **How does the color of a mineral compare with the color of its streak?** *(Often the streak color and the mineral color are different.)*

Teach Ask students to make a data table, list the mineral samples by number, and record the color and streak of each sample. Then ask them to use the mineral identification table at the back of the book to identify each mineral.

Apply Ask: **How do you perform a streak test every day in class?** *(By streaking the graphite in pencil lead)* **learning modality: kinesthetic**

Help Students Read L1

Relating Text and Figures Refer to the Content Refresher in this chapter, which provides the guidelines for relating text and figures.

Have students read the text on this page related to streak and luster. Then have them use Figure 4 to describe the luster of the pictured minerals. Ask: **Can you think of common materials that have a metallic luster?** *(Rings, watchbands, chrome stripping)*

Monitor Progress L2

Writing Have each student write a paragraph about why a mineral's streak color may differ from the mineral's color.

Answers

Figure 3 For all three minerals, the mineral's color and streak are the same.

Figure 4 Hematite

 Reading Checkpoint The quality of the light reflected from a mineral's surface

Math Skill Calculating density

Focus Remind students that mass will be divided by volume. Explain that one cubic centimeter is the volume of a cube with one-centimeter edges.

Teach In the example, the density of one sample of olivine is determined. This value is fairly typical of the mineral, but olivine's density varies with its chemical composition.

Answer
2.7 g/cm³

Measuring Mineral Hardness

Materials metal nail file, penny, glass baby food jar, mineral samples such as garnet, quartz, pyrite, magnetite, galena, halite, and talc

Focus Tell students that mineral hardness depends on the strength of the bonds in the mineral's crystal structure.

Teach Organize students into small groups. Then challenge each group to give each mineral sample a hardness rating and place the samples in sequence from softest to hardest, using the Mohs scale for reference. After all groups have finished, invite a member of each group to write results on the board.

Apply Ask: **How are hard minerals used in society?** *(Garnet and corundum are used as abrasives; diamond is used on saw blades.)* **How are soft minerals used?** *(Talc is used in talcum powder.)* **learning modality: kinesthetic**

Calculating Density
To calculate the density of a mineral, divide the mass of the mineral sample by its volume.

$$\text{Density} = \frac{\text{Mass}}{\text{Volume}}$$

For example, if a sample of olivine has a mass of 237 g and a volume of 72 cm³, then the density is

$$\frac{237 \text{ g}}{72 \text{ cm}^3} = 3.3 \text{ g/cm}^3$$

Practice Problem A sample of calcite has a mass of 324 g and a volume of 120 cm³. What is its density?

FIGURE 5
Mohs Hardness Scale
Geologists determine a mineral's hardness by comparing it to the hardness of the minerals on the Mohs scale.

Density Each mineral has a characteristic density. Recall that density is the mass in a given space, or mass per unit volume. No matter what the size of a mineral sample, the density of that mineral always remains the same.

You can compare the density of two mineral samples of about the same size. Just pick them up and heft them, or feel their weight, in your hands. You may be able to feel the difference between low-density quartz and high-density galena. If the two samples are the same size, the galena will be almost three times as heavy as the quartz.

But heft provides only a rough measure of density. When geologists measure density, they use a balance to determine the precise mass of a mineral sample. Then they place the mineral in water to determine how much water the sample displaces. The volume of the displaced water equals the volume of the sample. Dividing the sample's mass by its volume gives the density of the mineral:

$$\text{Density} = \frac{\text{Mass}}{\text{Volume}}$$

Hardness When you identify a mineral, one of the best clues you can use is the mineral's hardness. In 1812, Friedrich Mohs, an Austrian mineral expert, invented a test to describe the hardness of minerals. Called the **Mohs hardness scale,** this scale ranks ten minerals from softest to hardest. Look at Figure 5 to see which mineral is the softest and which is the hardest.

Talc The softest known mineral, talc flakes when scratched by a fingernail.

Gypsum A fingernail can easily scratch it.

Calcite A fingernail cannot scratch it, but a copper penny can.

Fluorite A steel knife can easily scratch it.

Apatite A steel knife can scratch it.

1 2 3 4 5

Mineral Density

Use the line graph of the mass and volume of pyrite samples to answer the questions.

1. **Reading Graphs** What is the mass of Sample B? What is the volume of Sample B?

2. **Calculating** What is the density of Sample B?

3. **Reading Graphs** What is the mass of Sample C? What is the volume of Sample C?

4. **Calculating** What is the density of Sample C?

5. **Comparing and Contrasting** Compare the density of Sample B to that of Sample C.

6. **Predicting** A piece of pyrite has a volume of 40 cm³. What is its mass?

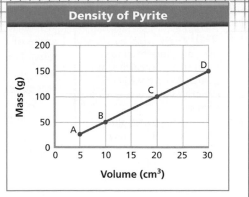

Density of Pyrite

Mass (g) vs. Volume (cm³)

7. **Drawing Conclusions** Does the density of a mineral depend on the size of the mineral sample? Explain.

Hardness can be determined by a scratch test. A mineral can scratch any mineral softer than itself, but can be scratched by any mineral that is harder. To determine the hardness of azurite, a mineral not on the Mohs scale, you could try to scratch it with talc, gypsum, or calcite. But none of these minerals scratch azurite. Apatite, rated 5 on the scale, does scratch azurite. Therefore, azurite's hardness is about 4.

Feldspar
It can't be scratched by a steel knife, but it can scratch window glass.

Quartz
It can scratch steel and hard glass easily.

Topaz
It can scratch quartz.

Corundum
It can scratch topaz.

Diamond
The hardest known mineral, diamond can scratch all other substances.

6 7 8 9 10

Chapter 4 F ◆ 119

Math Skill Making and Interpreting Graphs

Focus Tell students that line graphs are useful for showing the relationship between two variables in a simple equation, such as $d = m/v$.

Teach Ask: **Which variable is on the *x*-axis?** *(Volume)* **Which variable is on the *y*-axis?** *(Mass)* **What are the plotted points?** *(Each point is a sample of pyrite.)* Help students understand that connecting the points gives a line that represents the density of pyrite.

Answers
1. 50 g, 10 cm³
2. 5 g/cm³
3. 100 g, 20 g
4. 5 g/cm³
5. The density of samples B and C is the same.
6. 200 g
7. No; density does not depend on size. Larger samples have more mass, but the ratio between mass and volume is constant.

Help Students Read   L1

Relating Text and Figures Have students read about mineral hardness while referring to Figure 5. Ask: **Why might diamonds be valuable as tools?** *(They can cut or scratch all other substances.)*

Differentiated Instruction

**English Learners/Beginning   L1
Comprehension: Modified Cloze**
Distribute a simplified paragraph about hardness and density, but leave some words blank. Here is an example: "The _____ of a mineral is found by scratching it with other minerals or objects. A mineral's _____ is a measure of the mass that is in a given volume." Model how to fill in the blank, using a sample sentence on the board.

Provide students with the correct answers as choices. **learning modality: verbal**

**English Learners/Intermediate   L2
Comprehension: Modified Cloze**
Distribute the same paragraph, but include some additional terms as incorrect answer choices. After students complete the paragraph, have them work together to write definitions for the answer choices that were not used. **learning modality: verbal**

Monitor Progress   L2

Skills Check Have each student make a table that lists each mineral property, a description of each property, and a description of any test for that property. Students can place their tables in their portfolios.

Portfolio

Address Misconceptions [L2]

Mineral Crystals

Focus Many students think that crystal faces must be present for a mineral to have a crystal structure. Have them compare a sample of a mineral with well-shaped crystals and a sample of a mineral in which crystals are not clearly visible. Explain that crystals might be visible under a microscope.

Teach Help students understand that it is the arrangement of atoms in a mineral that determines its crystal structure. Crystal faces are only an external manifestation of this structure. Ask: **Is a mineral sample that does not have smooth faces still a crystal?** *(Yes; it still has the same atomic structure.)* **Would this mineral sample still belong to one of the six crystal systems?** *(Yes)*

Apply Show students a sample of a mineral that does not look like a crystal, such as borax. Ask: **How do you know that this mineral has crystals?** *(All minerals have crystals.)* **How would you describe the crystals in this mineral?** *(They have a repeating, orderly arrangement of atoms.)* **learning modality: logical/mathematical**

Lab zone Build Inquiry [L1]

Mineral Cleavage

Materials 2 paper towels per student

Time 10 minutes

Focus Tell students that cleavage in minerals occurs because minerals are more likely to break along planes of weakness.

Teach Provide each student with two paper towels. Ask: **In which direction do the paper towels split, or tear?** *(Students will find that the towels tear easily in the direction of the perforations, a line of weakness.)* Relate this behavior to minerals' breaking along planes of weakness.

Apply Show students a book of muscovite mica. Samples of muscovite mica are called books because the crystals form stacks of flat sheets that resemble pages of a book. Slowly tear some sheets of the mineral from the book. Tell students that the mineral sheets are separated by planes of weakness in the mineral's structure. **learning modality: kinesthetic**

Lab zone Skills Activity

Classifying

1. Use your fingernail to try to scratch talc, calcite, and quartz. Record which minerals you were able to scratch.

2. Now try to scratch the minerals with a penny. Were your results different? Explain.

3. Were there any minerals you were unable to scratch with either your fingernail or the penny?

4. In order of increasing hardness, how would you classify the three minerals?

FIGURE 6
Properties of Minerals
All crystals of the same mineral have the same crystal structure. Each mineral also has other characteristic properties.
Interpreting Data *Which mineral has the lowest density?*

Magnetite
Crystal System: Cubic
Color: Black
Streak: Black
Luster: Metallic
Hardness: 6
Density (g/cm³): 5.2
Special Property: Magnetic

Quartz
Crystal System: Hexagonal
Color: Transparent, various colors
Streak: Colorless
Luster: Glassy
Hardness: 7
Density (g/cm³): 2.6
Special Property: Fractures like broken glass

Rutile
Crystal System: Tetragonal
Color: Black or reddish brown
Streak: Light brown
Luster: Metallic or gemlike
Hardness: 6–6.5
Density (g/cm³): 4.2–4.3
Special Property: Not easily melted

120 ● F

Lab zone Skills Activity

Skills Focus Classifying [L2]

Materials penny; samples of talc, calcite, and quartz

Time 10 minutes

Tips Pair students of differing ability levels for this activity.

Expected Outcome A fingernail scratches talc but not calcite or quartz. A penny scratches talc and calcite but not

quartz. Quartz, then, cannot be scratched by either a fingernail or a penny. Therefore, the minerals in order of increasing hardness are talc, calcite, and quartz.

Extend Have students test other materials in the classroom, including chalk, wood, plastics, and various metals. To finish, have students collaborate to develop a hardness scale for all materials tested. **learning modality: kinesthetic**

Crystal Systems The crystals of each mineral grow atom by atom to form that mineral's crystal structure. Geologists classify these structures into six groups based on the number and angle of the crystal faces. These groups are called crystal systems. For example, all halite crystals are cubic. Halite crystals have six square faces that meet at right angles, forming a perfect cube.

Sometimes, the crystal structure is obvious from the mineral's appearance. Crystals that grow in an open space can be almost perfectly formed. But crystals that grow in a tight space are often incompletely formed. In other minerals, the crystal structure is visible only under a microscope. A few minerals, such as opal, are considered minerals even though their particles are not arranged in a crystal structure. Figure 6 shows minerals that belong to each of the six crystal systems.

Cleavage and Fracture The way a mineral breaks apart can help to identify it. A mineral that splits easily along flat surfaces has the property called **cleavage.** Whether a mineral has cleavage depends on how the atoms in its crystals are arranged. The arrangement of atoms in the mineral causes it to break apart more easily in one direction than another. Look at the photo of mica in Figure 7. Mica separates easily in only one direction, forming flat sheets. Therefore, mica has cleavage. Feldspar is another common mineral that has cleavage.

When quartz fractures, the break looks like the surface of a seashell.

Cleavage

Mica cleaves into thin, flat sheets that are almost transparent.

Most minerals do not split apart evenly. Instead, they have a characteristic type of fracture. **Fracture** describes how a mineral looks when it breaks apart in an irregular way. Geologists use a variety of terms to describe fracture. For example, quartz has a shell-shaped fracture. When quartz breaks, it produces curved, shell-like surfaces that look like chipped glass. Pure metals, like copper and iron, have a hackly fracture—they form jagged points. Some soft minerals that crumble easily like clay have an earthy fracture. Minerals that form rough, irregular surfaces when broken have an uneven fracture.

Reading Checkpoint Compare the fracture of quartz to the fracture of a pure metal, such as iron.

FIGURE 7
Cleavage and Fracture
How a mineral breaks apart can help to identify it.
Applying Concepts *How would you test a mineral to determine whether it has cleavage or fracture?*

Go Online
active art

For: Crystal Systems activity
Visit: PHSchool.com
Web Code: cfp-1041

Sulfur
Crystal System: Orthorhombic
Color: Lemon yellow to yellowish brown
Streak: White
Luster: Greasy
Hardness: 2
Density (g/cm³): 2.0–2.1
Special Property: Melts easily

Azurite
Crystal System: Monoclinic
Color: Blue
Streak: Pale blue
Luster: Glassy to dull or earthy
Hardness: 3.5–4
Density (g/cm³): 3.8
Special Property: Reacts to acid

Microcline Feldspar
Crystal System: Triclinic
Color: Pink, white, red-brown, or green
Streak: Colorless
Luster: Glassy
Hardness: 6
Density (g/cm³): 2.6
Special Property: Cleaves well in two directions

F ◆ 121

Help Students Read L1

Compare and Contrast Have students compare and contrast the way minerals break apart. Ask: **If you saw smooth, flat surfaces on a piece of mineral, what could you conclude?** *(The mineral has cleavage.)* **If you saw irregular surfaces on a mineral, what could you conclude?** *(The mineral has fractures.)* **learning modality: visual**

Go Online
active art

For: Crystal Systems Activity
Visit: PHSchool.com
Web Code: cfp-1041
Students explore three-dimensional models of the six crystal systems.

Monitor Progress L2

Drawing Have students make drawings of the six crystal systems. Ask students to label each of their drawings. Students can save their drawings in their portfolios.

Portfolio

Answers
Figure 6 Sulfur
Figure 7 You would break apart the mineral.

Reading Checkpoint Quartz has a shell-shaped fracture, sometimes called conchoidal fracture. Pure metals have a hackly fracture.

Reviewing Key Concepts

1. a. A mineral is a naturally occurring, inorganic solid that has a crystal structure and definite chemical composition. **b.** It was not formed by organisms or from the remains of organisms. **c.** No; amber is not inorganic.

2. a. Color, streak, luster, density, hardness, crystal system, cleavage and fracture, and special properties **b.** Cleavage is weakness along flat surfaces through a mineral. Fracture is a tendency for some minerals to break in irregular ways. **c.** It will probably break apart with cleavage because the carbon atoms in graphite form sheets that could split apart easily in layers.

Reteach   L1

Have each student create a concept map that includes a mineral's definition and properties. Distribute large sheets of paper, and challenge students to include as much information as possible in their concept maps.

Performance Assessment   L2

Oral Presentation Play a game using information from the mineral-identification table in the back of the book. Choose a mystery mineral, and begin the game by mentioning a property of that mineral. Announce more properties one by one until someone identifies the mineral.

All in One Teaching Resources

- Section Summary: *Properties of Minerals*
- Review and Reinforce: *Properties of Minerals*
- Enrich: *Properties of Minerals*

FIGURE 8
Special Properties
The special properties of minerals include fluorescence, magnetism, radioactivity, and reaction to acids. Other minerals have useful optical or electrical properties.

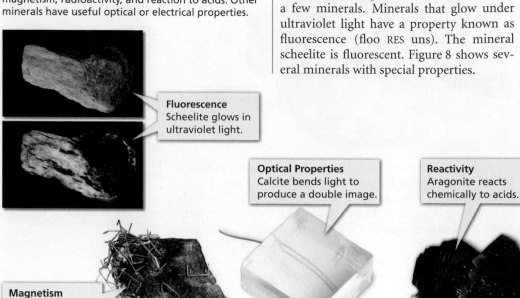

Fluorescence
Scheelite glows in ultraviolet light.

Optical Properties
Calcite bends light to produce a double image.

Reactivity
Aragonite reacts chemically to acids.

Magnetism
Magnetite attracts these iron staples.

Special Properties Some minerals can be identified by special physical properties. For example, magnetism occurs naturally in a few minerals. Minerals that glow under ultraviolet light have a property known as fluorescence (floo RES uns). The mineral scheelite is fluorescent. Figure 8 shows several minerals with special properties.

Section 1 Assessment

Target Reading Skill **Outlining** Use the information in your outline about the properties of minerals to help you answer the questions.

Reviewing Key Concepts

1. a. Defining Write a definition of "mineral" in your own words.
   b. Explaining What does it mean to say that a mineral is inorganic?
   c. Classifying Amber is a precious material used in jewelry. It forms when the resin of pine trees hardens into stone. Is amber a mineral? Explain.
2. a. Listing Name eight properties that can be used to identify minerals.
   b. Comparing and Contrasting What is the difference between fracture and cleavage?

c. Predicting Graphite is a mineral made up of carbon atoms that form thin sheets. But the sheets are only weakly held together. Predict whether graphite will break apart with fracture or cleavage. Explain.

Math Practice

3. Calculating Density The mineral platinum is an element that often occurs as a pure metal. If a sample of platinum has a mass of 430 g and a volume of 20 cm³, what is its density?

Math Practice

Math Skill Calculating density
Answer
3. 21.5 g/cm³
($430 \text{ g}/20 \text{ cm}^3 = 21.5 \text{ g/cm}^3$)

Lab zone Chapter Project

Keep Students on Track Have each student select a container for the crystal garden and make a sketch. Ask each student to select a crystal growth solution. Halite, Epsom salt, and alum are possibilities. Supervise students when they are using the solutions.

Finding the Density of Minerals

Problem

How can you compare the density of different minerals?

Skills Focus

measuring

Materials (per student)

- graduated cylinder, 100-mL
- 3 mineral samples: pyrite, quartz, and galena
- water
- balance

Procedure

1. Check to make sure the mineral samples are small enough to fit in the graduated cylinder.
2. Copy the data table into your notebook. Place the pyrite on the balance and record its mass in the data table.
3. Fill the cylinder with water to the 50-mL mark.
4. Carefully place the pyrite in the cylinder of water. Try not to spill any of the water.
5. Read the level of the water on the scale of the graduated cylinder. Record the level of the water with the pyrite in it.

Data Table			
	Pyrite	Quartz	Galena
Mass of Mineral (g)			
Volume of Water Without Mineral (mL)	50	50	50
Volume of Water With Mineral (mL)			
Volume of Water Displaced (mL)			
Volume of Water Displaced (cm³)			
Density (g/cm³)			

6. Calculate the volume of water displaced by the pyrite. To do this, subtract the volume of water without the pyrite from the volume of water with the pyrite. Record your answer.
7. Calculate the density of the pyrite by using this formula.

$$\text{Density} = \frac{\text{Mass of mineral}}{\text{Volume of water displaced by mineral}}$$

(Note: Density is expressed as g/cm³. One mL of water has a volume of 1 cm³.)

8. Remove the water and mineral from the cylinder.
9. Repeat Steps 2–8 for quartz and galena.

Analyze and Conclude

1. **Interpreting Data** Which mineral had the highest density? The lowest density?
2. **Measuring** How does finding the volume of the water that was displaced help you find the volume of the mineral itself?
3. **Drawing Conclusions** Does the shape of a mineral sample affect its density? Explain.
4. **Predicting** Would the procedure you used in this lab work for a substance that floats or one that dissolves in water?

Designing Experiments

Pyrite is sometimes called "fool's gold" because its color and appearance are similar to real gold. Design an experiment to determine if a sample that looks like gold is in fact real gold.

Analyze and Conclude

1. Galena, the highest; quartz, the lowest
2. The volume of water displaced equals the volume of the mineral itself.
3. No; shape or size does not affect density. The ratio of mass to volume is constant for any given mineral composition.
4. One that floats would not displace a volume of water equal to itself; one that dissolves would not displace any water.

Extend Inquiry

Designing an Experiment Advise students to consider properties of a mineral and how to test for them when designing their experiments.

Finding the Density of Minerals

Prepare for Inquiry

Key Concept

Each mineral has a characteristic density.

Skills Objectives

After this lab, students will be able to:
- measure the density of minerals
- draw conclusions about how knowing a mineral's density helps to identify it

 Prep Time 20 minutes
Class Time 40 minutes

Advance Planning

Collect an appropriate number of mineral samples. Make sure that each sample will fit into a graduated cylinder. Students may need calculators to determine the density of the samples.

All in One Teaching Resources
- Lab Worksheet: *Finding the Density of Minerals*

Guide Inquiry

Invitation

Ask: **What is density?** *(A measure of the mass in one unit volume of a substance)* Then have students relate that definition to the formula for density in step 7.

Introduce the Procedure

You may want to have students practice the procedure with a sample of known density. A piece of calcite has a density of about 2.71 g/cm³.

Troubleshooting the Experiment

- Emphasize that spilling any water when placing a sample in the graduated cylinder will cause the volume determination to be incorrect.
- Make sure that students know how to read volume from a graduated cylinder.

Expected Outcome

In students' data tables, values for *Volume of Water with Mineral and Volume of Water Displaced* will vary, depending on the sample sizes. Students' calculations of density should be close to these: galena, 7.4–7.6 g/cm³; pyrite, 5.0 g/cm³; quartz, 2.6 g/cm³.

Objectives

After this lesson, students will be able to

F.4.2.1 Explain how minerals form from magma and lava

F.4.2.2 Explain how minerals form from water solutions

Target Reading Skill ↻

Asking Questions Explain that changing a heading into a question helps students anticipate the ideas, facts, and events they are about to read.

Answers

Possible student questions and answers are these: **How do minerals form from magma?** (*They form when magma cools and crystals grow.*) **How do minerals form from solution?** (*They form when solutions evaporate or cool.*)

All in One Teaching Resources

• Transparency F37

Preteach

Build Background Knowledge ▪L2

Experience With Sugar Crystals

To help students understand how some crystals form, explain how cotton candy is made: Sugar is melted to a liquid and then spun into threads, which cool and crystallize back into sugar. Tell students that some minerals form in a similar way—minerals in rock melt to form magma, which is forced upward and then cools to form new mineral crystals.

Reading Focus

Key Concepts
• How do minerals form from magma and lava?
• How do minerals form from water solutions?

Key Terms
• geode • crystallization
• solution • vein

↻ Target Reading Skill

Asking Questions Before you read, preview the red headings. In a graphic organizer like the one below, ask a *how* or *what* question for each heading. As you read, write answers to your questions.

Formation of Minerals

Question	Answer
How do minerals form from magma?	

Amethyst geode ▼

124 ◆ F

Lab zone Discover **Activity**

How Does the Rate of Cooling Affect Crystals?

1. ☠ Put on your goggles. Use a plastic spoon to place a small amount of salol near one end of each of two microscope slides. You need just enough to form a spot 0.5 to 1.0 cm in diameter.

2. 🔥 🧤 Carefully hold one slide with tongs. Warm it gently over a lit candle until the salol is almost completely melted. **CAUTION:** *Move the slide in and out of the flame to avoid cracking the glass.*

3. Set the slide aside to cool slowly. While the first slide is cooling, hold the second slide with tongs and heat it as in Step 2.

4. Cool the second slide quickly by placing it on an ice cube. Carefully blow out the candle.

5. Observe the slides under a hand lens. Compare the appearance of the crystals that form on the two slides.

6. Wash your hands when you are finished.

Think It Over

Developing Hypotheses Which sample had larger crystals? If a mineral forms by rapid cooling, would you expect the crystals to be large or small?

On a rock-collecting field trip, you spot an egg-shaped rock about the size of a football. No, it's not a dinosaur egg—but what is it? You collect the rock and bring it to a geologic laboratory. There, you carefully split the rock open. The rock is hollow! Its inside surface sparkles with large, colorful amethyst crystals.

You have found a geode (JEE ohd). A **geode** is a rounded, hollow rock that is often lined with mineral crystals. Crystals form inside a geode when water containing dissolved minerals seeps into a crack or hollow in a rock. Slowly, crystallization occurs, lining the inside with large crystals that are often perfectly formed. **Crystallization** is the process by which atoms are arranged to form a material with a crystal structure. In general, minerals can form in two ways: by crystallization of magma and lava or by crystallization of materials dissolved in water.

Lab zone Discover **Activity**

Skills Focus Developing hypotheses ▪L3

Materials salol, plastic spoon, 2 microscope slides, tongs, candle, matches, ice cube, hand lens

Time 15 minutes

Tips CAUTION: Salol is phenyl salicylate, which is toxic if ingested. Tell students to

not touch the salol with their hands. Salol is combustible—handle with care.

Have students wear goggles. Caution them not to overheat the slide because it might break. Moving the slide from side to side over the flame will prevent overheating.

Expected Outcome The crystals on the two slides will be different sizes.

Think It Over The first sample, which cooled more slowly, should have larger crystals. Crystals that form by rapid cooling should be small.

Minerals From Magma and Lava

Many minerals form from magma and lava. **Minerals form as hot magma cools inside the crust, or as lava hardens on the surface. When these liquids cool to a solid state, they form crystals.** The size of the crystals depends on several factors. The rate at which the magma cools, the amount of gas the magma contains, and the chemical composition of the magma all affect crystal size.

When magma remains deep below the surface, it cools slowly over many thousands of years. Slow cooling leads to the formation of large crystals, like the amethyst crystals in a geode. If the crystals remain undisturbed while cooling, they grow by adding atoms according to a regular pattern.

Magma closer to the surface cools much faster than magma that hardens deep below ground. With more rapid cooling, there is no time for magma to form large crystals. Instead, small crystals form. If magma erupts to the surface and becomes lava, the lava will also cool quickly and form minerals with small crystals.

 Reading Checkpoint What size crystals form when magma cools rapidly?

Minerals From Solutions

Sometimes the elements and compounds that form minerals can be dissolved in water to form solutions. A **solution** is a mixture in which one substance is dissolved in another. **When elements and compounds that are dissolved in water leave a solution, crystallization occurs.** Minerals can form in this way underground and in bodies of water on Earth's surface.

FIGURE 9
Selenite Crystals
These huge selenite crystals in a cave in Mexico formed from the crystallization of minerals in a solution.

F ◆ 125

Lab zone Try This **Activity**

Crystal Hands

1. Put on your goggles.
2. ☠ Pour a solution of table salt into one shallow pan and a solution of Epsom salts into another shallow pan.
3. Put a large piece of black construction paper on a flat surface.
   Dip one hand in the table salt solution. Shake off the excess liquid and make a palm print on the paper. Repeat with the other hand and the Epsom salt solution, placing your new print next to the first one. Wash your hands after making your hand prints. **CAUTION:** *Do not do this activity if you have a cut on your hand.*
4. Let the prints dry overnight.

Observing Use a hand lens to compare the shape of the crystals. Which hand prints have more crystals?

Lab zone Try This **Activity**

Skills Focus Observing   L1

Materials table salt solution, Epsom salt solution, 2 shallow pans, large sheet of black construction paper

Time 10 minutes; then 1 day to dry

Tips When mixing the solutions, add table salt or Epsom salt to warm water until no more will dissolve. Stir frequently.

Expected Outcome The regions of crystal growth will have the shape of the student's palm print. Epsom salt crystals will be needle-shaped. Halite crystals will be cubic. Students probably will observe more Epsom salt crystals.

Extend Have students try the same exercise with sugar. **learning modality: kinesthetic**

Instruct

Minerals From Magma and Lava

Teach Key Concepts   L2

Crystal Size

Focus Ask: **How far can you walk in a short amount of time?** *(Not very far)* **How far can you walk in a long amount of time?** *(Much farther)* Tell students that atoms in magma or lava also can move farther when they have more time. With more time, atoms from a greater distance can move to a growing crystal, and the crystal can become large. With less time, a higher number of small crystals form because atoms don't have time to travel far.

Teach Ask: **Where would you expect molten rock to cool slowly and large crystals to form?** *(Deep beneath Earth's surface)* **Why?** *(The temperature is higher.)* **Where would you expect molten rock to cool quickly and small crystals to form?** *(On Earth's surface)* **Why?** *(The temperature is much lower.)*

Apply Tell students that volcanic glass contains no crystals. Ask them to hypothesize how fast it cooled. *(Very quickly)* **learning modality: logical/mathematical**

Independent Practice   L2

All in One Teaching Resources

- Guided Reading and Study Worksheet: *How Minerals Form*

🔘 **Student Edition on Audio CD**

Monitor Progress _____   L2

Skills Check Have students compare and contrast the formation of minerals from magma or lava and from water solutions.

Answer

 Reading Checkpoint Small crystals form.

Observing Granite and Rhyolite

Materials hand lens, samples of granite and rhyolite

Time 10 minutes

Focus Tell students that granite and rhyolite form from the same type of magma and have the same minerals.

Teach Invite students to examine the samples. Ask: **What can you infer about the conditions in which each formed?** *(Students should notice that granite is coarse-grained, whereas rhyolite is fine-grained. They should infer that granite formed from magma that cooled slowly; rhyolite formed from magma that cooled quickly.)*

Apply Ask students to infer where the granite and rhyolite formed. *(Beneath Earth's surface and on Earth's surface, respectively)*
learning modality: visual

Minerals From Solutions

Teach Key Concepts   `L2`
Recognizing Where Minerals Form

Focus Remind students that minerals can form from lava and magma or from solutions.

Teach Direct students' attention to Figure 10. Ask: **Where do large mineral crystals form from magma?** *(In magma chambers and conduits beneath Earth's surface)* **In which environment might vein minerals form?** *(Near magma bodies that produce hydrothermal solutions)* **In which type of environment do minerals crystallize from evaporating water?** *(Often in warm, shallow water in hot, arid regions)*

Apply Ask: **How could understanding how vein minerals form help geologists find valuable mineral deposits?** *(Geologists could explore in regions where hydrothermal solutions are likely to have existed in the past.)*
learning modality: visual

All in One Teaching Resources

• Transparency F38

Minerals formed
by evaporation

A gypsum "rose" forms by
evaporation of a mineral solution.

Water containing
dissolved minerals

Minerals Formed by Evaporation Some minerals form when solutions evaporate. If you stir salt crystals into a beaker of water, the salt dissolves, forming a solution. But if you allow the water in the solution to evaporate, it will leave salt crystals on the bottom of the beaker. In a similar way, deposits of the mineral halite formed over millions of years when ancient seas slowly evaporated. In the United States, such halite deposits are found in the Midwest, the Southwest, and along the Gulf Coast. Other useful minerals that can form by evaporation include gypsum and calcite.

Minerals From Hot Water Solutions Deep underground, magma can heat water to a high temperature. Sometimes, the elements and compounds that form a mineral dissolve in this hot water. When the water solution begins to cool, the elements and compounds leave the solution and crystallize as minerals. The silver in Figure 10 was deposited from a hot water solution.

Pure metals that crystallize from hot water solutions underground often form veins. A **vein** is a narrow channel or slab of a mineral that is different from the surrounding rock. Solutions of hot water and metals often flow through cracks within the rock. Then the metals crystallize into veins that resemble the streaks of fudge in vanilla fudge ice cream.

 Reading Checkpoint   What is a vein?

Go Online
PHSchool.com

For: More on mineral formation
Visit: PHSchool.com
Web Code: cfd-1042

Differentiated Instruction

Gifted and Talented   `L3`
Interpreting Data and Communicating
Have students research the areas of the United States beneath which evaporative mineral deposits occur. Students then should make a map to present to the class.
learning modality: visual

Special Needs   `L1`
Interpreting Diagrams and Communicating Refer students to Figure 10. Tell them to use the figure as a guide and make enlarged individual drawings of the different environments in which minerals form. Students should label the sketches and include short captions describing the processes that occur. **learning modality: visual**

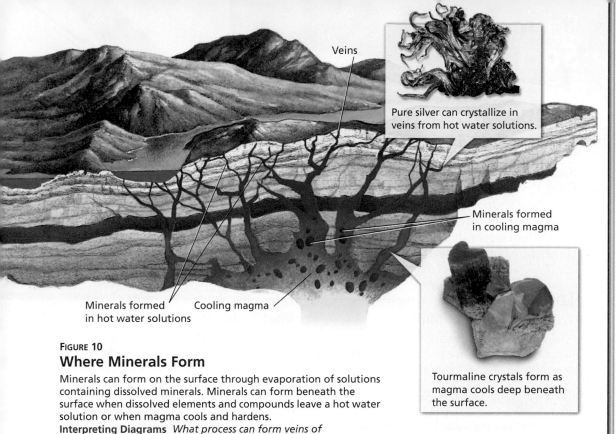

Veins

Pure silver can crystallize in veins from hot water solutions.

Minerals formed in cooling magma

Minerals formed in hot water solutions

Cooling magma

Tourmaline crystals form as magma cools deep beneath the surface.

FIGURE 10
Where Minerals Form
Minerals can form on the surface through evaporation of solutions containing dissolved minerals. Minerals can form beneath the surface when dissolved elements and compounds leave a hot water solution or when magma cools and hardens.
Interpreting Diagrams *What process can form veins of underground minerals?*

Section 2 Assessment

Target Reading Skill Asking Questions Use your chart to explain two ways in which minerals can form on Earth's surface.

Reviewing Key Concepts
1. **a. Defining** What is crystallization?
   b. Relating Cause and Effect What factors affect the size of the crystals that form as magma cools?
   c. Predicting Under what conditions will cooling magma produce minerals with large crystals?
2. **a. Defining** What is a solution?
   b. Explaining What are two ways in which minerals can form from a solution?
   c. Relating Cause and Effect Describe the process by which a deposit of rock salt, or halite, could form from a solution.

Writing in Science
Dialogue Suppose that you are a scientist exploring a cave. The light on your helmet suddenly reveals a wall covered with large crystals. Scientists on the surface ask you about your observations. Write a dialogue made up of their questions and your replies. Include the different ways in which the minerals you see might have formed.

Chapter 4 F ◆ 127

Lab zone Chapter **Project**

Keep Students on Track Make sure that students record daily observations about how their crystal gardens grow and that they sketch the different types of crystals. Ask students to compare the shapes and growth rates of the crystals grown from the various solutions. If crystals do not grow, add more of the correct solution.

Writing in Science

Writing Skill Explanation
Scoring Rubric
4 includes three or more relevant questions and replies and a hypothesis; dialogue is lively and realistic
3 includes all criteria
2 includes one or more questions and replies but no hypothesis
1 includes a general description only

Monitor Progress _____ L2
Answers
Figure 10 Solutions of hot water and metals flowing through cracks within the rock and then crystallizing

Reading Checkpoint A narrow channel or slab of a mineral that is different from the surrounding rock.

Assess

Reviewing Key Concepts
1. a. The process by which atoms are arranged to form a material with a crystal structure **b.** Rate at which magma cools, amount of gas the magma contains, and the chemical composition of the magma **c.** Slow cooling beneath Earth's surface
2. a. A mixture in which one substance dissolves in another **b.** Minerals can form when solutions containing dissolved minerals evaporate on Earth's surface and when crystallization occurs in hot water solutions containing metals deep underground. **c.** Evaporation of ocean water caused the concentration of dissolved salt to increase until some salt crystallized.

Reteach L1
Write these two headings on the board: *Minerals From Magma or Lava* and *Minerals From Solutions.* Work as a class to list as many examples of each as possible.

Performance Assessment L2
Skills Check Have each student make a concept map titled *The Formation of Minerals.* The map should include the two general ways in which minerals form and then branch out into specific processes and details.

All in One Teaching Resources
• Section Summary: *How Minerals Form*
• Review and Reinforce: *How Minerals Form*
• Enrich: *How Minerals Form*

F ● 127

Science and Society

Who Owns the Ocean's Minerals?

Key Concept
The ocean floor contains much mineral wealth. Nations must decide how this wealth will be divided.

Build Background Knowledge

Recalling How Ocean Minerals Form
Help students recall that minerals often form from solutions, both hot and cold. Ask: **How do minerals form from water solutions?** *(Minerals precipitate if water contains too much dissolved material, if water evaporates, or if water temperature changes.)* **Is ocean water a solution?** *(Yes; ocean water contains dissolved material.)* **Where could ocean water be heated to high temperatures?** *(Near mid-ocean ridges where submarine volcanism occurs)* Ask a student volunteer to read the captions of the insets on these pages. Explain to students that along the continental shelf, the water is shallow and the ocean floor slopes gently. When the continental slope is reached, the ocean floor begins to slope downward more steeply. Abyssal plains are the deep, relatively flat portions of the ocean floor.

Introduce the Debate
Show students a world map. Point out that many countries do not have access to oceans. Also make students aware that some nations are much wealthier than other nations are. Ask: **Which countries could most easily extract minerals from the ocean floor in the near future?** *(Wealthy countries that can afford to invest in deep ocean mining and countries that have easy access to the oceans)*

Science and Society

Who Owns the Ocean's Minerals?

Rich mineral deposits lie on and just beneath the ocean floor. Coastal nations have the right to mine deposits near their shores. Today, they are mining minerals from the continental shelf. But mineral deposits on the ocean floor beyond are open for all nations. Who owns these valuable underwater minerals?

The Issues

Who Can Afford to Mine?
Mining the ocean floor will cost a huge amount of money. New technologies must be developed to obtain mineral deposits from the ocean floor. Only wealthy industrial nations will be able to afford the costs. Industrial nations that have spent money on mining think that they should keep the profits. But developing nations that lack money and technology and landlocked nations disagree.

What Rights Do Nations Have?
By 2003, 157 nations had signed the Law of the Sea treaty. Among other things, this treaty stated that ocean mineral deposits are the common property of all people. It also stated that mining profits must be shared among all nations. Some people think that, because of the treaty, wealthy nations should share their technology and any profits they get from mining the ocean floor.

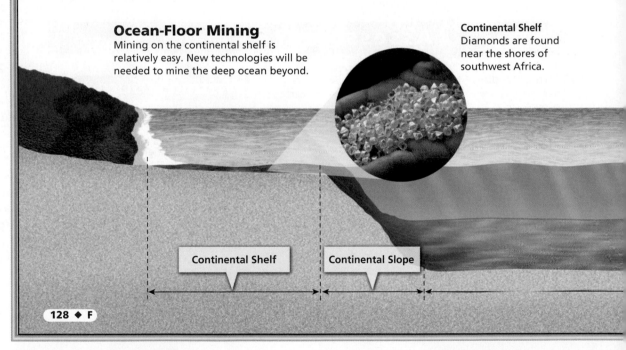

Ocean-Floor Mining
Mining on the continental shelf is relatively easy. New technologies will be needed to mine the deep ocean beyond.

Continental Shelf
Diamonds are found near the shores of southwest Africa.

Continental Shelf

Continental Slope

Facilitate the Debate
- Have students read the feature and answer the What Would You Do questions individually as a homework assignment. The next day, organize the class into small groups for discussion. Have students consider these questions: Who should own the minerals on the ocean floor? Do the people of wealthy nations have any obligation to share profits from mining of these minerals with people from developing nations? Do private companies from any nation have an obligation to share the profits with all the nations of the world?

- Organize the class into two groups. Arbitrarily assign one group to argue that wealthy nations and companies have no obligation to share profits from the mining of these minerals. Assign the other group to argue that the wealth should be shared equally among nations. Alternately call on students from each group to state the group's position or refute an idea from someone in the other group.

Remotely operated vehicles like this one can be used to search the ocean floor for minerals.

How Can the Wealth Be Shared?

What can nations do to prevent conflict over mining the ocean floor? They might arrange a compromise. Perhaps wealthy nations should contribute part of their profits to help developing or landlocked nations. Developing nations could pool their money for ocean-floor mining. Whatever nations decide, some regulations for ocean-floor mining are necessary. In the future, these resources will be important to everyone.

What Would You Do?

1. Identify the Problem
Summarize the controversy about ocean mineral rights.

2. Analyze the Options
Research this topic at the library or on the Internet. Then compare the concerns of wealthy nations with those of developing nations. How could you reassure developing nations that they will not be left out?

3. Find a Solution
Look at a map of the world. Who should share the mineral profits from the Pacific Ocean? From the Atlantic Ocean? Write one or two paragraphs stating your opinion. Support your ideas with facts.

For: More on who owns the ocean's minerals
Visit: PHSchool.com
Web Code: cfh-1040

Abyssal Plain
Minerals called manganese nodules form on the deep ocean floor. The metals cobalt, iron, nickel, and copper are also found here.

Mid-Ocean Ridge
Rich mineral deposits form from hot water solutions near mid-ocean ridges. Mining for gold, silver, copper, and other minerals might be possible here.

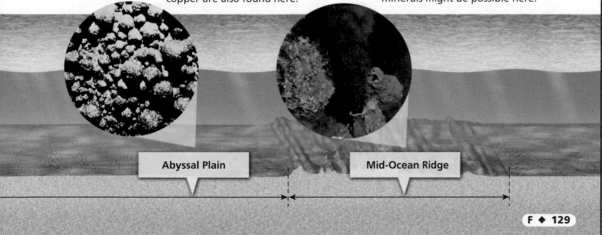

Abyssal Plain

Mid-Ocean Ridge

What Would You Do?
1. The controversy is how or whether mineral wealth from the deep oceans should be shared among wealthy and landlocked or developing countries.
2. Concerns of wealthy nations might include covering the costs of developing technology to mine at such depths. Developing nations might be concerned that they would not share the wealth of international waters. Students might suggest that developing nations pool resources to invest in mining projects and share in the profits.
3. Encourage students to provide justification for their opinions. (*Possible opinion: Countries should share in the profits in amounts proportional to their distance from one or both oceans.*)

 **For:** More on who owns the ocean's minerals
Visit: PHSchool.com
Web Code: cfh-1040

Students can research this issue online.

Extend
Encourage interested students to write to the U.S. State Department and to the U.S. Ambassador to the United Nations to learn the current U.S. position on the ownership and use of the ocean's mineral resources. A first step might be to find these agencies' Web pages on the Internet. The inquiry then could be made via e-mail, which might expedite a reply.

Background

Facts and Figures Manganese nodules are one of the most important deep-ocean metallic resources. They cover large parts of the deep ocean floor. The nodules generally are a few centimeters in diameter and consist of concentric layers of precipitated manganese-rich minerals. Sharks' teeth or sand grains often occur at the center of the nodules and probably provide a nucleus upon which mineral growth begins.

At mid-ocean ridges, seawater circulates through fractures in the ocean crust. The water is heated by the hot rock. Water and rock contribute metals to the solution through chemical reactions. As the solution reemerges into cool ocean water, ore minerals precipitate and cause the water to appear black. Such hydrothermal vents are called black smokers.

Objectives

After this lesson, students will be able to
F.4.3.1 Describe how minerals are used
F.4.3.2 Explain how ores are processed to obtain metals

Target Reading Skill

Using Prior Knowledge Explain that using prior knowledge helps students connect what they already know to what they are about to read.

Answers

Possible answers include the following:

What you know: 1. The gems used in jewelry are minerals. **2.** Metals come from Earth.

What you learned: 1. Minerals are also the source of metals and other useful materials, like quartz and gypsum. **2.** Most metals come from ores, which are mined and smelted before the metals can be used.

All in One Teaching Resources

• Transparency F39

Preteach

Build Background Knowledge   L1

Experience With Mineral Resources
Ask: **Which things that you use every day are made from minerals?** *(A typical answer may mention such things as bicycles, autos, and coins.)* **What process could use minerals mined from the ground to produce steel?** *(Some students might describe a steel mill, in which ore is smelted in furnaces.)*

Reading Focus

Key Concepts
• How are minerals used?
• How are ores processed to obtain metals?

Key Terms
• gemstone
• ore
• smelting
• alloy

Target Reading Skill

Using Prior Knowledge Before you read, look at the section headings and visuals to see what this section is about. Then write what you know about mineral resources in a graphic organizer like the one below. As you read, write what you learn.

What You Know
1. The gems used in jewelry are minerals.
2.

What You Learned
1.
2.

Lab zone Discover **Activity**

How Are Minerals Processed Before They Are Used?

1. Examine a piece of the mineral bauxite carefully. Use your knowledge of the properties of minerals to describe it.
2. Examine an aluminum can. (The metal aluminum comes from bauxite.) Compare the properties of the aluminum can with the properties of bauxite.
3. Examine a piece of the mineral graphite and describe its properties.
4. Examine the lead in a pencil. (Pencil lead is made from graphite.) Compare the properties of the pencil lead with the properties of graphite.

Think It Over
Posing Questions How does each mineral compare to the object made from it? To understand how bauxite and graphite are made into useful materials, what questions would you need to answer?

More than a thousand years ago, the Hopewell people lived in the Ohio River valley. These ancient Native Americans are famous for the mysterious earthen mounds they built near the river. There these people left beautiful objects made from minerals. Some of these objects are tools chipped from flint (a variety of quartz). Others are animals made from thin sheets of copper, like the fish in Figure 11.

To obtain these minerals, the Hopewell people traded with peoples across North America. The copper, for example, came from near Lake Superior. There, copper could be found as a pure metal. Because pure copper is soft, it was easy to shape into ornaments or weapons.

FIGURE 11
Hopewell Fish
The ancient Hopewell people used a thin sheet of copper to make this fish.

Lab zone Discover **Activity**

Skills Focus Posing questions

Materials samples of bauxite and graphite, aluminum can, pencil

Time 10 minutes

Tips Place samples of bauxite and graphite and the aluminum can on a table in a central location. Have students make notes of their observations.

L1 **Think It Over** Bauxite is often earthy or claylike. It appears very different from aluminum metal. Graphite is a soft, black, slippery mineral. Its character is mostly preserved in pencil lead. One would need to answer questions like these: How can pure aluminum be separated from bauxite? How is graphite mixed with clay to make pencil lead?

The Uses of Minerals

Like the Hopewell people, modern civilizations use many minerals. You are surrounded by materials that come from minerals, such as the metal body and window glass of a car. **Minerals are the source of gemstones, metals, and a variety of materials used to make many products.** How many products that are made from minerals can you name? You might be surprised at how important minerals are in everyday life.

Gemstones Beautiful gemstones such as rubies and sapphires have captured the imagination of people throughout the ages. Usually, a **gemstone** is a hard, colorful mineral that has a brilliant or glassy luster. People value gemstones for their color, luster, and durability, and for the fact that they are rare. Once a gemstone is cut and polished, it is called a gem. Gems are used mainly for jewelry and decoration. They are also used for mechanical parts and for grinding and polishing.

Metals Some minerals are the sources of metals such as aluminum, iron, copper, or silver. Metals are generally not as hard as gemstones. But metals are useful because they can be stretched into wire, flattened into sheets, and hammered or molded without breaking. Metal tools and machinery, the metal filament in a light bulb, aluminum foil, and the steel beams used to frame office buildings all began as minerals inside Earth's crust.

Other Useful Minerals There are many other useful minerals besides metals and gems. People use materials from these minerals in foods, medicines, fertilizers, and building materials. The very soft mineral talc is ground up to make talcum powder. Clear crystals of the mineral calcite are used in optical instruments such as microscopes. Quartz, a mineral found in sand, is used in making glass as well as in electronic equipment and watches. Gypsum, a soft, white mineral, is used to make wallboard, cement, and stucco.

 Reading Checkpoint How do people use talc and calcite?

FIGURE 12
Gems
Precious gems like the diamonds and large blue sapphires on this necklace are among the most valuable minerals.
Observing How would you describe the luster of these gems?

Minerals

Video Preview
▶ Video Field Trip
Video Assessment

Chapter 4 F ◆ 131

The Uses of Minerals

Teach Key Concepts L2
Mineral Resources

Focus Challenge students to identify items that are not made from minerals or rocks. *(The only items that qualify are those made from plant or animal material.)*

Teach Write on the board: *Gemstones, Metals From Ore, Other Uses of Minerals.* Ask the class for examples of each.

Apply Ask: **How did the use of minerals affect the development of society?** *(Society often advanced as new ways to use mineral resources were discovered, for example, the rush for gold led to the founding of towns and cities.)* **learning modality: logical/mathematical**

Independent Practice L2

 All in One Teaching Resources
• Guided Reading and Study Worksheet: *Using Mineral Resources*

💿 **Student Edition on Audio CD**

Video Field Trip

Minerals

Show the Video Field Trip to let students experience finding jade and gold. Discussion question: **How did the Maya use jade?** *(To inlay their teeth, make burial masks for their kings, and to make treasured objects)*

Monitor Progress _____ L2

Skills Check Have each student make a concept map of the uses of minerals.

Answers
Figure 12 Diamond has a brilliant luster; sapphire often has a glassy luster.

 Reading Checkpoint Talc is used for talcum powder; calcite is used in optical instruments.

Differentiated Instruction

Less Proficient Readers L1
Communicating Have students use sketches, photographs, and short captions to create a visual display about uses of minerals. Tell students to draw ideas from the headings and illustrations in the chapter. **learning modality: visual**

Gifted and Talented L3
Interpreting Data and Communicating Challenge students to investigate synthetic gem-quality diamonds: how they are made, their quality, their cost, and the effect they might have on the diamond market. Ask students to prepare a consumer report about the subject. **learning modality: visual**

Producing Metals From Minerals

Teach Key Concepts L2

Prospecting, Mining, and Processing

Focus Ask: **What steps must occur so that pure metals can be available to society?** *(Ores must be found, mined, and processed to extract the metals.)*

Teach Work together as a class to create a sequence-of-events concept map that includes the processes of prospecting for, mining, and processing ore. When the sequence map is complete, add explanation and detail to each step. Have students copy the completed map in their journals.

Apply Give students this fictional scenario: A shortage of iron has developed in the United States. As geologists, mining engineers, and chemists, work together as a class to develop a plan to increase domestic supplies. *(One plan is to locate, mine, and process new iron ore deposits; some students may suggest mining garbage dumps and recycling the steel.)* **learning modality: visual**

Lab zone Teacher Demo

Types of Mines L1

Materials photographs of strip mines, open pit mines, and shaft mines

Time 10 minutes

Focus To help students understand the different types of mining, have them recall eating fudge-ribbon ice cream. One can scrape a ribbon of fudge off the surface (strip mining), dig a hole to reach a region that has a concentration of fudge (open pit mining), or follow a sloping ribbon (shaft mining).

Teach Show students the photographs of examples of mines. Work together as a class to classify each mine as strip, open pit, or shaft.

Apply Ask: **What would be the best way to mine a large copper deposit that extends several hundred meters beneath the surface?** *(Open pit)* **A shallow layer of coal?** *(Strip)* **A rich but narrow gold vein?** *(Shaft)* **learning modality: visual**

Producing Metals From Minerals

How is a mineral containing metal made into a finished product? **To produce metal from a mineral, a rock containing the mineral must be located through prospecting and mined, or removed from the ground. Then the rock must be processed to extract the metal.** Look at the Tech & Design in History timeline to see how the technology of producing metals has developed through the ages.

A rock that contains a metal or other useful mineral that can be mined and sold at a profit is called an **ore.** Unlike the copper used by the Hopewell people, most metals do not occur in a pure form. A metal usually occurs as a mineral that is a combination of that metal and other elements. Much of the world's copper, for example, comes from ores containing the mineral chalcopyrite (kal koh PY ryt). In addition to copper, chalcopyrite contains iron and sulfur.

• Tech & Design in History •

Advances in Metal Technology
For thousands of years, people have been inventing and improving methods for smelting metals and making alloys.

4000 B.C. Copper
The island of Cyprus was one of the first places where copper was mined and smelted. In fact, the name of the island provided the name of the metal. In Latin, *aes cyprium* meant "metal of Cyprus." It was later shortened to *cuprum*, meaning "copper." The sculpted figure is carrying a large piece of smelted copper.

1500 B.C. Iron
The Hittites learned to mine and smelt iron ore. Because iron is stronger than copper or bronze, its use spread rapidly. Tools and weapons could be made of iron. This iron dagger was made in Austria several hundred years after the Hittites' discovery.

3500 B.C. Bronze
Metalworkers in Sumer, a city between the Tigris and Euphrates rivers, made an alloy of tin and copper to produce a harder metal—bronze. Bronze was poured into molds to form statues, weapons, or vessels for food and drink.

4000 B.C.	2500 B.C.	1000 B.C.

Prospecting A prospector is anyone who searches, or prospects, for an ore deposit. Geologists prospect for ores by observing rocks on the land surface and by studying maps of rocks beneath the surface. Geologists can often map the size and shape of an ore deposit by making careful measurements of Earth's magnetic field over the deposit. This works well for minerals that contain magnetic elements such as iron and nickel.

Mining The geologist's map of an ore deposit helps miners decide how to remove the ore from the ground. There are three types of mines: strip mines, open pit mines, and shaft mines. In strip mining, earthmoving equipment scrapes away soil to expose ore. In open pit mining, miners use giant earthmoving equipment to dig a tremendous pit and remove ore deposits. For ore deposits that occur in veins, miners dig shaft mines. Shaft mines often have a network of tunnels that extend deep into the ground, following the veins of ore.

A.D. 500 Early Steel-Making
Sri Lankans made steel in outdoor furnaces. Steady winds blowing over the top of the furnace's front wall created the high temperatures needed to make steel. Because their steel was so much harder than iron, the Sri Lankans were able to trade it throughout the Indian Ocean region.

A.D. 1860s Modern Steel-Making
Steel-making techniques invented by Henry Bessemer and William Siemens made it possible to produce steel cheaply on a large scale. Siemens' invention, the open-hearth furnace, is still widely used, although more modern methods account for most steel production today.

A.D. 1960s Space-Age Alloys
Scientists working on the space program have developed light and strong alloys for use in products ranging from bicycles to soda cans. For example, a new alloy of nickel and titanium can "remember" its shape. It is used for eyeglasses that return to their original shape after being bent.

A.D. 500

A.D. 2000

Chapter 4 F ◆ 133

Use Visuals: Figure 13 L2

Smelting Iron Ore

Focus Tell students that the chemical formula of hematite is Fe_2O_3. Ask: **What do the chemical symbols in this formula stand for?** (*Fe is iron, and O is oxygen.*)

Teach Ask: **What is the purpose of smelting?** (*To separate the iron from the oxygen in the iron ore*) **What is added to accomplish this task?** (*Coke and limestone*) **Where does the oxygen go?** (*It goes into the carbon dioxide gas.*)

Apply Ask students to name items that are made of iron produced through smelting. (*Possible answers: Skillets made of cast iron, knives made of stainless steel*) **learning modality: visual**

 **Teaching Resources**

• Transparency F40

Lab zone Teacher Demo

Smelting Copper Oxide L3

Materials black copper oxide, powdered charcoal, test tube, test tube holder, Bunsen burner, jar, water

Time 15 minutes

Focus Tell students that smelting is not used only for iron ore. Many different metals can be extracted from ore by use of various smelting procedures.

Teach Demonstrate how to extract copper from copper oxide. First, mix copper oxide with bits of charcoal at the bottom of a test tube. Then, wearing goggles and holding the test tube with a test tube holder, heat the mixture over a Bunsen burner. Finally, pour the heated mixture into a jar of cold water. Students should note that pieces of shiny orange copper fall to the bottom of the jar and that the charcoal floats. Explain that the heating of the mixture freed the copper from the oxygen in the copper oxide.

Apply Ask students to explain how this demonstration is similar to smelting iron ore. (*Separating oxygen from copper oxide is part of the process used to refine copper; separating oxygen from iron is part of the process of refining iron ore.*) **learning modality: visual**

Smelting Ores must be processed before the metals they contain can be used. In the process of **smelting,** an ore is mixed with other substances and then melted to separate the useful metal from other elements the ore contains. Look at Figure 13 to see how smelting separates iron metal from hematite, a common form of iron ore.

❶ Iron ore is crushed and mixed with crushed limestone and coke (baked coal), which is rich in carbon.

❷ The mixture is placed in a blast furnace, where extremely hot air is blown through, making the coke burn easily.

❸ As the coke burns, chemical changes in the mixture produce carbon dioxide gas and molten iron.

❹ The dense, molten iron sinks to the bottom of the furnace. Impurities left in the ore combine with the limestone to create slag.

❺ The slag and molten iron are poured off through taps.

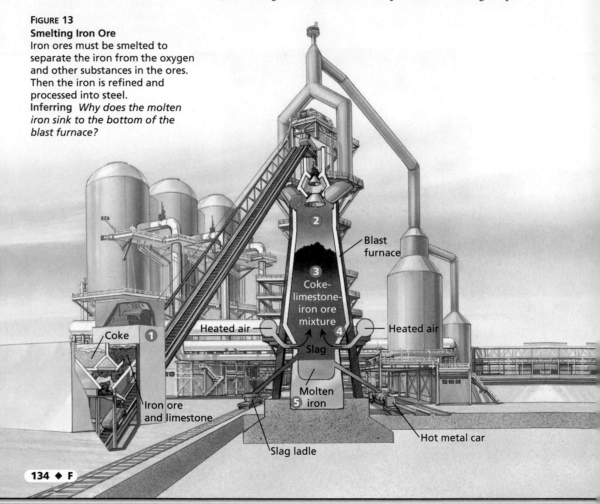

FIGURE 13
Smelting Iron Ore
Iron ores must be smelted to separate the iron from the oxygen and other substances in the ores. Then the iron is refined and processed into steel.
Inferring *Why does the molten iron sink to the bottom of the blast furnace?*

134 ◆ F

Further Processing After smelting, additional processing is needed to remove impurities from the metal. After the iron is purified, a small amount of carbon may be added to it. The result is steel, which is harder and stronger than iron. Steel is an **alloy**, a solid mixture of two or more elements, at least one of which is a metal. To be considered an alloy, the mixture must have the characteristic properties of a metal.

After adding carbon to iron, steelmakers may add other elements to create alloys with specific properties. For stronger steel, the metal manganese is added. For rust-resistant steel, the metals chromium and nickel are added. Figure 14 shows how rust-resistant stainless steel was used in the construction of one of America's most famous monuments.

 Reading Checkpoint What is an alloy?

FIGURE 14
The Gateway Arch
The Gateway Arch in St. Louis, Missouri, is covered in stainless steel.

Section 3 Assessment

Target Reading Skill **Using Prior Knowledge** Review your graphic organizer and revise it based on what you just learned in the section.

Reviewing Key Concepts

1. **a. Defining** What are gemstones? Why are they valuable?
   b. Listing What properties of metals make them useful to humans?
   c. Problem Solving Suppose that you are designing a machine with many small, moving parts that will need to run constantly. Would you make the parts from metal or gemstone? Explain your answer.

2. **a. Identifying** What is an ore?
   b. Summarizing Explain the steps that must take place before an ore can be made into a useful product.
   c. Inferring Which material formed during smelting is denser—molten metal or slag? How can you tell?

Lab zone At-Home Activity

Rust Protection You can demonstrate to your family how rust damages objects that contain iron. Obtain three iron nails. Coat one of the nails with petroleum jelly and coat the second nail with clear nail polish. Do not put anything on the third nail. Place all the nails in a glass of water with a little vinegar. (The vinegar speeds up the rusting process.) Allow the nails to stand in the glass overnight. Which nails show signs of rusting? Explain these results to your family.

Chapter 4 F ◆ 135

Go Online
SciLINKS NSTA
For: Links on mining minerals
Visit: www.SciLinks.org
Web Code: scn-1043

Download a worksheet that will guide students' review of mining minerals.

Monitor Progress ____ L2

Answers
Figure 13 Because it is so dense

Reading Checkpoint A solid mixture of two or more elements, at least one of which is a metal

Assess

Reviewing Key Concepts

1. **a.** Gemstones are hard, colorful minerals that have a brilliant or glassy luster. **b.** Some are soft, malleable, and good conductors; others are hard and durable; some are lightweight. **c.** Answers may vary. It would be difficult to fashion gemstones into machine parts, but parts made from gemstones would last longer because gems such as diamond, ruby, and topaz are harder than metals.
2. **a.** Ore is rock that contains a metal or other useful material that can be mined and sold at a profit. **b.** It must be mined and processed to extract the pure metal. **c.** Molten metal; it sinks to the bottom of the furnace.

Reteach L1

Have each student make a table that lists the minerals studied in this section in the left column and their uses in the right column.

Performance Assessment L2

Skills Check Have each student make a flowchart that describes the formation of an ore and the procedures necessary to find, mine, and process the ore.

All in One Teaching Resources

- Section Summary: *Using Mineral Resources*
- Review and Reinforce: *Using Mineral Resources*
- Enrich: *Using Mineral Resources*

Lab zone At-Home Activity

Rust Protection L2 Family members will notice that the uncoated nail shows signs of rusting after a night in the water but the coated nails do not. Remind students that stainless steel is made so that it does not readily rust. It is an alloy that includes iron, chromium, and nickel.

A Mouthful of Minerals

Prepare for Inquiry

Key Concept
Toothpaste contains various minerals that polish and clean teeth. Some toothpastes are more effective than are others.

Skills Objectives
After this lab, students will be able to
- observe the characteristics of different toothpastes as cleaning agents
- control variables as they conduct an experiment to test the effectiveness of different toothpastes
- draw conclusions as to which toothpaste cleaned most effectively

 Prep Time 25 minutes
Class Time 40 minutes

Advance Planning
Small, unglazed, white porcelain tiles can be obtained from the local hardware store. Stain the tiles by coloring three small areas of the unglazed sides of the tiles with a blue permanent marker.
- Local dentists might be able to supply at least some of the pastes and brushes. Make sure that at least one of the pastes tested contains the mineral sodium bicarbonate (baking soda). Do *not* use whitening toothpaste containing hydrogen peroxide if you plan to have students try the Design Your Own Experiment.

Safety
Remind students not to taste or ingest any of the toothpastes. Review Safety Guidelines in Appendix A.

Alternative Materials
In place of the unglazed ceramic tiles, the shells of hardboiled eggs can be used.

All in One Teaching Resources
- Lab Worksheet: *A Mouthful of Minerals*

Guide Inquiry

Invitation
Survey students as to the type or brand of toothpaste each uses. Tally the results on the board. Ask: **Why do you use that particular type or brand?** (*Most students probably use a particular toothpaste because of its taste or because of advertising claims.*) Ask: **Do you think all toothpaste is equally effective in cleaning teeth?** (*Answers will vary, but most students should state that different kinds and brands of toothpaste are probably not equally effective at cleaning teeth.*)

Introduce the Procedure
Demonstrate how much toothpaste should be used in each trial. Only a pea-sized amount is necessary. Remind students not to ingest any of the toothpaste they will be testing and that swallowing too much toothpaste while brushing can be harmful.

Troubleshooting the Experiment
- Stress the importance of completely cleaning the toothbrush before testing a new toothpaste.
- Explain to students that they must completely rinse the toothpaste off of the tile before they compare the effectiveness of the pastes. Residual paste can cause the tiles to appear "cleaner" than they actually are.

A Mouthful Of Minerals

Problem
What effect do the minerals in toothpaste have on the toothpaste's ability to clean?

Skills Focus
observing, controlling variables, drawing conclusions

Materials
- samples of 3 different types of toothpaste
- worn-out toothbrushes
- tap water
- a ceramic tile stained on the unglazed side with a felt-tip marker or pen

Procedure

1. Copy the data table into your notebook.
2. Your teacher will give you samples of toothpaste, a list of the mineral or minerals in each type of toothpaste, a toothbrush, and a ceramic tile.
3. In your data table, record the substances found in each toothpaste sample. Common minerals in toothpaste include mica, calcite, and quartz (silica). Toothpaste also may include compounds such as sodium bicarbonate (baking soda), sodium fluoride, aluminum or calcium phosphates, and titanium dioxide.
4. For each toothpaste sample, predict how effective you think it will be in removing the stain from the tile. Record your predictions in the data table.
5. Put a pea-sized amount of the first toothpaste onto a toothbrush. **CAUTION:** *Do not ingest any of the toothpaste.*
6. Brush one of the stain marks on the tile 50 times. As you brush, try to use the same amount of force for each stroke.
7. Using tap water, rinse the tile to remove all of the paste. Then rinse the toothpaste out of the toothbrush.
8. Repeat Steps 5–7 for the other toothpaste samples, using a different stain mark for each test. Be sure to brush with the same amount of force and for the same number of times.
9. Compare how well the different toothpastes cleaned the stains. Record your observations in the data table.

Analyze and Conclude

1. **Classifying** Which mineral or minerals were found in all of the toothpastes tested? Did any toothpaste contain minerals not found in the other toothpastes?
2. **Observing** Which toothpaste was most effective in removing stains from the tile?
3. **Interpreting Data** Were your predictions about which toothpaste would be most effective correct?
4. **Interpreting Data** Does the toothpaste that was most effective in cleaning the tile differ in mineral content from the other toothpastes that were tested?

Data Table			
Toothpaste	Minerals Present	Predictions	Observations
1			
2			
3			

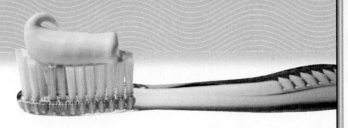

5. **Controlling Variables** What was the independent variable in this experiment? What was the dependent variable? Why did you use the same amount of toothpaste, force, and number of brushstrokes in each trial?

6. **Drawing Conclusions** How do the minerals in toothpaste affect the toothpaste's cleaning ability? Explain.

7. **Developing Hypotheses** Your teeth have the same composition as apatite, which has a hardness of 5 on the Mohs scale. What would be the advantages and disadvantages of using a toothpaste containing a mineral that is harder than apatite? Softer than apatite? Explain.

8. **Communicating** Write a lab report for this experiment. In your report, describe your predictions, your procedure, how you controlled variables, and whether or not your results supported your predictions.

Design Your Own Experiment

Some brands of toothpaste claim that they whiten teeth. Design an experiment to test the effectiveness of different kinds of whitening toothpaste. Make a data table to organize your findings. *Obtain your teacher's permission before carrying out your investigation.*

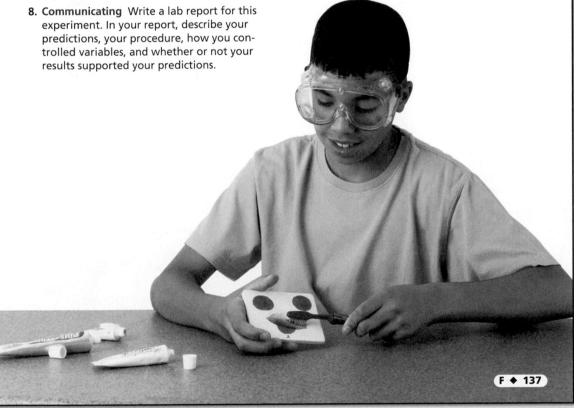

Extend Inquiry

Design Your Own Experiment The active ingredients in "whitening" toothpaste are often either baking soda (sodium bicarbonate) and/or hydrogen peroxide. Students' proposed procedures should be similar to that used in this experiment. Students' results should show that toothpaste containing both sodium bicarbonate and hydrogen peroxide will be more effective at whitening teeth than either of these ingredients alone. Point out that using such pastes over long periods of time can actually damage teeth.

Expected Outcome
Effectiveness of cleaning will vary with the types and brands of paste tested. The paste containing the baking soda, however, should be more effective at removing or lightening stains than the pastes without this ingredient.

Analyze and Conclude
Answers
1. Most toothpaste contains silica, phosphate minerals, and sodium fluoride. Some toothpaste also contains calcite.

2. Harder minerals will polish and clean teeth more effectively than softer minerals. Using such minerals, however, will damage the teeth by removing some of the teeth's enamel when used for extended periods of time.

3. Answers will vary, depending on the toothpaste tested.

4. The paste with the baking soda, which is the mineral sodium bicarbonate, was probably the most effective at removing the stains.

5. The independent variable was the type/brand of toothpaste. The dependent variable was the effectiveness of the paste in removing stains. Because any valid scientific experiment tests only one variable at a time, the amount of paste, the number of brushstrokes, and force were the same.

6. Answers will depend on the type and brand of toothpaste used. Paste containing baking soda is generally more effective at removing surface stains from teeth than paste without this mineral.

7. Toothpastes with minerals harder than apatite will remove stains but will also scratch the surface of the tooth. Minerals softer than apatite would not scratch the surface of the tooth but would not remove stains as quickly.

8. Students' lab reports should clearly demonstrate that they followed scientific methods and compared their results with their predictions.

Study Guide

The BIG Idea

Have students read the answer to the Essential Question. Encourage them to evaluate and revise their own answers as needed.

Help Students Read

Building Vocabulary

Word Origin Have students look up the origins of the words *ally* and *alloys*. They will discover that both come from the Latin word *alligare*, meaning "to bind." Ask students how *alloy* is similar in meaning to *ally*. (*People who are allies join together, just as an alloy is a mixture of elements that join together.*)

Words in Context Help students learn the meaning of new words or phrases by examining context. Tell students to look for familiar words or phrases that surround a new term—these are clues to the new term's meaning. Have students reread the first paragraph under the heading *Smelting* in Section 3. Ask: **Which word that appears in the same sentence as smelting helps you to remember its meaning?** (*Melted*)

Connecting Concepts

Concept Maps Help students develop one way to show how the information in this chapter is related. Minerals, formed by magma or by elements or compounds in hot solutions, share five characteristics that make them valuable resources. Have students brainstorm to identify the key concepts, key terms, details, and examples, then write each one on a sticky note and attach it at random on chart paper or on the board.

Tell students that this concept map will be organized in hierarchical order and to begin at the top with the key concepts. Ask students these questions to guide them to categorize the information on the stickies: **What are the characteristics of a mineral? How are minerals formed, identified, and used?**

Prompt students by using connecting words or phrases, such as "to form," "are identified by," and "have properties of," to indicate the basis for the organization of the map. The phrases should form a sentence between or among a set of concepts.

The BIG Idea

Properties of Matter Minerals are naturally occurring, inorganic solids with a crystal structure and a definite chemical composition. Minerals are used as gemstones, metals, and raw materials for many products.

① Properties of Minerals

Key Concepts

- A mineral is a naturally occurring, inorganic solid that has a crystal structure and a definite chemical composition.
- Each mineral has characteristic properties that can be used to identify it.
- Density can be determined with the following formula:

$$\text{Density} = \frac{\text{Mass}}{\text{Volume}}$$

Key Terms
mineral
inorganic
crystal
streak
luster
Mohs hardness scale
cleavage
fracture

② How Minerals Form

Key Concepts

- Minerals form as hot magma cools inside the crust, or as lava hardens on the surface. When these liquids cool to a solid state, they form crystals.
- When elements and compounds that are dissolved in water leave a solution, crystallization of minerals occurs.

Key Terms
geode
crystallization
solution
vein

③ Using Mineral Resources

Key Concepts

- Minerals are the source of gemstones, metals, and a variety of materials used to make many products.
- To produce metal from a mineral, a rock containing the mineral must be located through prospecting and mined, or removed from the ground. Then the rock must be processed to extract the metal.

Key Terms
gemstone
ore
smelting
alloy

Answer

Accept logical presentations by students.

All in One Teaching Resources

- Key Terms Review: *Minerals*
- Connecting Concepts: *Minerals*

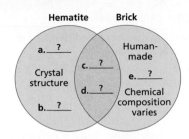

Go Online
PHSchool.com
For: Self-assessment
Visit: PHSchool.com
Web Code: cfa-1040

Organizing Information

Comparing and Contrasting Fill in the Venn diagram to compare the characteristics of a mineral and a material that is not a mineral.

Hematite   Brick

a. _?_

Crystal structure

c. _?_

d. _?_

b. _?_

Human-made

e. _?_

Chemical composition varies

Reviewing Key Terms

Choose the letter of the best answer.

1. Because minerals do not come from once-living material, they are said to be
   a. crystalline.
   b. solid.
   c. colorful.
   d. inorganic.

2. In a mineral, the particles line up in a repeating pattern to form a(n)
   a. element.
   b. crystal.
   c. mixture.
   d. compound.

3. Which characteristic is used to determine the color of a mineral's powder?
   a. luster
   b. fracture
   c. cleavage
   d. streak

4. Halite is a mineral formed through the evaporation of
   a. magma.
   b. a vein.
   c. a solution.
   d. lava.

5. Minerals from which metals can be removed in usable amounts are called
   a. gemstones.   **b.** crystals.
   c. alloys.   **d.** ores.

If the statement is true, write *true*. If it is false, change the underlined word or words to make the statement true.

6. A hollow rock lined with crystals is a <u>geode</u>.

7. <u>Fracture</u> is the term that describes how a mineral reflects light from its surface.

8. Mineral deposits beneath Earth's surface that are different from the surrounding rocks are called <u>veins</u>.

9. Hard, shiny crystals used in jewelry are called <u>ores</u>.

10. Steel is an example of a(n) <u>alloy</u>.

Writing in Science

Descriptive Paragraph Choose a mineral such as gold or jade. Write a paragraph about the properties of this mineral. Explain why it is valuable and how it is useful to society.

Minerals

Video Preview
Video Field Trip
▶ Video Assessment

Go Online
PHSchool.com
For: Self-Assessment
Visit: PHSchool.com
Web Code: cfa-1040

Students can take an online practice test that is automatically scored.

Teaching Resources
- Transparency F41: *Venn Diagram*
- Chapter Test
- Performance Assessment Teacher Notes
- Performance Assessment Student Worksheet
- Performance Assessment Scoring Rubric

ExamView® **Computer Test Bank CD-ROM**

Organizing Information
a. naturally occurring
b. definite chemical composition
c. solid or inorganic
d. inorganic or solid
e. no crystal structure

Reviewing Key Terms
1. d **2.** b **3.** d **4.** c **5.** d
6. true
7. Luster
8. true
9. gemstones
10. true

Writing in Science

Writing Skill Description
Scoring Rubric
4 includes requirements and exceeds what is asked for. It may add information about how the metal used to be used or how it may be used in the future, for example.
3 includes all criteria
2 includes only two criteria
1 includes only brief or inaccurate information

DISCOVERY CHANNEL SCHOOL
Video Assessment

Minerals

Show the Video Assessment to review chapter content and as a prompt for the writing assignment. Discussion questions: **What makes a mineral a gemstone?** (*It can be polished and is highly valued.*) **Why do you think jade and gold are highly valued?** (*Because of their beauty and rareness and the difficulty in acquiring them*)

Checking Concepts

11. Most minerals contain two or more elements. A pure element is composed of atoms of a single element.

12. Although the color of a mineral might vary, the color of a mineral's streak is always the same.

13. Minerals are grouped into six crystal systems according to their crystal shapes.

14. In general, minerals can form through crystallization of magma or lava and through crystallization of minerals from solutions. In the first way, minerals form as magma cools beneath Earth's surface or as lava cools on Earth's surface. In the second way, minerals crystallize as solutions cool or evaporate.

15. Corundum would make the best gemstone. It is hardest and has a glassy luster.

16. A mineral is combined with other minerals and heated, causing a chemical change that separates out the metal in the mineral.

Thinking Critically

17. Obsidian cannot be classified as mineral because the atoms are not arranged in an orderly, repeating pattern.

18. Color and luster are similar because they are both visually observable properties. They are different because color describes the type of light reflected from a mineral's surface; luster describes the quality or general appearance of the reflected light, whatever its color.

19. Hot fluids move along faults or other cracks in rock. As the fluids cool or otherwise change, minerals precipitate along the crack to form the vein. The energy source is Earth's internal heat.

20. Without enough chromium and nickel in the steel, iron oxide could form on the steel; that is, the steel could rust.

Math Practice

21. 19 g/cm^3

22. 3.52 g/cm^3

Applying Skills

23. The color is yellowish orange, the luster is glassy or brilliant, and the crystals appear rectangular (tetragonal).

24. The fairly large size of the crystals suggests that the wulfenite formed slowly.

25. A hardness of 3 is very low on the Mohs hardness scale. Because it is desirable for gems to be hard, wulfenite probably would not be hard enough to use as a gem. The mineral might be used as an ore of the metals it contains.

Review and Assessment

Checking Concepts

11. How does the composition of most minerals differ from a pure element?

12. How can the streak test be helpful in identifying minerals?

13. How do geologists use different types of crystal shapes to classify minerals?

14. Describe two ways that minerals can form.

15. Which mineral in the table below would make the best gemstone? Explain your answer.

Properties of Minerals

Mineral	Hardness	Density (g/cm³)	Luster
Galena	2.5	7.5	metallic
Fluorite	4.0	3.3	glassy
Corundum	9.0	4.0	glassy
Talc	1.0	2.8	pearly

16. Describe what happens to a mineral during smelting.

Thinking Critically

17. Classifying Obsidian is a solid that occurs in volcanic areas. Obsidian forms when magma cools very quickly, creating a type of glass. In glass, the particles are not arranged in an orderly pattern as in a crystal. Should obsidian be classified as a mineral? Explain why or why not.

18. Comparing and Contrasting Color and luster are both properties of minerals. How are they similar? How are they different? How can each be used to help identify a mineral?

19. Relating Cause and Effect Describe how a vein of ore forms underground. What is the energy source for this process?

20. Predicting What would happen if steelmakers forgot to add enough chromium and nickel to a batch of stainless steel?

Math Practice

21. Calculating A platinum ring has a volume of 0.8 cm^3 and a mass of 15.2 g. What is its density?

22. Calculating A diamond has a mass of 10.56 g and a volume of 3 cm^3. Calculate the density of the diamond.

Applying Skills

Use the photograph below to answer Questions 23–25.

You have found a sample of the mineral wulfenite. The wulfenite has a hardness of about 3 on the Mohs hardness scale and a density of 6.8 g/cm^3. The mineral contains oxygen as well as the metals lead and molybdenum.

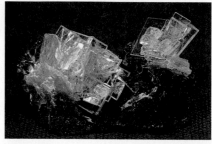

23. Observing Describe wulfenite's color and luster and the shape of its crystals.

24. Inferring Did the wulfenite form slowly or quickly? Explain your answer.

25. Drawing Conclusions Is wulfenite hard enough for use as a gem? What would you use these crystals for? Explain.

Lab zone Chapter **Project**

Performance Assessment Share your crystal garden with a classmate. Can your classmate identify which solution created which crystals? Do your data show differences in crystal growth rates? Which materials worked best for crystals to grow on? Share the answers to these questions when you present your project.

Lab zone Chapter **Project**   L3

Performance Assessment Talk with each student or group before the presentation. Make suggestions and offer encouragement. Assess the presentations on the quality of the garden scenes, the growth of the crystals in the garden, the growth data kept by the students, and the coherence of the presentation.

In assessing their crystal gardens, students should reflect on the materials used, the quality and attractiveness of the scenes that they made, and the growth rate of the different kinds of crystals. Students should assess how their gardens compared with others in the class and suggest ways in which they could have improved their own outcomes.

Standardized Test Prep

Choose the letter of the best answer.

1. Which of the following is a mineral?
 A salt
 B pearl
 C coal
 D cement

2. You could distinguish gold from pyrite (fool's gold) by
 F comparing their hardness.
 G testing their chemical composition.
 H comparing their density.
 J all of the above

3. Veins of silver can be found in rock. These veins formed when
 A hot water solutions escaped from cracks in the rock.
 B hot water solutions crystallized in cracks in the rock.
 C magma crystallized in cracks in the rock.
 D hot water solutions evaporated in cracks in the rock.

4. An ore is a mineral that
 F is beautiful and rare.
 G can be mined at a profit.
 H is dense and metallic.
 J is light and durable.

5. The following diagrams show four different mineral samples. Based on these diagrams, what property is the same for all four minerals?

 A crystal structure
 B cleavage
 C hardness
 D color

Constructed Response

6. A geologist finds an unknown mineral while working in a national park. The geologist is carrying a kit that contains a geologic hammer, a jackknife, a hand lens, a piece of tile, and a penny. In a paragraph, describe how the geologist could use these items to determine some of the mineral's properties.

Standardized Test Practice

1. A **2.** J **3.** B **4.** G **5.** B

6. The geologist could describe the mineral's hardness, cleavage or fracture, streak, luster, and crystal shape. Hardness could be approximated by performing scratch tests using the penny and jackknife. The hammer could be used to break the mineral to make fresh cleavage or fracture surfaces. A streak test could be performed using the piece of tile, and the hand lens could be used to better observe the mineral's luster and crystal shape.

Chapter at a Glance

PRENTICE HALL
TeacherEXPRESS™
Plan • Teach • Assess

 Chapter Project *Collecting Rocks*

All in One Teaching Resources
- Chapter Project Teacher Notes, pp. 300–301
- Chapter Project Student Overview, pp. 302–303
- Chapter Project Student Worksheets 1–2, pp. 304–305
- Chapter Project Scoring Rubric, p. 306

	Technology	**Local Standards**
	Video Preview	

 Classifying Rocks

1 period
1/2 block

F.5.1.1 List the characteristics used to identify rocks.
F.5.1.2 Identify and describe the three major groups of rocks.

 Igneous Rocks

1 period
1/2 block

F.5.2.1 Identify the characteristics used to classify igneous rocks.
F.5.2.2 Describe ways in which igneous rocks are used.

 Video Field Trip

 Sedimentary Rocks

1 period
1/2 block

F.5.3.1 Describe how sedimentary rocks form.
F.5.3.2 List and describe the three major types of sedimentary rocks.
F.5.3.3 Explain how sedimentary rocks are used.

 Rocks From Reefs

1 period
1/2 block

F.5.4.1 Describe the formation of coral reefs.
F.5.4.2 Explain how limestone deposits from coral reefs provide information about Earth's history.

 PLANET DIARY

Metamorphic Rocks

2 periods
1 block

F.5.5.1 Describe the conditions under which metamorphic rocks form.
F.5.5.2 Identify the ways in which geologists classify metamorphic rocks.
F.5.5.3 Explain how metamorphic rocks are used.

The Rock Cycle

2 period
1 block

F.5.6.1 Describe the rock cycle.
F.5.6.2 Explain the role of plate tectonics in the rock cycle.

 *active art*

Review and Assessment

All in One Teaching Resources
- Key Terms Review, p. 357
- Transparency F52
- Performance Assessment Teacher Notes, p. 364
- Performance Assessment Scoring Rubric, p. 365
- Performance Assessment Student Worksheet, p. 366
- Chapter Test, p. 367–370

 PHSchool.com

 Video Preview

Test Preparation

Test Preparation Blackline Masters

Lab zone Chapter Activities Planner

For more activities

LAB ZONE
Easy Planner
CD-ROM

Student Edition	Inquiry	Time	Materials	Skills	Resources
Chapter Project, p. 143	Open-Ended	Ongoing (2–3 weeks)	**All in One** Teaching Resources, p. 300	Observing, classifying	**Lab zone Easy Planner**
Section 1					
Discover Activity, p. 144	Guided	10 minutes	Samples of marble and conglomerate, hand lens, penny	Observing	**Lab zone Easy Planner**
Section 2					
Discover Activity, p. 148	Guided	10 minutes	Samples of granite and obsidian, hand lens	Inferring	**Lab zone Easy Planner**
Section 3					
Discover Activity, p. 152	Guided	15 minutes	Sheet of paper, 2 slices of bread, stack of books, plastic knife	Observing	**Lab zone Easy Planner**
Try This, p. 155	Directed	15 minutes setup; 10 next day	Samples of sandstone and shale, hand lens, balance, pan, water	Drawing conclusions	**Lab zone Easy Planner**
Section 4					
Discover Activity, p. 157	Guided	15 minutes	Samples of limestone and coquina, dilute hydrochloric acid, plastic dropper, running water, hand lens	Drawing conclusions	**Lab zone Easy Planner**
Section 5					
Discover Activity, p. 160	Guided	15 minutes	Samples of gneiss and granite, hand lens	Inferring	**Lab zone Easy Planner**
Try This, p. 161	Directed	15 minutes	Modeling compound, metric rulers, 25 sequins, 30-cm string, 2 blocks of wood	Making models	**Lab zone Easy Planner**
Skills Lab, p. 163	Open-Ended	Prep: 30 minutes Class: 30 minutes	1 nonrock solid object such as brick or bone, 2 igneous rock samples such as granite and basalt, 2 sedimentary rock samples such as sandstone and conglomerate, 2 metamorphic rock samples such as gneiss and slate, hand lens	Inferring, classifying	**Lab zone Easy Planner** **Lab Activity Video** **All in One** Teaching Resources Skills Lab: *Mystery Rocks*, p. 346–348
Section 6					
Discover Activity, p. 164	Guided	10 minutes	3 index cards, colored pencils	Developing hypotheses	**Lab zone Easy Planner**
Design Your Own Lab, p. 167	Open-Ended	Prep: 30 minutes Class: 40 minutes	steel nail; wire brush; plastic dropper; hand lens; samples of igneous, sedimentary, and metamorphic rocks with flat surfaces; greasy materials, such as butter and crayons; materials that stain, such as ink and paint	Design an experiment, controlling variables, drawing conclusions	**Lab zone Easy Planner** **Lab Activity Video** **All in One** Teaching Resources Design Your Own Lab: *Testing Rock Flooring*, p. 355–356

Section 1 Classifying Rocks

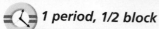 *1 period, 1/2 block*

Objectives

F.5.1.1 List the characteristics used to identify rocks.

F.5.1.2 Identify and describe the three major groups of rocks.

Key Terms

• rock-forming mineral • granite • basalt • grains • texture • igneous rock
• sedimentary rock • metamorphic rock

Local Standards

Preteach

Build Background Knowledge

Students share their knowledge of rocks and rock types. Display samples or pictures of rocks with which most students will be familiar.

Lab zone Discover Activity *How Do Rocks Compare?* L1

Targeted Print and Technology Resources

All in One Teaching Resources

L2 Reading Strategy Transparency F42: Asking Questions

PresentationExpress™ CD-ROM

Instruct

Mineral Composition and Color Explain that rocks are mixtures of minerals and other materials, and show students how to connect a rock's color to the types of minerals that may be present.

Texture Ask students to suggest adjectives to describe the size, shape, and arrangement of grains in rocks.

How Rocks Form Ask leading questions to help students connect rock formation to locations that provide the conditions necessary for the different types of rocks to form.

Targeted Print and Technology Resources

All in One Teaching Resources

L2 Guided Reading, pp. 309–312

PHSchool.com Web Code: cfd-1051

Student Edition on Audio CD

Assess

Section Assessment Questions

Have students use their completed graphic organizers to answer the questions.

Reteach

Students classify rocks based on their description and how they were formed.

Targeted Print and Technology Resources

All in One Teaching Resources

• Section Summary, p. 308
L1 Review and Reinforce, p. 313
L3 Enrich, p. 314

Section 2 Igneous Rocks

 1 period, 1/2 block

Objectives

F.5.2.1 Identify the characteristics used to classify igneous rocks.
F.5.2.2 Describe ways in which igneous rocks are used.

Key Terms

• extrusive rock • intrusive rock

Local Standards

Preteach

Build Background Knowledge

Students answer questions that help them recall their knowledge about molten material and where it rises.

 **Discover Activity** *How Do Igneous Rocks Form?* **L1**

Targeted Print and Technology Resources

 Teaching Resources

L2 Reading Strategy Transparency F43: Identifying Main Idea

 PresentationExpress™ CD-ROM

Instruct

Classifying Igneous Rocks Discuss classification criteria used to describe the origin, texture, and mineral composition of igneous rocks.

Uses of Igneous Rocks Help students to connect the properties of obsidian, granite, and other igneous rocks to their uses.

Targeted Print and Technology Resources

 Teaching Resources

L2 Guided Reading, pp. 317–320

L2 Transparency F44

www.SciLinks.org Web Code: scn-1052

DISCOVERY CHANNEL SCHOOL
Video Field Trip

 Student Edition on Audio CD

Assess

Section Assessment Questions

 Have students use their completed graphic organizers with main ideas to answer the questions.

Reteach

Students create a table to show how some common igneous rocks are classified.

Targeted Print and Technology Resources

All in One **Teaching Resources**

• Section Summary, p. 316

L1 Review and Reinforce, p. 321

L3 Enrich, p. 322

Section 3  Sedimentary Rocks

1 period, 1/2 block

ABILITY LEVELS
L1 Basic to Average
L2 For All Students
L3 Average to Advanced

Objectives

F.5.3.1 Describe how sedimentary rocks form.

F.5.3.2 List and describe the three major types of sedimentary rocks.

F.5.3.3 Explain how sedimentary rocks are used.

Local Standards

Key Terms

• sediment • erosion • deposition • compaction • cementation • clastic rock
• organic rock • chemical rock

Preteach

Build Background Knowledge

Students recall a beach they have walked on and infer what causes sand to harden into sandstone. If they need help, stack books on top of one another to illustrate.

 **Discover Activity** *How Does Pressure Affect Particles of Rock?* **L1**

Targeted Print and Technology Resources

All in One Teaching Resources

L2 Reading Strategy Transparency F45: Outlining

 PresentationExpress™ CD-ROM

Instruct

From Sediment to Rock Guide students to discuss types of sediment and how they form, and help them apply their knowledge to a piece of sandstone.

Types of Sedimentary Rock Discuss the formation of the three major groups of sedimentary rocks . Help students name the types of rock that might form in various environments.

Uses of Sedimentary Rocks Challenge students to identify common uses of sedimentary rock and to identify sedimentary rock resources in your state.

Targeted Print and Technology Resources

All in One Teaching Resources

L2 Guided Reading, pp. 325–329

L2 Transparency F46

www.SciLinks.org Web Code: scn-1053

Student Edition on Audio CD

Assess

Section Assessment Questions

Have students use their completed outlines to answer the questions.

Reteach

Students gather photographs that illustrate examples of erosion and deposition.

Targeted Print and Technology Resources

All in One Teaching Resources

• Section Summary, p. 324

L1 Review and Reinforce, p. 330

L3 Enrich, p. 331

Section 4 Rocks From Reefs

 1 period, 1/2 block

ABILITY LEVELS
L1 Basic to Average
L2 For All Students
L3 Average to Advanced

Objectives

F.5.4.1 Describe the formation of coral reefs.

F.5.4.2 Explain how limestone deposits from coral reefs provide information about Earth's history.

Local Standards

Key Terms

• coral reef

Preteach

Build Background Knowledge

Students share their knowledge of coral reefs. They answer questions about where reefs occur and how to describe reef structure.

 **Discover Activity** *How Does a Rock React to Acid?* L3

Targeted Print and Technology Resources

 Teaching Resources

L2 Reading Strategy Transparency F47: Using Prior Knowledge

 PresentationExpress™ CD-ROM

Instruct

Coral Reefs Use leading questions to develop an understanding of how reefs form and why they are important.

Limestone From Coral Reefs Demonstrate how limestone deposits that began as coral reefs provide evidence of how plate motions have changed Earth's surface. Open a discussion of the conditions under which ancient coral reefs formed.

Targeted Print and Technology Resources

Teaching Resources

L2 Guided Reading, pp. 334–336

PHSchool.com Web Code: cfd-1054

 Student Edition on Audio CD

Assess

Section Assessment Questions

Have students use their completed graphic organizers to answer the questions.

Reteach

Students discuss the structure of a coral animal.

Targeted Print and Technology Resources

Teaching Resources
• Section Summary, p. 333
L1 Review and Reinforce, p. 337
L3 Enrich, p. 338

Section 5 Metamorphic Rocks

 *2 periods, 1 block*

ABILITY LEVELS
L1 Basic to Average
L2 For All Students
L3 Average to Advanced

Objectives

F.5.5.1 Describe the conditions under which metamorphic rocks form.
F.5.5.2 Identify the ways in which geologists classify metamorphic rocks.
F.5.5.3 Explain how metamorphic rocks are used.

Key Terms

• foliated

Local Standards

Preteach

Build Background Knowledge

Students recall forces that can change rocks by answering questions about plate boundaries and plate collisions.

 Discover Activity *How Do Grain Patterns Compare?* **L1**

Targeted Print and Technology Resources

 **Teaching Resources**

L2 Reading Strategy Transparency F48: Previewing Visuals

PresentationExpress™ CD-ROM

Instruct

Types of Metamorphic Rocks Review with students the difference between foliated and nonfoliated rocks, and how these characteristics form. Help students apply their knowledge to a given example.

Uses of Metamorphic Rock Describe the properties of marble and slate that make them useful in statues and buildings. Guide a discussion of these properties and help students apply their knowledge to other uses.

Skills Lab *Mystery Rocks* **L3**

Targeted Print and Technology Resources

 Teaching Resources

L2 Guided Reading, pp. 341–343
L3 Transparency F49
L2 Skills Lab: *Mystery Rocks,* pp. 346–348

Lab Activity Video/DVD
Skills Lab: *Mystery Rocks*

www.SciLinks.org Web Code: cfa-1055

Student Edition on Audio CD

Assess

Section Assessment Questions

 Have students use the questions and answers they prepared by previewing visuals to answer the questions.

Reteach

Students discuss places where metamorphic rocks might form.

Targeted Print and Technology Resources

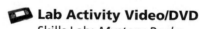 **Teaching Resources**

• Section Summary, p. 340
L1 Review and Reinforce, p. 344
L3 Enrich, p. 345

Section 5 Metamorphic Rocks

Metamorphic Index Minerals The intrusion of a granite batholith heats the surrounding rock layers. The temperature is highest in the rocks closest to the intrusion. This causes the rocks nearest the intrusion to undergo a higher amount of metamorphism. The amount of change that a metomorphic rock was undergone is known as the metamorphic grade. As metamorphic grade changes away from a granite intrusion temperature, different minerals occur in the rock. If the surrounding rock is shale, the sequence of minerals and metamorphic rocks shown in the diagram below will form. By mapping the extent of these index minerals in the rocks, geologists can determine the temperatures that occurred during metamorphism. Mapping the metamorphic grade might also help to locate the intruding igneous body.

Index minerals are also useful for determining the grade of metomorphic rocks that form during mountain building. Such rocks are exposed to both high temperature and high pressure. Identifying the metamorphic grade provides information about the burial depth and history of these rocks.

Metamorphism of Shale

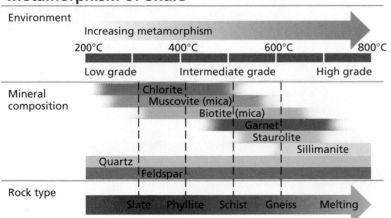

Section 6 The Rock Cycle

Reading the Rocks By studying rocks, faults, and folds over a large area, geologists try to figure out what that area looked like at different times in the geologic past. Rocks provide clues to past environments and geologic events. To help understand these rock clues, geologists study modern environments and geologic events. For example, in order to understand what an ancient river deposit would look like, geologists study modern river sediments. To understand ancient lava flows, scientists study the active lava flows of volcanoes, such as Kilauea. Each rock sample preserves clues to its origin and history. Reading the rocks is like solving a complex puzzle, in order to understand Earth's history.

Help Students Read

Sequencing
Ordering Events

Strategy Help students understand and visualize the steps in a process or the order in which events occur. Readers can construct graphic organizers to help themselves visualize and comprehend a sequence. For most sequences, flowcharts are the graphic organizer of choice. However, cycle diagrams are more appropriate for cycles. Before students begin, locate a description in the text of a several-step process or a chain of causes and effects, such as those in *Sedimentary Rocks*, related to the formation of sedimentary rocks, or in *Rocks From Reefs*, related to how coral reefs form.

Example

1. Review the passage, listing the steps or events in order.
2. If the passage describes a chain of events or steps, draw a flowchart on the board, having students tell the sequence of events, steps, or causes and effects, and writing each part of the process in a separate box of the flowchart.
3. Have students locate additional examples of sequential relationships in the text or visuals of the chapter. Students can depict the steps or events using graphic organizers.

The BIG Idea

The Big Idea is the major scientific concept of the chapter. It is followed by the Essential Question. Read aloud the question to students. As students study the chapter, tell them to think about the Essential Question. Explain that they will discover the answer to the question as they read. The chapter Study Guide provides a sample answer.

Objectives

Rocks are an important part of the natural world that remain mostly unnoticed by many students. Collecting rocks in the field will enrich students' understanding of Earth. After this project, students will be able to

- observe and recognize rock characteristics
- classify rock samples
- draw conclusions about how their rocks formed
- communicate their results by making a display

Skills Focus

Observing, classifying, drawing conclusions, communicating

Project Time Line 2 to 3 weeks

All in One Teaching Resources

- Chapter Project Teacher Notes
- Chapter Project Overview
- Chapter Project Worksheet 1
- Chapter Project Worksheet 2
- Chapter Project Scoring Rubric

Developing a Plan

Students will brainstorm locations where rocks can be collected safely and legally. They will plan excursions to places where they are likely to find many kinds of rocks, and they will collect rocks at several of these locations. They will examine the collected rocks and classify and identify each sample through observation and tests. After students have classified their rocks, they will create a display.

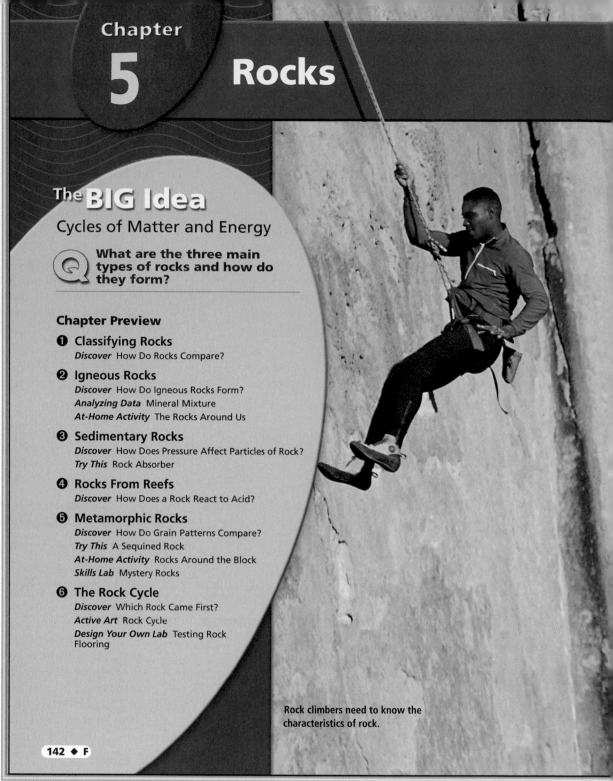

The BIG Idea

Cycles of Matter and Energy

Q **What are the three main types of rocks and how do they form?**

Chapter Preview

Rock climbers need to know the characteristics of rock.

Possible Materials

For the collection phase of the project, students will need a heavy bag in which to carry the rock samples. A canvas bag is traditional for this purpose, but an old backpack also works well. Resealable plastic sandwich bags are useful for storing individual rock samples. In the lab, students will need a hand lens and a fingernail file for doing scratch tests. For creating a display, students might use egg cartons or some other container with compartments. Rock and mineral guidebooks will help students identify the rocks they collect.

Possible Shortcuts

- You might want to organize the class into small groups to conduct this project.
- You can make this project shorter and less involved by having pairs of students collect

Section 6 The Rock Cycle

 2 periods, 1 block

ABILITY LEVELS
L1 Basic to Average
L2 For All Students
L3 Average to Advanced

Objectives

F.5.6.1 Describe the rock cycle.

F.5.6.2 Explain the role of plate tectonics in the rock cycle.

Key Terms

• rock cycle

Local Standards

Preteach

Build Background Knowledge

Students brainstorm a list of Earth processes that affect rock in Earth's crust and explain why rocks are not permanent.

 **Discover Activity** *Which Rock Came First?* L1

Targeted Print and Technology Resources

All in One Teaching Resources

L2 Reading Strategy Transparency F50: Sequencing

 PresentationExpress™ CD-ROM

Instruct

A Cycle of Many Pathways Review with students the meaning of *cycle* and discuss products and processes in the rock cycle. Help students apply their knowledge to real-world events and use the Active Art to connect products and processes to the various pathways in the rock cycle.

The Rock Cycle and Plate Tectonics Help students develop an understanding of the rock cycle products and processes that occur at various plate tectonic settings.

 **Design Your Own** *Testing Rock Flooring* L2

Targeted Print and Technology Resources

All in One Teaching Resources

L2 Guided Reading, pp. 351–352

L2 Transparency F51

L2 Design Your Own Lab: *Testing Rock Flooring*, pp. 355–356

Lab Activity Video/DVD
Design Your Own Lab: *Testing Rock Flooring*

PHSchool.com Web Code: cfp-1056

 Student Edition on Audio CD

Assess

Section Assessment Questions

Have students use their completed graphic organizers showing the sequence of steps in the rock cycle to answer the questions.

Reteach

Students work together to explain how a silicon atom in a sand grain could someday erupt from a volcano.

Targeted Print and Technology Resources

All in One Teaching Resources

• Section Summary, p. 350

L1 Review and Reinforce, p. 353

L3 Enrich, p. 354

Chapter 5 Content Refresher

Go Online

NSTA-PDi LINKS

For: Professional development support
Visit: www.SciLinks.org/PDLinks
Web Code: scf-1050

Professional Development

Section 1 Classifying Rocks

Thin Sections Geologists sometimes view thin slices of rocks under a microscope. These slices, called thin sections, need to be thin enough for light to pass through. A special microscope called a petrographic microscope is used. Two lenses in the microscope work like polarizing sunglasses. When one lens is rotated into the light path, only light that vibrates parallel to the direction of the polarizing lens can pass. When both lenses are in the light path, light normally is blocked. However, if a thin section is on the microscope's stage, colors produced by interference of light waves are observed. These colors and other optical properties are useful for identifying and characterizing minerals.

Section 2 Igneous Rocks

Pegmatites Intrusive igneous rocks are coarser-grained than extrusive rocks because they cooled more slowly. Slow cooling rates allow crystals to grow larger. Most granite crystals are between about 1 mm and 1 cm in size. Pegmatites are intrusive rocks that are very coarse-grained, with most crystals larger than 1-3 centimeters. Some pegmatites have extremely large crystals. One in the Black Hills of South Dakota had a crystal 12 meters long that weighed 80 tons!

Pegmatites normally have a mineral composition similar to that of granite. They form from the last portions of the magma to solidify. The last magma to cool commonly contains higher concentrations of rare elements. For this reason, pegmatites sometimes contain rare and unusual minerals. Many of the spectacular mineral specimens in museums were collected from pegmatites.

Section 3 Sedimentary Rocks

Environment of Deposition

Knowing the environment in which sedimentary rocks formed can tell us about the geologic history of an area. This history is important because fossil fuels are found in sedimentary rocks.

Grain size can tell a lot about the environment of deposition. As shown in the diagram, grain size

Address Misconceptions

Some students may think that sedimentary rock forms rather quickly. For a strategy for overcoming this misconception, see **Address Misconceptions** on page 155.

decreases as sediment is transported by running water. The finer the grain size, the farther the sediment has been carried from its source. This information, along with grain composition, can indicate where the sediment came from. The range of grain sizes (sorting) also provides information. For example, running water usually deposits sediment that is well sorted (the sediment is all about the same size). Sediment deposited by ice is poorly sorted (has a wide range of grain sizes).

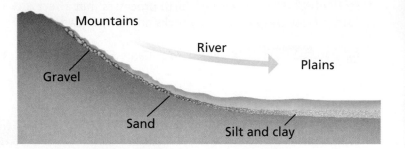

Section 4 Rocks From Reefs

Ancient Reefs Corals have been major reef-builders for about the last 210 million years. But reefs can be formed by any organisms that are attached to the sea bottom and produce rigid carbonate skeletons. Organisms that have been important reef-builders in the past include sponges, bryozoans, and algae. Bryozoans are animals that form branching or fan-shaped, skeletons. Some types of algae form calcite skeletons and grow in branching forms or by encrusting on other organisms or on rocks. These algae are often called calcareous algae or coralline algae. Along with corals, coralline algae are important reef-building organisms in modern reefs.

DISCOVERY
CHANNEL
SCHOOL

Rocks

▶ Video Preview
Video Field Trip
Video Assessment

DISCOVERY
CHANNEL
SCHOOL
Video
Preview

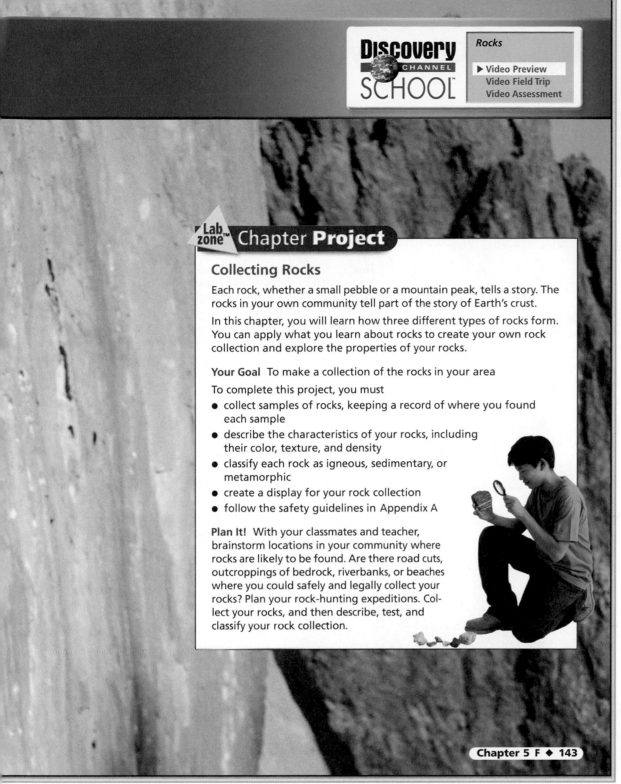

Lab zone™ Chapter **Project**

Collecting Rocks

Each rock, whether a small pebble or a mountain peak, tells a story. The rocks in your own community tell part of the story of Earth's crust.

In this chapter, you will learn how three different types of rocks form. You can apply what you learn about rocks to create your own rock collection and explore the properties of your rocks.

Your Goal To make a collection of the rocks in your area

To complete this project, you must
- collect samples of rocks, keeping a record of where you found each sample
- describe the characteristics of your rocks, including their color, texture, and density
- classify each rock as igneous, sedimentary, or metamorphic
- create a display for your rock collection
- follow the safety guidelines in Appendix A

Plan It! With your classmates and teacher, brainstorm locations in your community where rocks are likely to be found. Are there road cuts, outcroppings of bedrock, riverbanks, or beaches where you could safely and legally collect your rocks? Plan your rock-hunting expeditions. Collect your rocks, and then describe, test, and classify your rock collection.

Chapter 5 F ◆ 143

Rocks

Show the Video Preview to introduce the Chapter Project and overview the chapter content. Discussion question: **Why do climbers prefer climbing granite walls over other kinds of rock?** *(Their rough surfaces and crack lines provide good handholds and footholds, and sometimes even ledges for resting.)*

only two or three rocks each and bring the rocks to class. Then, either small groups or the class as a whole can classify and identify the most interesting samples. These rocks then can be made into a display.

Launching the Project

Show students a rock collection in a professional display. Point out that the display shows various kinds of rocks, each with a specific name. Ask: **Where in our community are some good places to collect different kinds of rocks?** *(A typical answer might mention parks, road cuts, or stream beds.)* Explain that in the Chapter Project students will collect, classify, and identify rock samples and then create a display. Emphasize that students should collect rocks only where it is safe and legal to do so.

Performance Assessment

Use the Chapter Project Scoring Rubric to assess students' work. Students will be assessed on
- how many rock samples they collect and describe
- how well they classify and identify their rock samples and how well they create an attractive display
- how effectively they present their rock collections to the class
- how well they participated in a group, if they worked in groups

Portfolio

Objectives

After the lesson, students will be able to

F.5.1.1 list the characteristics used to identify rocks

F.5.1.2 identify and describe the three major groups of rocks

Target Reading Skill

Asking Questions Explain that changing a heading into a question helps students anticipate the ideas, facts, and events they are about to read.

Answers

Students will create a two-column table. Column 1 has the headings restated as questions, Column 2 the answers.

All in One Teaching Resources

• Transparency F42

Preteach

Build Background Knowledge   L2

Common Rock Types

Display samples or pictures of sandstone and marble. Ask: **How would you describe the difference between sandstone and marble?** *(A typical answer might describe a difference in texture—sandstone is grainy, whereas marble is smooth and crystalline.)*

Lab zone Build Inquiry   L2

Identifying the Minerals in Granite

Focus Ask: **How can you tell the difference between granite and its component minerals?** *(A mineral usually looks homogeneous to the unaided eye. Coarse-grained rocks, such as granite, appear heterogeneous.)*

Teach Provide students with a sample of granite and samples of the major minerals in the rock. Have them use Figure 2 to match the mineral samples with crystals in the rock and make a labeled drawing of the granite sample.

Apply Ask students to describe the arrangement of mineral crystals in the rock. *(The crystals in granite normally will have random orientation and an interlocking appearance.)* **learning modality: visual**

Reading Focus

Key Concepts

• What characteristics do geologists use to identify rocks?

• What are the three main groups of rocks?

Key Terms

• rock-forming mineral • granite
• basalt • grains • texture
• igneous rock
• sedimentary rock
• metamorphic rock

Target Reading Skill

Asking Questions Before you read, preview the red headings. In a graphic organizer like the one below, ask a *what* or *how* question for each heading. As you read, write answers to your questions.

Question	Answer
What does a rock's color tell about the rock?	

Lab zone Discover Activity

Conglomerate

Marble

How Do Rocks Compare?

1. Look at samples of conglomerate and marble with a hand lens.

2. Describe the two rocks. What is the color and texture of each?

3. Try scratching the surface of each rock with the edge of a penny. Which rock seems harder?

4. Hold each rock in your hand. Allowing for the fact that the samples aren't exactly the same size, which rock seems denser?

Think It Over

Observing Based on your observations, how would you compare the physical properties of marble and conglomerate?

If you were a geologist, how would you examine a rock for the first time? You might use a camera or notebook to record information about the setting where the rock was found. Then, you would use a chisel or the sharp end of a rock hammer to remove samples of the rock. Finally, you would break open the samples with a hammer to examine their inside surfaces. You must look at the inside of a rock because the effects of ice, liquid water, and weather can change the outer surface of a rock.

You can find interesting rocks almost anywhere. The rock of Earth's crust forms mountains, hills, valleys, beaches, even the ocean floor. **When studying a rock sample, geologists observe the rock's mineral composition, color, and texture.**

FIGURE 1
Inspecting a Rock
This geologist is using a hand lens to observe a piece of shale.

Lab zone Discover Activity

Skills Focus Observing

Materials samples of marble and conglomerate, hand lens, penny

Time 10 minutes

Tips If you have only a few samples of each kind of rock, pair samples of about the same size and invite students to examine them.

L1 Think It Over Students should discover that marble has a crystalline texture that can be seen easily. Conglomerate has a grainy texture and is composed of rock fragments and smaller sediment grains. The color of marble and conglomerate varies. Marble generally will be denser than conglomerate. Hardness will vary with specimens and with the location chosen for the scratch test.

Quartz

Feldspar

Hornblende

Mica

Granite

Mineral Composition and Color

Rocks are made of mixtures of minerals and other materials. Some rocks contain only a single mineral. Others contain several minerals. For example, the granite in Figure 2 is made up of the minerals quartz, feldspar, hornblende, and mica. About 20 minerals make up most of the rocks of Earth's crust. These minerals are known as **rock-forming minerals.** Appendix B at the back of this book lists some of the most common rock-forming minerals.

A rock's color provides clues to the rock's mineral composition. For example, **granite** is generally a light-colored rock that has high silica content. **Basalt,** shown in Figure 3, is a dark-colored rock that is low in silica. But as with minerals, color alone does not provide enough information to identify a rock.

Geologists observe the shape and color of crystals in a rock to identify the minerals that the rock contains. In identifying rocks, geologists also use some of the tests that are used to identify minerals. For example, testing the surface of a rock with acid determines whether the rock includes minerals made of compounds called carbonates.

Reading Checkpoint How would you define "rock-forming mineral"?

FIGURE 2
Minerals in Granite
Granite is made up of quartz, feldspar, hornblende, and mica. It may also contain other minerals.
Observing *Which mineral seems most abundant in the sample of granite shown?*

FIGURE 3
Basalt
Basalt is a dark-colored rock that has low silica content. Unlike granite, basalt has mineral crystals that are too small to be seen without a hand lens.

F ◆ 145

Texture

Teach Key Concepts

Elements of Rock Texture

Focus Explain that a complete description of rock texture can include several different types of information, such as grain size, grain shape, and how the grains are arranged.

Teach Ask students to suggest adjectives for describing grain size, grain shape, and grain pattern. (*For grain size, students might suggest* coarse-grained *and* fine-grained. *For grain shape, they might use* granular, rounded, *or* jagged. *For grain pattern, students might suggest* layered, swirled, *or* random.)

Apply Have students describe the textures of some common items, such as rice-marshmallow treats, sugar cubes, and a piece of concrete. **learning modality: visual**

Help Students Read

Previewing Visuals Before students read *Texture*, have them preview the visuals on the page. Have each student write a sentence about what he or she has learned from the visuals. Then, after students have read the section, have them read their sentences and compare them with what they have just learned from the text. **learning modality: visual**

How Rocks Form

Teach Key Concepts

Groups of Rocks

Focus Prompt students to tell you why it is useful to group objects.

Teach Ask: **What criterion is used to divide rocks into three groups?** (*The way that the rocks form*) **How does each group of rocks form?** (*Igneous rocks form when lava or magma cools. Sedimentary rocks form when sediment is compacted and cemented together. Metamorphic rock forms when preexisting rock is subjected to high heat, pressure, or hot fluids deep within Earth.*)

Apply Have students describe locations in which each of the different types of rock might form. (*Igneous: on or beneath a volcano; sedimentary: in an ocean basin; metamorphic: deep beneath a mountain range, such as the Himalaya*) **learning modality: logical/mathematical**

Texture

As with minerals, color alone does not provide enough information to identify a rock. But a rock's texture is very useful in identifying a rock. Most rocks are made up of particles of minerals or other rocks, which geologists call **grains**. Grains give the rock its texture. To a geologist, a rock's **texture** is the look and feel of the rock's surface. Some rocks are smooth and glassy. Others are rough or chalky. To describe a rock's texture, geologists use terms based on the size, shape, and pattern of the grains.

Rock Textures
Texture helps classify rocks.
Comparing and Contrasting *How would you compare the texture of diorite with the texture of gneiss?*

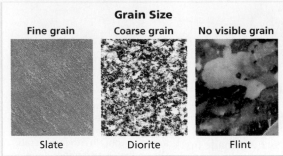

Grain Size
Fine grain   Coarse grain   No visible grain

Slate   Diorite   Flint

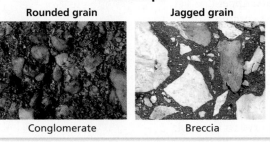

Grain Shape
Rounded grain   Jagged grain

Conglomerate   Breccia

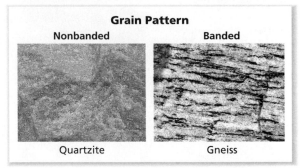

Grain Pattern
Nonbanded   Banded

Quartzite   Gneiss

Grain Size Often, the grains in a rock are large and easy to see. Such rocks are said to be coarse-grained. In other rocks, the grains are so small that they can only be seen with a microscope. These rocks are said to be fine-grained. Notice the difference in texture between the fine-grained slate and the coarse-grained diorite in Figure 4 at left. Some rocks have no visible grain even when they are examined under a microscope.

Grain Shape The grains in a rock vary widely in shape. Some grains look like tiny particles of sand. Others look like small seeds or exploding stars. In some rocks, such as granite, the grain results from the shapes of the crystals that form the rock. In other rocks, the grain shape results from fragments of several rocks. These fragments can be smooth and rounded or they can be jagged.

Grain Pattern The grains in a rock often form patterns. Some grains lie in flat layers that look like a stack of pancakes. Other grains form swirling patterns. Some rocks have grains of different colors in bands, like the gneiss (NYS) in Figure 4. In other rocks, the grains occur randomly throughout.

 Reading Checkpoint What does it mean to say that a rock is coarse-grained?

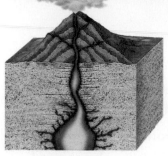  

Igneous Rock forms when magma or lava cools and hardens.

Sedimentary Rock forms when pieces of rock are pressed and cemented together.

Metamorphic Rock forms from other rocks that are changed by heat and pressure.

How Rocks Form

Using color, texture, and mineral composition, geologists can classify a rock according to its origin. A rock's origin is how the rock formed. **Geologists classify rocks into three major groups: igneous rock, sedimentary rock, and metamorphic rock.**

Each of these groups of rocks forms in a different way. **Igneous rock** (IG nee us) forms from the cooling of magma or lava. Most **sedimentary rock** (seduh MEN turee) forms when particles of other rocks or the remains of plants and animals are pressed and cemented together. Sedimentary rock forms in layers that are buried below the surface. **Metamorphic rock** (metuh MAWR fik) forms when an existing rock is changed by heat, pressure, or chemical reactions. Most metamorphic rock forms deep underground.

FIGURE 5
Kinds of Rocks
Rocks can be igneous, sedimentary, or metamorphic, depending on how the rock formed.

For: More on rock identification
Visit: PHSchool.com
Web Code: cfd-1051

Section 1 Assessment

⟳ **Target Reading Skill** Asking Questions Work with a partner to check the answers in your graphic organizer about the section headings.

Reviewing Key Concepts

1. **a. Naming** What three characteristics do geologists use to identify rocks?
   b. Defining What are the grains of a rock?
   c. Comparing and Contrasting In your own words, compare the grain size, shape, and pattern of the conglomerate and breccia in Figure 4.
2. **a. Reviewing** What are the three main groups of rocks?
   b. Explaining How do igneous rocks form?
   c. Classifying Gneiss is a kind of rock that forms when heat and pressure inside Earth change granite. To what group of rocks does gneiss belong?

Writing in Science

Wanted Poster Write a paragraph for a wanted poster in which you describe the characteristics of granite. In your wanted poster, be sure to describe granite's mineral composition, color, and texture. Also mention the group of rocks to which granite belongs.

Monitor Progress [L2]

Answers
Figure 4 Diorite is more coarse, and the grains are not in bands.

✔ **Reading Checkpoint** It has grains or crystals that can be seen with the unaided eye.

Assess

Reviewing Key Concepts

1. a. Mineral composition, color, and texture **b.** The particles of minerals or other rocks that give a rock its texture. **c.** Both rocks have a coarse, granular texture. The major difference is that the grains in conglomerate are rounded, whereas the grains in breccia are angular.
2. a. Igneous rock, sedimentary rock, and metamorphic rock. **b.** Igneous rocks form when lava or magma cools on or beneath Earth's surface. **c.** Metamorphic rock

Reteach [L1]
Write descriptions of several different rocks on the board. One possible example is this: sandstone—a rock made of sand grains that were deposited and cemented together. Have students classify the rocks as igneous, sedimentary, or metamorphic.

Performance Assessment [L2]
Have students explain in their own words what characteristics geologists use to identify rocks.

All in One Teaching Resources
- Section Summary: *Classifying Rocks*
- Review and Reinforce: *Classifying Rocks*
- Enrich: *Classifying Rocks*

Lab zone Chapter Project

Keep Students on Track Students should begin to identify locations in which they can collect rock samples. Be sure that they collect samples only in the areas permitted and that they include safety in their plans. Caution students to collect samples only when in groups or with an adult. After students have selected sites, have them begin collecting rocks of various colors and textures.

Writing in Science

Writing Skill Description
Scoring Rubric
4 includes description that addresses all of the criteria and states that granite is an igneous rock; provides a variety of sensory details
3 includes all criteria

2 includes three of the four criteria with brief descriptions
1 includes one or two criteria or accurate details

Objectives

After this lesson, students will be able to
F.5.2.1 identify the characteristics used to classify igneous rocks
F.5.2.2 describe ways in which igneous rocks are used

Target Reading Skill

Identifying Main Ideas Explain that identifying main ideas and details helps students sort the facts from the information into groups. Each group can have a main topic, subtopics, and details.

Answers

Main Idea: Igneous rocks are classified by origin, texture, and mineral composition.
Details: An igneous rock can be extrusive or intrusive; its texture depends on the size and shape of its mineral crystals; its color depends on its mineral composition.

All in One **Teaching Resources**

• Transparency F43

Preteach

Build Background Knowledge **L1**

Lava

Help students recall knowledge about lava. Ask: **Where does molten material rise to Earth's surface?** (*Volcanoes, fissures*) **What happens when it rises close to or onto the surface?** (*It cools and becomes rock.*)

For: more on igneous rock
Visit: www.SciLinks.org
Web Code: scn-1052

Download a worksheet that will guide students' review of Internet resources on igneous rocks.

Section
2
Igneous Rocks

Section
2
Igneous Rocks

Reading Focus

Key Concepts

• What characteristics are used to classify igneous rocks?
• How are igneous rocks used?

Key Terms

• extrusive rock   • intrusive rock

Target Reading Skill

Identifying Main Ideas As you read Classifying Igneous Rocks, write the main idea in a graphic organizer like the one below. Then write three supporting details that further explain the main idea.

Main Idea

Igneous rocks are classified by origin, texture, and composition.

Detail   **Detail**   **Detail**

For: Links on igneous rocks
Visit: www.SciLinks.org
Web Code: scn-1052

Discover Activity

Obsidian

Granite

How Do Igneous Rocks Form?

1. Use a hand lens to examine samples of granite and obsidian.
2. Describe the texture of both rocks using the terms coarse, fine, or glassy.
3. Which rock has coarse-grained crystals? Which rock has no crystals or grains?

Think It Over
Inferring Granite and obsidian are igneous rocks. From your observations, what can you infer about how each type of rock formed?

The time is 4.6 billion years ago. You are in a spacecraft orbiting Earth. Do you see the blue and green globe of Earth that astronauts today see from space? No—instead, Earth looks like a charred and bubbling marshmallow heated over hot coals.

Soon after Earth formed, the planet's interior became so hot that magma formed. Lava repeatedly flowed over the surface. The lava quickly hardened, forming a rocky crust. Because this early crust was denser than the material beneath it, chunks of crust sank into Earth's interior. This allowed more lava to erupt over the surface and harden to form rock.

Classifying Igneous Rocks

The first rocks to form on Earth probably looked like the igneous rocks that can be seen today. Igneous rock is any rock that forms from magma or lava. The name *igneous* comes from the Latin word *ignis*, meaning "fire." **Igneous rocks are classified according to their origin, texture, and mineral composition.**

Origin Igneous rock may form on or beneath Earth's surface. **Extrusive rock** is igneous rock formed from lava that erupted onto Earth's surface. Basalt is the most common extrusive rock. Basalt forms much of the crust, including the oceanic crust, shield volcanoes, and lava plateaus.

Discover Activity

Skills Focus Inferring   **L1**

Materials samples of granite and obsidian, hand lens

Time 10 minutes

Tips If samples of granite and obsidian are unavailable, use any two igneous rocks with similar composition but obviously different textures, such as gabbro and basalt or diorite and andesite.

Expected Outcome Granite and obsidian have similar compositions but different textures. Students should observe that granite has a coarse, crystalline texture, whereas obsidian has a glassy texture.

Think It Over The large crystals in granite form when magma cools slowly beneath Earth's surface. Glassy obsidian forms when lava cools so rapidly on Earth's surface that crystals cannot form.

Igneous rock that formed when magma hardened beneath Earth's surface is called **intrusive rock.** The most abundant intrusive rock in continental crust is granite. Batholiths made of granite form the core of many mountain ranges.

Texture The texture of an igneous rock depends on the size and shape of its mineral crystals. The only exceptions to this rule are the different types of volcanic glass—igneous rock that lacks a crystal structure.

Igneous rocks may be similar in mineral composition and yet have very different textures. Rapidly cooling lava forms fine-grained igneous rocks with small crystals. Slowly cooling magma forms coarse-grained rocks with large crystals. Therefore, intrusive and extrusive rocks usually have different textures.

Intrusive rocks have larger crystals than extrusive rocks. If you examine a coarse-grained rock such as granite, you can easily see that the crystals vary in size and color. Some intrusive rocks, like the porphyry in Figure 6, have a texture that looks like a gelatin dessert with chopped-up fruit mixed in.

Extrusive rocks have a fine-grained or glassy texture. Basalt is a fine-grained extrusive rock. It consists of crystals too small to be seen without a microscope. Obsidian is an extrusive rock that cooled very rapidly without forming crystals. As a result, obsidian has the smooth, shiny texture of a thick piece of glass.

Discovery CHANNEL SCHOOL

Rocks

Video Preview
▶ Video Field Trip
Video Assessment

FIGURE 6
Igneous Rock Textures
Igneous rocks such as rhyolite, pegmatite, and porphyry can vary greatly in texture depending on whether they are intrusive or extrusive.
Relating Cause and Effect *What conditions caused rhyolite to have a fine-grained texture?*

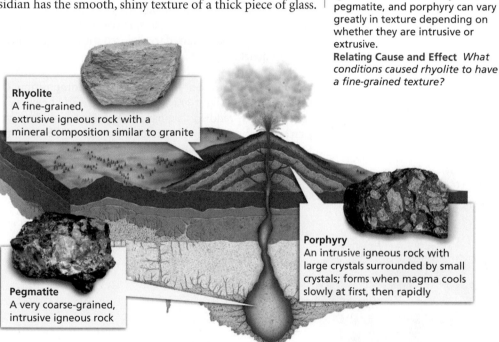

Rhyolite
A fine-grained, extrusive igneous rock with a mineral composition similar to granite

Pegmatite
A very coarse-grained, intrusive igneous rock

Porphyry
An intrusive igneous rock with large crystals surrounded by small crystals; forms when magma cools slowly at first, then rapidly

F ◆ 149

Instruct

Classifying Igneous Rocks

Teach Key Concepts L2
Classification Criteria

Focus Remind students that classification systems use criteria to group objects. Criteria used to classify igneous rocks include origin, texture, and mineral composition.

Teach List the three criteria discussed in this chapter on the board, and discuss possible choices for each: **origin** *(intrusive or extrusive),* **texture** *(fine-grained, coarse-grained, or glassy),* and **mineral composition** *(light-colored, intermediate-colored, dark-colored depending on silica content).*

Apply Ask students to identify an extrusive rock that has a fine-grained texture and a dark color. *(basalt)* **learning modality: logical/mathematical**

All in One Teaching Resources
• Transparency F44

Discovery CHANNEL SCHOOL Video Field Trip

Rocks

Show the Video Field Trip to let students experience geology at Yosemite and understand how the cliffs there formed. Discussion question: **What is the main type of rock that is found in the cliffs of Yosemite?** *(Igneous)*

Independent Practice L2

All in One Teaching Resources
• Guided Reading and Study Worksheet: *Igneous Rocks*

Monitor Progress _____ L2

Skills Check Ask each student to make a concept map summarizing the relationships between cooling rate, origin, and crystal size in igneous rocks. Students can save their concept maps in their portfolios. **Portfolio**

Answer
Figure 6 Rapid cooling of lava on Earth's surface

Differentiated Instruction

Gifted and Talented L3
Writing Hypotheses Show students samples of pumice and scoria. Have students write hypotheses about why these rocks contain holes. Then ask them to research the subject and report their findings. *(The holes in pumice and scoria are gas pockets formed by the gas that was given off by the erupting lava.)* **learning modality: logical/mathematical**

Less Proficient Readers L1
Making a Display Have students listen to this section using the *Student Edition on Audio CD.* Then, ask them to prepare a display using sketches, photographs, or samples that illustrate igneous rock origin, texture, and mineral composition.
learning modality: visual

Math Skill Making and Interpreting Graphs

Focus Explain that circle graphs often are the best choice for showing parts of a whole.

Teach Remind students that a graph's title often contains important information. Ask: **What does this circle graph represent?** *(The minerals in granite)* **What is the sum of all of the percentages shown in the graph?** (100%)

Answers

1. Feldspar

2. 10%

3. $100\% - (35\% + 10\%) = 55\%$

4. The overall color would be darker.

Lab zone Build **Inquiry** L2

Comparing and Contrasting Granite and Basalt

Materials hand lens, samples of granite and basalt

Time 15 minutes

Focus Explain that granite and basalt are the two most common igneous rocks.

Teach Invite students to handle the samples and then to sketch and describe each one. Descriptions should include origin, texture, color, density, and any minerals students can identify.

Apply Ask: **Which parts of the crust are composed mostly of basalt, and which are mostly granite?** *(Dense oceanic crust is composed mostly of rock such as basalt. Less dense continental crust is composed mostly of rock such as granite.)* **learning modality: kinesthetic**

Math ▸ Analyzing Data

Mineral Mixture

Granite is a mixture of light-colored minerals such as feldspar and quartz and dark-colored minerals including hornblende and mica. But, granite can vary in mineral composition, affecting its color and texture.

Study the circle graph and then answer the questions.

1. **Reading Graphs** What mineral is most abundant in granite?
2. **Reading Graphs** About what percentage of granite is made up of dark minerals?
3. **Calculating** If the amount of quartz increases to 35 percent and the amount of dark-colored minerals stays the same, what percentage of the granite will be made up of feldspar?

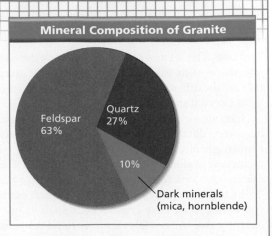

Mineral Composition of Granite

Feldspar 63%
Quartz 27%
10%
Dark minerals (mica, hornblende)

4. **Predicting** How would the color of the granite change if it contained less feldspar and more mica and hornblende?

Mineral Composition You may recall that the silica content of magma and lava can vary. Lava that is low in silica usually forms dark-colored rocks such as basalt. Basalt contains feldspar as well as certain dark-colored minerals, but does not contain quartz.

Magma that is high in silica usually forms light-colored rocks, such as granite. Granite's mineral composition determines its color—light gray, red, pink, or nearly black. Granite that is rich in reddish feldspar is a speckled pink. But granite rich in hornblende and dark mica is light gray with dark specks. Quartz crystals in granite add light gray or smoky specks.

Geologists can make thin slices of a rock, such as the gabbro in Figure 7. They study the rock's crystals under a microscope to determine the rock's mineral composition.

✓ Reading Checkpoint How can mineral composition affect a rock's color?

FIGURE 7
Thin Section of a Rock
This thin slice of gabbro, viewed under a microscope, contains olivine, feldspar, and other minerals.

Uses of Igneous Rocks

Many igneous rocks are hard, dense, and durable. **People throughout history have used igneous rock for tools and building materials.**

Building Materials Granite has a long history as a building material. More than 3,500 years ago, the ancient Egyptians used granite for statues like the ones shown in Figure 8. About 600 years ago, the Incas of Peru carefully fitted together great blocks of granite and other igneous rocks to build a fortress near Cuzco, their capital city. In the United States during the 1800s and early 1900s, granite was widely used to build bridges and public buildings and for paving streets with cobblestones. Today, thin, polished sheets of granite are used in curbstones, floors, and kitchen counters. Basalt is crushed to make gravel that is used in construction.

Other Uses Igneous rocks such as pumice and obsidian also have important uses. The rough surface of pumice makes it a good abrasive for cleaning and polishing. Ancient native Americans used obsidian to make sharp tools for cutting and scraping. Perlite, formed from the heating of obsidian, is often mixed with soil for starting vegetable seeds.

FIGURE 8
Durable Granite
The ancient Egyptians valued granite for its durability. These statues from a temple in Luxor, Egypt, were carved in granite.

 Reading Checkpoint What igneous rock is most often used as a building material?

Section 2 Assessment

 Target Reading Skill Identifying Main Ideas Use your graphic organizer about the characteristics of igneous rock to help you answer Question 1 below.

Reviewing Key Concepts

1. a. **Explaining** How are igneous rocks classified?
   b. **Defining** What are extrusive rocks and intrusive rocks?
   c. **Comparing and Contrasting** Compare granite and basalt in terms of their origin and texture. Which is extrusive? Which is intrusive?
2. a. **Summarizing** What are two common uses of igneous rocks?
   b. **Reviewing** What characteristics make igneous rocks useful?
   c. **Making Judgments** Would pumice be a good material to use to make a floor? Explain.

Lab zone At-Home **Activity**

The Rocks Around Us Many common household products contain minerals found in igneous rock. For example, glass contains quartz, which is found in granite. Research one of the following materials and the products in which it is used: garnet, granite, perlite, pumice, or vermiculite. Explain to family members how the rock or mineral formed and how it is used.

Lab zone At-Home **Activity**

The Rocks Around Us L2 Encourage students to do this activity at home. Then compare student research in class. (*Possible answers: Garnet, an abrasive; granite, countertops, minerals in granite [quartz and feldspar], used in the manufacture of glass; perlite and vermiculite, soil additives; pumice, abrasive cleanser*)

Uses of Igneous Rocks

Teach Key Concepts   L2

Uses of Igneous Rocks

Focus Ask students to describe uses of igneous rock in their community.

Teach Explain that igneous rocks are used because of their properties and beauty. Ask: **Why can obsidian be used for cutting?** (*It breaks with hard, sharp edges.*) **Why is polished granite sometimes used on floors or walls of buildings?** (*Durability and attractive color make it attractive for these purposes.*)

Apply Have students suggest ways to use igneous rock in buildings of their own design. **learning modality: logical/mathematical**

Monitor Progress _____   L2

Answers

Reading Checkpoint The minerals have different colors, so rocks with different proportions of them have different colors.

Reading Checkpoint Granite

Assess

Reviewing Key Concepts

1. a. By origin, texture, mineral composition **b.** Extrusive rocks form from lava that has erupted onto Earth's surface. Intrusive rock forms when magma hardens beneath Earth's surface. **c.** They are similar because both form when molten rock cools. Granite is a light-colored, intrusive rock with a coarse-grained texture. Basalt is a dark-colored, extrusive rock with a fine-grained texture.
2. a. Building materials, abrasives **b.** They are hard, dense, and durable. **c.** No; pumice is too abrasive and full of holes.

Reteach   L1

Have students create a table that shows how common igneous rocks are classified. Use mineral composition (as a color index) across the top and grain size along the side.

All in One Teaching Resources

- Section Summary: *Igneous Rocks*
- Review and Reinforce: *Igneous Rocks*
- Enrich: *Igneous Rocks*

Objectives
After the lesson, students will be able to
F.5.3.1 describe how sedimentary rocks form
F.5.3.2 list and describe the three major types of sedimentary rocks
F.5.3.3 explain how sedimentary rocks are used

Target Reading Skill
Outlining Explain that using an outline format helps students organize information by main topic, subtopics, and details.

Answers
Sedimentary Rock
I.   From Sediment to Rock
  A. Erosion
  B. Deposition
  C. Compaction
  D. Cementation
II. Types of Sedimentary Rock
  A. Clastic Rocks
  B. Organic Rocks
  C. Chemical Rocks
III. Uses of Sedimentary Rocks

All in One Teaching Resources

• Transparency F45

Preteach

Build Background Knowledge   L2

How Sandstone Forms
Invite students to think of a sandy beach along an ocean or lake. Ask: **What could cause the sand to harden into sandstone?** *(Possible answer: the weight of sand piled deeply enough could press the grains together. Some students might suggest that something would have to hold the sand grains together.)*

Help Students Read   L1

Sequencing
Refer to the Content Refresher in this chapter, which provides the guidelines for sequencing. Have students read the text on the following page about how sedimentary rock forms. Then have them use what they have just read and Figure 9 to draw a flowchart describing the process.

Reading Focus
Key Concepts
• How do sedimentary rocks form?
• What are the three major types of sedimentary rocks?
• How are sedimentary rocks used?

Key Terms
• sediment • erosion
• deposition • compaction
• cementation • clastic rock
• organic rock • chemical rock

Target Reading Skill
Outlining As you read, make an outline about sedimentary rocks. Use the red section headings for the main topics and the blue headings for the subtopics.

Sedimentary Rocks
I. From sediment to rock
A. Erosion
B.
II.
A.

Lab zone   Discover **Activity**

How Does Pressure Affect Particles of Rock?
1. Place a sheet of paper over a slice of soft bread.
2. Put a stack of several heavy books on top of the paper. After 10 minutes, remove the books. Observe what happened to the bread.
3. Slice the bread so you can observe its cross section.
4. Carefully slice a piece of fresh bread and compare its cross section to that of the pressed bread.

Think It Over
Observing How did the bread change after you removed the books? Describe the texture of the bread. How does the bread feel? What can you predict about how pressure affects the particles that make up sedimentary rocks?

Visitors to Badlands National Park in South Dakota see some of the strangest scenery on Earth. The park contains jagged peaks, steep cliffs, and deep canyons sculpted in colorful rock that is layered like a birthday cake. The layers of this cake are red, orange, pink, yellow, or tan. These rocks formed over millions of years as particles of mud, sand, and volcanic ash were deposited in thick layers. The mud and sand slowly changed to sedimentary rock. Then, uplift of the land exposed the rocks to the forces that wear away Earth's surface.

Badlands National Park ▲

From Sediment to Rock
If you have ever walked along a stream or beach you may have noticed tiny sand grains, mud, and pebbles. These are particles of sediment. **Sediment** is small, solid pieces of material that come from rocks or living things. In addition to particles of rock, sediment may include shells, bones, leaves, stems, and other remains of living things. Sedimentary rocks form when sediment is deposited by water and wind. **Most sedimentary rocks are formed through a series of processes: erosion, deposition, compaction, and cementation.** Figure 9 shows how sedimentary rocks form.

Lab zone   Discover **Activity**

Skills Focus Observing   L1

Materials sheet of paper, 2 slices of bread, stack of books, plastic knife

Time 15 minutes

Tips To keep the bread from sticking to the tabletop, have students fold the sheet of paper and place the slice of bread inside the fold.

Expected Outcome Students will observe that the bread is thinner than before. The weight of the books compacts the bread and reduces the amount of pore space. This is similar to compaction of sediment.

Think It Over The bread's texture is harder and more dense than before. A typical prediction will suggest that pressure affects sediment grains similarly.

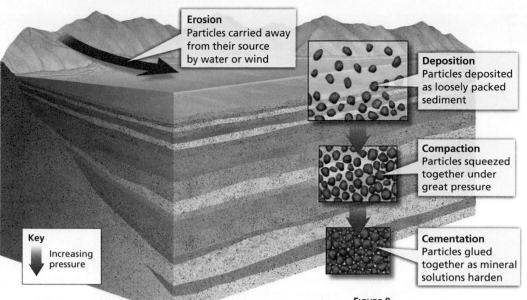

Erosion
Particles carried away from their source by water or wind

Deposition
Particles deposited as loosely packed sediment

Compaction
Particles squeezed together under great pressure

Cementation
Particles glued together as mineral solutions harden

Key
↓ Increasing pressure

FIGURE 9
How Sedimentary Rocks Form
Sedimentary rocks form through the deposition, compaction, and cementation of sediments over millions of years.
Relating Cause and Effect What conditions are necessary for sedimentary rocks to form?

Erosion Destructive forces are constantly breaking up and wearing away, or weathering, all the rocks on Earth's surface. These forces include heat and cold, rain, waves, and grinding ice. The forces of erosion form sediment. In **erosion,** running water, wind, or ice loosen and carry away fragments of rock.

Deposition Eventually, the moving water, wind, or ice slows and deposits the sediment in layers. If water is carrying the sediment, rock fragments and other materials sink to the bottom of a lake or ocean. **Deposition** is the process by which sediment settles out of the water or wind carrying it.

Compaction The process that presses sediments together is **compaction.** Thick layers of sediment build up gradually over millions of years. These heavy layers press down on the layers beneath them. The weight of new layers further compacts the sediments, squeezing them tightly together. The layers often remain visible in sedimentary rock.

Cementation While compaction is taking place, the minerals in the rock slowly dissolve in the water. **Cementation** is the process in which dissolved minerals crystallize and glue particles of sediment together. In cementation, dissolved minerals seep into the spaces between particles and then harden.

 Reading Checkpoint What is deposition?

 Go Online
SciLINKS NSTA
For: Links on sedimentary rocks
Visit: www.SciLinks.org
Web Code: scn-1053

From Sediment to Rock

Teach Key Concepts L2
Formation of Sedimentary Rock

Focus Ask: **How would you describe sand? Mud?** *(Small pieces of rock or mineral; sand grains are larger than the grains in mud)* **Has anyone been on a beach made of gravel or pieces of shell?** *(Gravel beaches are common along the west coast; shell beaches are common in tropical areas.)* Tell students that all of these materials are sediment.

Teach Emphasize that sedimentary rock consists of sediment, and discuss the processes of erosion, deposition, compaction, and cementation.

Apply Show students a piece of sandstone. Ask them to describe how it formed.
learning modality: logical/mathematical

All in One Teaching Resources
• Transparency F46

 **Go Online**
SciLINKS NSTA
For: Links on sedimentary rocks
Visit: www.SciLinks.org
Web Code: scn-1053

Download a worksheet that will guide students' review of Internet resources on sedimentary rock.

Independent Practice

All in One Teaching Resources
• Guided Reading and Study Worksheet: *Sedimentary Rocks*

💿 **Student Edition on Audio CD**

Differentiated Instruction

Special Needs
Comparing Sediment and Rock
Obtain some sediment samples such as clay, sand, and gravel. Have students compare the sediment samples with the corresponding clastic sedimentary rocks (shale, sandstone, and conglomerate).

L1 Encourage students to examine the sediment and sedimentary rocks with a magnifying lens. After students have examined the samples, engage them in a discussion about how sediment becomes sedimentary rock.
learning modality: kinesthetic

Monitor Progress L2

Drawing Have each student draw a close-up view of a sedimentary rock that includes grains and cement.

Answers
Figure 9 Sediment must be deposited and then changed to rock through compaction and cementation.

 Reading Checkpoint The process by which sediment settles out onto the land

Types of Sedimentary Rock

Teach Key Concepts   L2

Sedimentary Rock Classification

Focus Explain that sedimentary rocks are categorized according to how they form.

Teach To classify sedimentary rocks, students must understand three basic processes. Use the following strategies: 1) Compare the formation of chemical rocks with salt crystallizing on a car after splashed water evaporates. 2) To help students understand organic rocks, remind them of seashell sand on a beach and coral reefs. 3) Tell students that *clastic* rocks form from *clasts,* which are pieces of preexisting rock.

Apply Quiz students about the types of rock that might form in various modern environments: **an evaporating desert lake** *(Chemical);* **a desert dune** *(Clastic);* **an accumulation of peat in a swamp** *(Organic).* **learning modality: logical/mathematical**

Classifying Sedimentary Rocks

Materials hand lens and samples of sandstone, conglomerate, breccia, shale, organic limestone, rock gypsum

Time 15 minutes

Focus Remind students that texture and composition are important rock characteristics.

Teach Provide groups of students with representative samples of the three major groups of sedimentary rocks. Challenge each group to develop a rationale for classifying the samples into three types.

Apply Ask students to examine table salt with a hand lens and identify the sedimentary rock type. *(Chemical)* **learning modality: logical/mathematical**

Shale
Fossils are often found in shale, which splits easily into flat pieces.

Clastic

Sandstone
Many small holes between sand grains allow sandstone to absorb water.

Conglomerate
Rock fragments with rounded edges make up conglomerate.

FIGURE 10
Clastic Rocks
Clastic rocks such as shale, sandstone, conglomerate, and breccia are sedimentary rocks that form from particles of other rocks.

Lab zone Try This **Activity**

Rock Absorber
Here's how to find out if water can soak into rock.

1. Using a hand lens, compare samples of sandstone and shale.
2. Use a balance to measure the mass of each rock.
3. Place the rocks in a pan of water and watch closely. Which sample has bubbles escaping? Predict which sample will gain mass.
4. Leave the rocks submerged in the pan overnight.
5. The next day, remove the rocks from the pan and find the mass of each rock.

Drawing Conclusions How did the masses of the two rocks change after soaking? What can you conclude about each rock?

154 ◆ F

Types of Sedimentary Rock

Geologists classify sedimentary rocks according to the type of sediments that make up the rock. **There are three major groups of sedimentary rocks: clastic rocks, organic rocks, and chemical rocks.** Different processes form each of these types of sedimentary rocks.

Clastic Rocks Most sedimentary rocks are made up of broken pieces of other rocks. A **clastic rock** is a sedimentary rock that forms when rock fragments are squeezed together. These fragments can range in size from clay particles that are too small to be seen without a microscope to large boulders that are too heavy for you to lift. Clastic rocks are grouped by the size of the rock fragments, or particles, of which they are made. Common clastic rocks include shale, sandstone, conglomerate, and breccia (BRECH ee uh), shown in Figure 10.

Shale forms from tiny particles of clay. Water must deposit the clay particles in thin, flat layers. Sandstone forms from the sand on beaches, the ocean floor, riverbeds, and sand dunes. Most sand particles consist of quartz.

Some sedimentary rocks contain a mixture of rock fragments of different sizes. If the fragments have rounded edges, they form a clastic rock called conglomerate. A rock made up of large fragments with sharp edges is called breccia.

Organic Rocks Not all sedimentary rocks are made from particles of other rocks. **Organic rock** forms where the remains of plants and animals are deposited in thick layers. The term "organic" refers to substances that once were part of living things or were made by living things. Two important organic sedimentary rocks are coal and limestone, shown in Figure 11.

Lab zone Try This **Activity**

Skills Focus Drawing conclusions   L2

Materials samples of sandstone and shale, hand lens, balance, pan, water

Time 15 minutes for setup; 10 minutes the next day

Tips Each sample must be at least 25 g to show a significant change in mass. Be sure that the sandstone sample is porous (grains should fall off). If there are not enough samples for every student, divide the class into small groups.

Expected Outcome Students observe that sandstone is rough and coarse-grained, whereas shale is smooth and fine-grained. The mass of the shale changes little or not at all, but the mass of the sandstone increases.

Water can enter the pores in sandstone, but shale is impermeable to water.

Extend Have students try the same activity with other rock samples. **learning modality: logical/mathematical**

Organic

Breccia
Rock fragments with sharp edges form breccia.

Coal
Swamp plants that formed millions of years ago slowly changed to form coal.

Limestone
Coquina is a form of limestone in which the shells that makeup the rock are easy to see.

FIGURE 11
Organic Rocks
Organic rocks such as coal and limestone are sedimentary rocks that form from the remains of living things.

Coal forms from the remains of swamp plants buried in water. As layer upon layer of plant remains build up, the weight of the layers squeezes the decaying plants. Over millions of years, they slowly change into coal.

Limestone forms in the ocean, where many living things, such as coral, clams, and oysters, have hard shells or skeletons made of calcite. When these animals die, their shells pile up on the ocean floor. Over millions of years, these layers of sediment can grow to a depth of hundreds of meters. Slowly, compaction and cementation change the sediment to limestone.

Chemical Rocks When minerals that are dissolved in a solution crystallize, **chemical rock** forms. For example, limestone can form when calcite that is dissolved in lakes, seas, or underground water comes out of solution and forms crystals. This kind of limestone is considered a chemical rock. Chemical rocks can also form from mineral deposits left when seas or lakes evaporate. For example, rock salt is made of the mineral halite, which forms by evaporation.

 **Reading Checkpoint** How does coal form?

FIGURE 12
Chemical Rocks
These rock "towers" in Mono Lake California, are made of tufa, a form of limestone. Tufa is a chemical rock that forms from solutions containing dissolved materials. **Classifying** *What type of sedimentary rock is tufa?*

Formation of Sedimentary Rock

Focus Ask: **Why can't we see children grow?** (*Because they grow so slowly that it is difficult to observe*) Point out to students that it is difficult to observe the formation of sedimentary rocks for the same reason.

Teach Ask: **How long does it take for a sedimentary rock to form?** (*Many students will think that this occurs quickly, such as when puddles dry.*) Emphasize that sedimentary rock layers form through many thousands or millions of years. Ask: **Did humans contribute to the formation of sedimentary rocks?** (*Many students will think that humans had a role in forming sedimentary rocks.*) Explain that sedimentary rock layers form through natural processes.

Apply Show students a sample of sandstone. Ask them to explain where it came from. Help them to understand that this rock is a piece from a large layer of rock and that the layer of rock formed over a long period of time. **learning modality: logical/ mathematical**

Uses of Sedimentary Rocks

Teach Key Concepts L2
Common Uses

Focus Tell students that sedimentary rock is in their homes, gardens, and school.

Teach Challenge students to identify common uses of sedimentary rock. (*Possible answers: rock gypsum to make wallboard, phosphorite rock for fertilizer, and rock salt to spread on sidewalks to melt ice*)

Apply Ask students to identify sedimentary rock resources in your state. (*A possible answer that applies to all states is sand and gravel to make concrete and for fill.*) **learning modality: logical/mathematical**

Monitor Progress _____ L2

Writing Ask students to write a short paragraph explaining how a clamshell might become part of a sedimentary rock.

Answers
Figure 12 Chemical sedimentary rock

Reading Checkpoint Coal forms from the remains of swamp plants. The remains are buried and changed by heat and pressure.

Answer

 Reading Checkpoint — They are common and soft enough to be easily cut into blocks and slabs.

Assess

Reviewing Key Concepts

1. a. Small, solid pieces of material that come from rocks or living things **b.** Erosion, deposition, compaction, cementation **c.** Oldest layers will be on the bottom unless sedimentary layers have been folded or faulted.

2. a. Clastic, organic, chemical **b.** Organic; shell fragments can be deposited and cemented together, plant matter can change to coal under the influence of heat and pressure. **c.** Evaporation of seawater; chemical

3. a. Building materials, making cement, arrowheads **b.** No. Repeated wetting and drying sometimes can cause shale to fall apart.

Reteach   L1

Have student groups gather photographs that illustrate examples of erosion and deposition.

Performance Assessment   L2

Skills Check Have each student make a comparison-and-contrast table that includes all of the sedimentary rocks discussed in the section. The table should have columns for name, major group, and characteristics.

All in One Teaching Resources

* Section Summary: *Sedimentary Rocks*
* Review and Reinforce: *Sedimentary Rocks*
* Enrich: *Sedimentary Rocks*

FIGURE 13
Carving Limestone
This stone carver is sculpting designs on a sphere of white limestone.

Uses of Sedimentary Rocks

People have used sedimentary rocks throughout history for many different purposes, including building materials and tools. For example, people made arrowheads out of flint for thousands of years. Flint is a hard rock, yet it can be shaped to a point. Flint is formed when small particles of silica settle out of water.

Sedimentary rocks such as sandstone and limestone have been used as building materials for thousands of years. Both types of stone are soft enough to be cut easily into blocks or slabs. You may be surprised to learn that the White House in Washington, D.C., is built of sandstone. Builders today use sandstone and limestone on the outside walls of buildings. Limestone also has many industrial uses. For example, limestone is used in making cement and steel.

Reading Checkpoint — Why are sandstone and limestone useful as building materials?

Section 3 Assessment

Target Reading Skill Outlining Use the information in your outline about sedimentary rocks to help you answer the questions below.

Reviewing Key Concepts

1. a. Defining What is sediment?
  b. Sequencing Place these steps in the formation of sedimentary rock in the proper sequence: compaction, erosion, cementation, deposition.
  c. Inferring In layers of sedimentary rock, where would you expect to find the oldest sediment? Explain your answer.
2. a. Listing What are the three main types of sedimentary rock?
  b. Explaining Which type of sedimentary rock forms from the remains of living things? Explain how this sedimentary rock forms.
  c. Relating Cause and Effect What process causes deposits of rock salt to form? What type of sedimentary rock is rock salt?

3. a. Listing What are some uses of sedimentary rocks?
  b. Predicting The particles of sediment that make up shale are not usually well cemented. Would shale be a good choice of building material in a wet climate?

Writing in Science

Explaining a Process Suppose that a large mass of granite lies exposed on Earth's surface. Explain the steps in the process by which the granite could become sedimentary rock. Your answer should also state which of the main types of sedimentary rock will result from this process.

Writing in Science

Writing Mode Explanation

Scoring Rubric

4 includes description of steps and the type of rock; steps are detailed and drawings are present
3 includes all criteria
2 includes most steps with brief description
1 includes one or two steps, or inaccurate information

Lab zone Chapter Project

Keep Students on Track With an adult, have students visit an area to collect samples of rock. They should note whether the rock is a loose fragment, a piece broken from an outcrop, or a cobble in a stream. Have students classify their rocks in groups. Ask them to describe the textures and list any recognizable minerals.

Reading Focus

Key Concepts
• How do coral reefs form?
• What evidence do limestone deposits from coral reefs provide about Earth's history?

Key Term
• coral reef

Target Reading Skill
Using Prior Knowledge
Before you read, look at the section headings to see what this section is about. Then write what you know about coral reefs in a graphic organizer like the one below. As you read, write what you learn.

What You Know
1. Coral reefs grow in the oceans.
2.

What You Learned
1.
2.

 **Discover Activity**

How Does a Rock React to Acid?

1. Using a hand lens, observe the color and texture of limestone and coquina.
2. Put on your goggles and apron.
3. Obtain a small amount of dilute hydrochloric acid from your teacher. Hydrochloric acid is used to test rocks for the presence of the mineral calcite.
   Using a plastic dropper, place a few drops of dilute hydrochloric acid on the limestone. **CAUTION:** *Hydrochloric acid can cause burns.*
4. Record your observations.
5. Repeat Steps 2 through 4 with the sample of coquina and observe the results.
6. Rinse the rock samples with lots of water before returning them to your teacher. Wash your hands.

Think It Over
Drawing Conclusions How did the two rocks react to the test? A piece of coral reacts to hydrochloric acid the same way as limestone and coquina. What could you conclude about the mineral composition of coral?

Off the coast of Florida lies a "city" in the sea. It is a coral reef providing both food and shelter for many sea animals. The reef shimmers with life—clams, sponges, sea urchins, starfish, marine worms and, of course, fish. Schools of brilliantly colored fish dart in and out of forests of equally colorful corals. Octopuses lurk in underwater caves, scooping up crabs that pass too close. A reef forms a sturdy wall that protects the shoreline from battering waves. This city was built by billions of tiny, soft-bodied animals that have skeletons made of calcite.

FIGURE 14
A City in the Sea
A coral reef provides food and shelter for many different kinds of living things.

F ◆ 157

Section
4
Rocks From Reefs

Objectives
After this lesson, students will be able to
F.5.4.1 describe the formation of coral reefs
F.5.4.2 explain how limestone deposits from coral reefs provide information about Earth's history

Target Reading Skill

Using Prior Knowledge Explain that using prior knowledge helps students connect what they already know to what they are about to read.

Answers
Graphic organizers should have two columns: "What you know" and "What you learned." Have students write what they know in the first column. Then, as they read, they can add new facts to the second column.

All in One Teaching Resources
• Transparency F47

Preteach

Build Background Knowledge   L1

Experience With Reefs
Encourage students to share their knowledge of coral reefs, either from direct experience or from nature shows on television. Ask: **Where do coral reefs occur?** *(In warm ocean waters, such as in the Caribbean)* **How would you describe the structure of a coral reef?** *(A typical answer might describe a barrier-like structure that lies underwater.)*

 Discover Activity

Skills Focus Drawing conclusions
Materials samples of limestone and coquina, dilute hydrochloric acid, plastic dropper, running water, hand lens
Time 15 minutes
Tips Coquina is a rock composed of shells and shell fragments. A fossil shell can be used as an alternative. Caution students

L3 that the dilute (1%) hydrochloric acid must be handled with extreme care.

Expected Outcome Students will notice that coquina is a rock consisting of loosely cemented shell fragments. The limestone sample will be denser and well cemented. The dilute acid should fizz on both samples.

Think It Over Fizzing occurred on both samples. Coral also is made of calcite.

Coral Reefs

Teach Key Concepts **L2**

Coral Animals and Reefs

Focus Remind students that corals are animals. Ask: **What is a coral?** (*A polyp-like animal with a calcium carbonate skeleton*)

Teach Ask: **How do reefs form?** (*Through time, coral skeletons accumulate.*) **How long does it take for reefs to form?** (*Thousands of years*)

Apply Ask: **Why are reefs important?** (*They provide habitat for a huge number of species.*) **learning modality: verbal**

Go Online
PLANET DIARY
For: More on coral landforms
Visit: PHSchool.com
Web Code: cfd-1054

Download a worksheet that will guide students' review of Internet resources on coral landforms.

Limestone From Coral Reefs

Teach Key Concepts **L2**

Interpreting Earth's History From Reefs

Focus Remind students that modern coral reefs form in shallow, warm, ocean water within about 30 degrees of the equator.

Teach Ask students to imagine that they are observing an ancient coral reef preserved in a rock quarry. **Ask: What was the environment here when the reef formed?** (*The area was a shallow, warm ocean.*) **How could an underwater reef now be above sea level?** (*The land rose because of plate tectonics or the sea level dropped.*)

Apply Ask: **How could an ancient reef be preserved in the northern United States?** (*North America was near the equator when the reef formed.*) **learning modality: visual**

Independent Practice

All in One Teaching Resources

• Guided Reading and Study Worksheet: *Rocks From Reefs*

 Student Edition on Audio CD

Go Online
PLANET DIARY
For: More on coral landforms
Visit: PHSchool.com
Web Code: cfd-1054

FIGURE 15
Coral Animals and Reefs
The coral animals in the close-up feed on tiny organisms carried their way by the movement of ocean water. (The view has been magnified to show detail.) The aerial photograph shows an island in the South Pacific Ocean that is ringed by a coral reef (light blue areas). **Inferring** *Why are there no coral reefs in the dark blue areas of ocean water?*

158 ◆ F

Coral Reefs

Coral animals are tiny relatives of jellyfish that live together in vast numbers. They produce skeletons that grow together to form a structure called a **coral reef.**

How Coral Animals Live Most coral animals are smaller than your fingernail. Each one looks like a small sack with a mouth surrounded by tentacles. These animals use their tentacles to capture and eat microscopic creatures that float by.

Tiny algae grow within the body of each coral animal. The algae provide substances that the coral animals need to live. In turn, the coral animals provide a framework for the algae to grow on. Like plants, algae need sunlight. Below 40 meters, there is not enough light for the algae to grow. For this reason, almost all coral growth occurs within 40 meters of the water's surface.

How a Coral Reef Forms To form their skeletons, coral animals absorb the element calcium from the ocean water. The calcium is then combined with carbon and oxygen to form calcite. Recall that calcite is a mineral. **When coral animals die, their skeletons remain. More corals build on top of them, gradually forming a coral reef.**

Coral animals cannot grow in cold water. As a result, coral reefs form only in the warm, shallow water of tropical oceans. Reefs are most abundant around islands and along the eastern coasts of continents. In the United States, only the coasts of southern Florida and Hawaii have coral reefs.

Over thousands of years, reefs may grow to be hundreds of kilometers long and hundreds of meters thick. Reefs usually grow outward toward the open ocean. If the sea level rises or if the sea floor sinks, the reef will grow upward, too.

Reading Checkpoint What conditions of light and temperature do coral animals require?

Differentiated Instruction

Gifted and Talented **L3**
Research Mutualism Have students research the topic of mutualism, which is a mutually beneficial relationship between two species. The students should explain how coral polyps and zooxanthellae algae are dependent on each other. Ask students to suggest other examples of mutualism in nature. **learning modality: logical/mathematical**

Special Needs **L1**
Oral Presentation on Coral Reefs Show students a video about coral reefs. After the students have watched the video, ask them to prepare oral presentations explaining what they learned. **learning modality: visual**

Limestone From Coral Reefs

A coral reef is really organic limestone. **Limestone deposits that began as coral reefs provide evidence of how plate motions have changed Earth's surface. These deposits also provide evidence of past environments.**

Limestone from coral reefs has been forming in Earth's oceans for more than 400 million years. The limestone formed when shallow seas covered the low-lying parts of the continents. The limestone was exposed when the seas retreated. Later, plate motions slowly moved these limestone deposits far from the tropical oceans where they formed. In the United States, reefs that formed millions of years ago are exposed in Wisconsin, Illinois, Indiana, Texas, New Mexico, and many other places.

Deposits of organic limestone help geologists understand past environments. Where geologists find fossils of an ancient coral reef, they know that the reef formed in an area with a warm climate and shallow ocean water. In North America, these conditions existed for millions of years when much of the continent lay closer to the equator than it does today. Shallow seas covered the central part of North America, allowing large coral reefs to form. Today, the reefs are thick deposits of sedimentary rock.

FIGURE 16
Limestone From Coral
A band of light-colored limestone marks an ancient reef that forms part of Guadalupe Peak in Texas. This reef is now 2,600 meters above sea level!

Section 4 Assessment

Target Reading Skill Using Prior Knowledge Review your graphic organizer about coral reefs and revise it based on what you just learned.

Reviewing Key Concepts

1. **a. Describing** What is a coral animal?
   b. Summarizing How do coral animals build a coral reef?
   c. Predicting If sea level rises above a coral reef, what may happen to the reef?
2. **a. Identifying** What type of rock is made up of ancient coral?
   b. Inferring A geologist finds an area where the rocks were formed from an ancient coral reef. What can the geologist infer about the ancient environment where the rocks formed?

Lab zone At-Home **Activity**

Earth's Coral Reefs Obtain a globe or world map. Find the lines that represent the tropic of Cancer and the tropic of Capricorn. The area that lies between these two lines, called the Tropics, is where most coral reefs form in warm ocean water. Locate the northeast coast of Australia, the Red Sea, and groups of tropical islands in the Caribbean Sea, Indian Ocean, and Pacific Ocean. Point out these features to family members and explain that these are areas where coral reefs occur today.

Sequencing
Refer to the Content Refresher in this chapter, which provides the guidelines for sequencing.

Have students describe the forming of a coral reef as a sequence of steps, starting with "coral animals absorb the element calcium from the ocean water." *The sequence may look like the following: 1) The calcium is combined with carbon and oxygen to form calcite. 2) Coral animals die and their skeletons remain. 3) More coral animals build on top of them. 4) A coral reef forms.*

Monitor Progress L2

Answers
Figure 15 When the water is too deep, coral animals cannot survive.

 Coral animals need sunlight and warm water.

Assess

Reviewing Key Concepts

1. **a.** A small animal with tentacles and a skeleton made of calcite **b.** Coral skeletons are built on top of older skeletons. **c.** If sea level rises slowly, the reef might build upward. If sea level rises too quickly, the reef could die.
2. **a.** Types of organic limestone **b.** At the time the reef formed, the area was in a warm climate and was covered by shallow ocean water.

Reteach L1

Show students an illustration of a coral animal. Discuss the skeleton, tentacles, and other important structures.

Performance Assessment L2

Skills Check Have students create art or build a model of a reef illustrating how a reef forms. They might choose a fringing reef or an atoll. Some students may want to add details that illustrate a reef ecosystem.

All in One Teaching Resources

- Section Summary: *Rocks From Reefs*
- Review and Reinforce: *Rocks From Reefs*
- Enrich: *Rocks From Reefs*

Lab zone At-Home **Activity**

Earth's Coral Reefs L2 Encourage students to do this activity at home. Then have a class discussion about why coral reefs occur where they do. (*Coral reefs need warm, shallow, clear water that is not too rich in nutrients.*)

Lab zone Chapter **Project**

Keep Students on Track Ask students to make an introduction card for each of their rocks and decide how they will store their rocks. Each rock's card should include the following information: where and when collected, geologic feature from which collected, the rock's texture, a description of the rock's minerals, and the results of any tests performed on the rock.

Objectives

After this lesson, students will be able to

F.5.5.1 describe the conditions under which metamorphic rocks form

F.5.5.2 identify the ways in which geologists classify metamorphic rocks

F.5.5.3 explain how metamorphic rocks are used

Target Reading Skill

Previewing Visuals Explain that looking at the visuals before they read helps students activate prior knowledge and predict what they are about to read.

Answers

Students will pose and answer questions in a graphic organizer. Possible questions and answers: **Why do the crystals in gneiss line up in bands?** (*Gneiss is a type of metamorphic rock that is foliated—the crystals are flattened to form parallel lines.*) **How does quartzite form from sandstone?** (*High temperature and pressure on the minerals in sandstone cause them to be changed into minerals that make up quartzite.*)

All in One Teaching Resources

- Transparencies F48 and F49

Preteach

Build Background Knowledge ▪L2▪

Knowledge About Forces in Earth

Have students recall forces that can change rocks beneath Earth's surface. Ask: **What occurs at convergent plate boundaries?** (*Plates collide, resulting in subduction, volcanic activity, and mountain building.*)

Go Online
SciLINKS NSTA
For: Links on metamorphic rocks
Visit: www.SciLinks.org
Web Code: scn-1055

Download a worksheet that will guide students' review of Internet resources on metamorphic rocks.

Reading Preview

Key Concepts

- Under what conditions do metamorphic rocks form?
- How do geologists classify metamorphic rocks?
- How are metamorphic rocks used?

Key Term

- foliated

Target Reading Skill

Previewing Visuals Before you read, preview Figure 17. Then write two questions that you have about metamorphic rocks in a graphic organizer like the one below. As you read, answer your questions.

Metamorphic Rocks

Q. Why do the crystals in gneiss line up in bands?
A.
Q.

Go Online
SciLINKS NSTA

For: Links on metamorphic rocks
Visit: www.SciLinks.org
Web Code: scn-1055

Lab zone Discover Activity

How Do Grain Patterns Compare?

1. Using a hand lens, observe samples of gneiss and granite. Look carefully at the grains or crystals in both rocks.
2. Observe how the grains or crystals are arranged in both rocks. Draw a sketch of both rocks and describe their textures.

Think It Over

Inferring Within the crust, some granite becomes gneiss. What do you think must happen to cause this change?

Every metamorphic rock is a rock that has changed its form. In fact, the word *metamorphic* comes from the Greek words *meta*, meaning "change," and *morphosis*, meaning "form." But what causes a rock to change into metamorphic rock? The answer lies inside Earth.

Heat and pressure deep beneath Earth's surface can change any rock into metamorphic rock. When rock changes into metamorphic rock, its appearance, texture, crystal structure, and mineral content change. Metamorphic rock can form out of igneous, sedimentary, or other metamorphic rock.

Collisions between Earth's plates can push the rock down toward the heat of the mantle. Pockets of magma rising through the crust also provide heat that can produce metamorphic rocks. The deeper a rock is buried in the crust, the greater the pressure on that rock. Under high temperature and pressure many times greater than at Earth's surface, the minerals in a rock can be changed into other minerals. The rock has become a metamorphic rock.

Types of Metamorphic Rocks

While metamorphic rocks are forming, high temperatures change the size and shape of the grains, or mineral crystals, in the rock. Extreme pressure squeezes rock so tightly that the mineral grains may line up in flat, parallel layers. **Geologists classify metamorphic rocks according to the arrangement of the grains that make up the rocks.**

Lab zone Discover Activity

Skills Focus Inferring

Materials samples of gneiss and granite, hand lens

Time 15 minutes

Tips Because the color of gneiss and granite varies, obtain samples of similar colors to focus students' attention on the more relevant characteristic of texture.

▪L1▪ **Expected Outcome** Crystals in granite have random distribution and orientation. Crystals in gneiss are segregated into light and dark bands. Platy minerals all lie flat in a plane.

Think It Over Granite changes to gneiss at high temperature and pressure deep in Earth's crust.

Foliated Rocks Metamorphic rocks that have their grains arranged in parallel layers or bands are said to be **foliated.** The term *foliated* comes from the Latin word for "leaf." It describes the thin, flat layering found in most metamorphic rocks. Foliated rocks—including slate, schist, and gneiss—may split apart along these bands. In Figure 17, notice how the crystals in granite have been flattened to create the foliated texture of gneiss.

One common foliated rock is slate. Heat and pressure change the sedimentary rock shale into slate. Slate is basically a denser, more compact version of shale. During the change, new minerals such as mica form in the slate.

Nonfoliated Rocks Some metamorphic rocks are nonfoliated. The mineral grains in these rocks are arranged randomly. Metamorphic rocks that are nonfoliated do not split into layers. Marble and quartzite are two metamorphic rocks that have a nonfoliated texture. Quartzite forms out of sandstone. The weakly cemented quartz particles in the sandstone recrystallize to form quartzite, which is extremely hard. Notice in Figure 17 how much smoother quartzite looks than sandstone.

 Reading Checkpoint What is a foliated rock?

FIGURE 17
Forming Metamorphic Rocks
Great heat and pressure can change one type of rock into another. **Observing** *How does slate differ from shale?*

Granite
igneous

Sandstone
sedimentary

Shale
sedimentary

Heat and pressure

Heat and pressure

Heat and pressure

Gneiss
metamorphic, foliated

Quartzite
metamorphic, nonfoliated

Slate
metamorphic, foliated

F ◆ 161

Lab zone Try This **Activity**

A Sequined Rock
1. Make three balls of clay about 3 cm in diameter. Gently mix about 25 sequins into one ball.
2. Use a 30-cm piece of string to cut the ball in half. How are the sequins arranged?
3. Roll the clay with the sequins back into a ball. Stack the three balls with the sequin ball in the middle. Set these on a block of wood. With another block of wood, press slowly down until the stack is about 3 cm high.
4. Use the string to cut the stack in half. How are the sequins arranged?

Making Models What do the sequins in your model rock represent? Is this rock foliated or nonfoliated?

Uses of Metamorphic Rock

Uses of Metamorphic Rock

Teach Key Concepts

Useful Metamorphic Rocks

Focus Ask students to describe places where marble or slate is used in building.

Teach Ask: **What properties make marble useful for statues and buildings?** *(It can be carved and cut easily, has attractive texture and color, and takes a polish.)* **Why is slate used as roofing material?** *(It breaks into flat pieces and is impermeable to water.)*

Apply Have students suggest uses for marble and slate in a school building.
learning modality: visual

Monitor Progress

Answer

 It splits into flat pieces, has color, and is impermeable to water.

Assess

Reviewing Key Concepts

1. a. "Change form" **b.** Beneath Earth's surface under high heat and pressure
2. a. The size and arrangement of the grains and the minerals present **b.** When stress, or pressure, and heat causes mineral grains to form parallel layers **c.** Slate and gneiss; they have parallel layering.
3. a. Material for buildings and sculpture **b.** Marble; slate is difficult to carve.

Reteach

Tell students that metamorphic rocks form in three regions: a halo around a magma body, beneath a rising mountain belt, and deep in Earth's crust. Have the class describe conditions in each region. *(High temperature near a magma body, high pressure in a rising mountain belt, both high pressure and temperature deep in Earth's crust)*

All in One Teaching Resources

- Section Summary: *Metamorphic Rocks*
- Review and Reinforce: *Metamorphic Rocks*
- Enrich: *Metamorphic Rocks*

FIGURE 18
The Lincoln Memorial
The statue of Abraham Lincoln in the Lincoln Memorial in Washington, D.C., is made of gleaming white marble.

Certain metamorphic rocks are important materials for building and sculpture. Marble and slate are two of the most useful metamorphic rocks. Marble usually forms when limestone is subjected to heat and pressure deep beneath the surface. Because marble has a fine, even grain, it can be cut into thin slabs or carved into many shapes. And marble is easy to polish. These qualities have led architects and sculptors to use marble for many buildings and statues. For example, one of America's most famous sculptures is in the Lincoln Memorial in Washington, D.C. Sculptor Daniel Chester French carved this portrait of Abraham Lincoln in gleaming white marble.

Like marble, slate comes in a variety of colors, including gray, black, red, and purple. Because it is foliated, slate splits easily into flat pieces. These pieces can be used for flooring, roofing, outdoor walkways, chalkboards, and as trim for stone buildings.

 What characteristics of slate make it useful?

Section 5 Assessment

Target Reading Skill Previewing Visuals Compare your questions and answers about Figure 17 with those of a partner.

Reviewing Key Concepts

1. a. Explaining What does *metamorphic* mean?
  b. Relating Cause and Effect Where and under what conditions are metamorphic rocks formed?
2. a. Identifying What characteristic of metamorphic rocks do geologists use to classify them?
  b. Explaining How does a foliated metamorphic rock form?
  c. Classifying Which of the rocks in Figure 17 is foliated? How can you tell?
3. a. Identifying What is the main use of metamorphic rocks?
  b. Making Judgments Which might be more useful for carving chess pieces—marble or slate? Explain your answer.

Lab zone At-Home Activity

Rocks Around the Block How are rocks used in your neighborhood? Take a walk with your family to see how many uses you can observe. Identify statues, walls, and buildings made from rocks. Can you identify which type of rock was used? Look for limestone, sandstone, granite, and marble. Share a list of the rocks you found with your class. For each rock, include a description of its color and texture, where you observed the rock, and how it was used.

Lab zone At-Home Activity

Rocks Around the Block **L2** Review the characteristics of marble, granite, limestone, and sandstone so that students can recognize these rocks. Invite volunteers to present their findings to the class.

Mystery Rocks

Problem

What properties can be used to classify rocks?

Skills Focus

inferring, classifying

Materials

- 1 "mystery rock"
- 2 unknown igneous rocks
- 2 unknown sedimentary rocks
- 2 unknown metamorphic rocks
- hand lens

Procedure

1. For this activity, you will be given six rocks and one sample that is not a rock. They are labeled A through G.
2. Copy the data table into your notebook.
3. Using the hand lens, examine each rock for clues that show the rock formed from molten material. Record the rock's color and texture. Observe if there are any crystals or grains in the rock.
4. Use the hand lens to look for clues that show the rock formed from particles of other rocks. Observe the texture of the rock to see if it has any tiny, well-rounded grains.
5. Use the hand lens to look for clues that show the rock formed under heat and pressure. Observe if the rock has a flat layer of crystals or shows colored bands.
6. Record your observations in the data table.

Data Table

Sample	Color	Texture (fine, medium, or coarse-grained)	Foliated or Non-foliated	Rock Group (igneous, metamorphic, sedimentary)
A				
B				

Analyze and Conclude

1. **Inferring** Infer from your observations the group in which each rock belongs.
2. **Classifying** Which of the samples could be classified as igneous rocks? What physical properties do these rocks share with the other samples? How are they different?
3. **Classifying** Which of the samples could be classified as sedimentary rocks? How do you think these rocks formed? What are the physical properties of these rocks?
4. **Classifying** Which of the samples could be classified as metamorphic rocks? What are their physical properties?
5. **Drawing Conclusions** Decide which sample is not a rock. How did you determine that the sample you chose is not a rock? What do you think the "mystery rock" is? Explain.
6. **Communicating** What physical property was most useful in classifying rocks? Which physical property was least useful? Explain your answer.

More to Explore

Can you name each rock? Use a field guide to rocks and minerals to find the specific name of each rock sample.

F ◆ 163

---

identify their samples. Have students share results and resolve differences.

Analyze and Conclude

1. Students will classify two rocks each as igneous, sedimentary, and metamorphic.

2. Answers will vary. Students may say that all of the rocks have grains. These rocks have no evidence of sediment or metamorphic change.

3. Answers will vary. Students may mention evidence of sediments or cementation. Students should describe in general terms how sedimentary rocks form.

4. Answers will vary. Students may mention foliation or evidence of pressure and heat.

5. Students' reasons for identifying the nonrock will depend on what it is.

6. Answers will vary. Students may suggest that texture was most useful because it reflects how rocks form.

Mystery Rocks   L3

Prepare for Inquiry

Key Concept

Properties of rocks can be used to classify rock samples as igneous, sedimentary, or metamorphic.

Skills Objectives

After this lab, students will be able to
- infer the identity of a "mystery rock" by observing the properties of each rock sample
- classify each rock sample into one of the three major groups of rocks

 Prep Time 30 minutes
Class Time 30 minutes

Advance Planning

Select and label the samples ahead of time. Suggested rock samples and labels: A. sandstone, B. gneiss, D. granite, E. conglomerate, F. slate, G. basalt. Label as C the "mystery rock," an object that is not a rock. This could be a piece of brick, bone, wood, or pottery. Label the samples by painting a small spot of correcting fluid on each and then using a marker to write the letter on the spot. Provide each group or student with a complete set of seven samples.

Safety

Remind students to handle rocks carefully and to wash their hands when they are finished. Review Safety Guidelines in Appendix A.

All in One Teaching Resources
- Lab Worksheet: *Mystery Rocks*

Guide Inquiry

Introduce the Procedure

- **Why is a hand lens helpful for observing the texture of rocks?** (*The individual grains of fine-grained rocks are too small to be seen with the unaided eye.*)

Troubleshooting the Experiment

- Demonstrate how to examine a rock sample and record observations in a data table. Use a sample not found in the students' samples, such as marble.

Extend Inquiry

More to Explore Provide students with rock and mineral field guides so that they can

Objectives

After this lesson, students will be able to
F.5.6.1 describe the rock cycle
F.5.6.2 explain the role of plate tectonics in the rock cycle

Target Reading Skill

Sequencing Explain that organizing information from beginning to end helps students anticipate the ideas, facts, and events they are about to read.

Answers

1. Magma
2. Igneous rock
3. Sedimentary rock
4. Metamorphic rock

All in One Teaching Resources

• Transparency F50

Preteach

Build Background Knowledge
L2

Recalling Earth Processes
Encourage students to brainstorm a list of Earth processes that affect rock in Earth's crust. *(Weathering, erosion, melting, metamorphism)* Ask: **Do you think that rocks last forever?** *(No. Rocks may seem permanent, but they constantly are being formed and destroyed through long periods of time.)*

Reading Preview

Key Concepts
• What is the rock cycle?
• What is the role of plate tectonics in the rock cycle?

Key Term
• rock cycle

Target Reading Skill
Sequencing As you read, make a cycle diagram that shows the stages in the rock cycle. Write each stage of the rock cycle in a separate circle in your diagram.

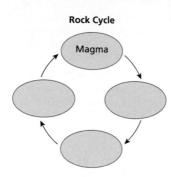

Rock Cycle

Magma

Lab zone Discover Activity

Which Rock Came First?

1. Referring to the photos below, make sketches of quartzite, granite, and sandstone on three index cards.
2. Observe the color and texture of each rock. Look for similarities and differences.
3. To which major group does each rock belong?

Think It Over
Developing Hypotheses How are quartzite, granite, and sandstone related? Arrange your cards in the order in which these three rocks formed. Given enough time in Earth's crust, what might happen to the third rock in your series?

Sandstone   **Quartzite**   **Granite**

Earth's rocks are not as unchanging as they seem. **Forces deep inside Earth and at the surface produce a slow cycle that builds, destroys, and changes the rocks in the crust.** The **rock cycle** is a series of processes on Earth's surface and in the crust and mantle that slowly change rocks from one kind to another.

A Cycle of Many Pathways

Here's one possible pathway through the rock cycle, shown in Figure 19. The igneous rock granite formed beneath the surface. Then, the forces of mountain building slowly pushed the granite upward, forming a mountain. Slowly, water and wind wore away the granite. These granite particles became sand, carried by streams to the ocean. Over millions of years, layers of sandy sediment piled up on the ocean floor. Slowly, the sediment changed to sandstone, a sedimentary rock. Over time, the sandstone became deeply buried. Heat and pressure changed the rock's texture from gritty to smooth. The sandstone changed into the metamorphic rock quartzite. But metamorphic rock does not end the rock cycle, which continues for millions of years.

Lab zone Discover Activity

Skills Focus Developing hypotheses L1
Materials 3 index cards, colored pencils
Time 15 minutes
Tips If possible, provide samples of quartzite, granite, and sandstone to give students real objects to examine and draw.

Expected Outcome Students' sketches should show the colors and textures of the rocks pictured in their text. They should identify quartzite as metamorphic, granite as igneous, and sandstone as sedimentary.

Think It Over Answers will vary. A typical answer suggests that granite from magma

formed first. Weathering, erosion, deposition, compaction, and cementation then formed sandstone from granite particles. Pressure and high temperatures then changed the sandstone to quartzite.

FIGURE 19
The Rock Cycle

Igneous, sedimentary, and metamorphic rocks change continuously through the rock cycle. **Interpreting Diagrams** *What process leads to the formation of sediment?*

Go Online
active art

For: Rock Cycle activity
Visit: PHSchool.com
Web Code: cfp-1056

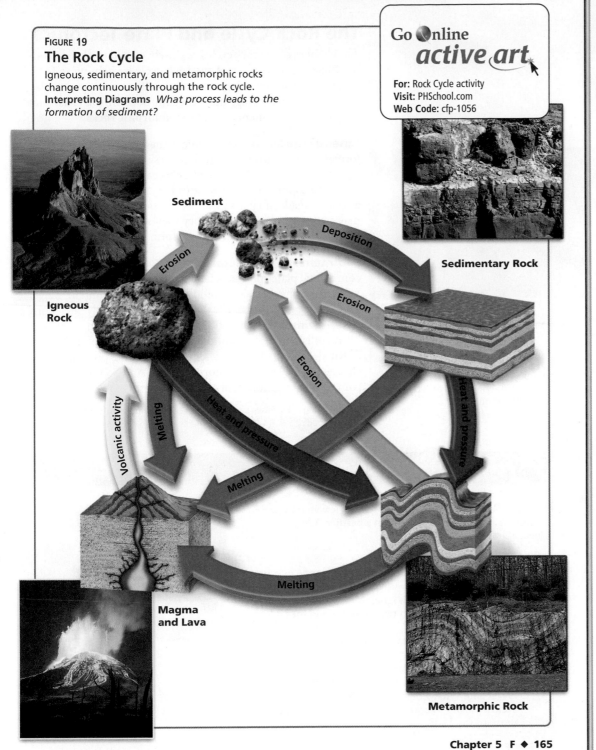

Sediment

Deposition

Erosion

Sedimentary Rock

Igneous Rock

Erosion

Erosion

Volcanic activity

Melting

Heat and pressure

Heat and pressure

Melting

Magma and Lava

Melting

Metamorphic Rock

Instruct

A Cycle of Many Pathways

Teach Key Concepts   L2

The Rock Cycle

Focus Help students understand a cycle. Ask: **Does the rock cycle have a beginning or an end?** (*No*)

Teach Tell students about the products and the processes. Ask: **What products occur in the rock cycle?** (*Magma, igneous rock, sediment, sedimentary rock, metamorphic rock*) **What processes occur in the rock cycle?** (*Melting, cooling, weather erosion, deposition, compaction, cementation*)

Apply Have students identify events that are part of the rock cycle. (*Possible answers: eruption of Kilauea, landslide in California*)

Extend The Active Art will help students connect products and processes of the rock cycle. **learning modality: visual**

Go Online
active art

For: Rock cycle activity
Visit: PHSchool.com
Web Code: cfp-1056
Students determine a rock's path through the rock cycle and watch it change over time.

Independent Practice   L2

All in One Teaching Resources
• Guided Reading and Study Worksheet: *The Rock Cycle*
• Transparency F51

Student Edition on Audio CD

Monitor Progress   L2

Oral Presentation Have students work in groups to draw a pathway through the rock cycle and develop a brief presentation of the pathway that they drew.

Answer
Figure 19 Erosion

Differentiated Instruction

Special Needs   L1
Describing Natural Cycles Challenge students to describe other natural cycles. These might include the cycle of seasons, the cycle of night and day, the water cycle, and the carbon-oxygen cycle. Point out that, like the rock cycle, these cycles are continuous, with no beginning or end.
learning modality: verbal

Less Proficient Readers   L1
Interpreting the Rock Cycle Prepare three or four sequence drawings that illustrate various products and processes in the rock cycle. Include short captions that describe the scenarios. Ask students to read and interpret each sequence. **learning modality: visual**

The Rock Cycle and Plate Tectonics

Teach Key Concepts　L2

Effects of Plate Tectonics

Focus Remind students that Earth's plates are in constant motion.

Teach Describe rock cycle processes and products that occur at various plate tectonic settings.

Apply Remind students that the rock cycle and plate tectonics have affected Earth through long periods of time. Ask: **What are some of these effects?** *(Raising and lowering of mountains, and forming and destroying of oceans)* **learning modality: visual**

Monitor Progress _____ L2

Answer

✓ Reading Checkpoint When plates collide, rock can be subducted and crust can be thickened. Rock also experiences tectonic stresses that can cause metamorphism.

Assess

Reviewing Key Concepts

1. a. Possible answer: A series of processes that change rock through time **b.** Possible answer: the igneous rock is buried, exposed to heat and pressure, and becomes a metamorphic rock, which eventually is uplifted and eroded to form sediment and then sedimentary rock.

2. a. Subduction of a plate causes melting and volcanism. Volcanism also occurs where plates separate. **b.** During the collision, mountains form. Through time, the mountains are weathered and eroded to produce sediment. The sediment is compacted and cemented to form sedimentary rock. **c.** Melting and metamorphism probably would not occur.

Reteach　L1

Have students work together to explain how a silicon atom in a sand grain could someday erupt from a volcano.

All in One Teaching Resources

- Section Summary: *The Rock Cycle*
- Review and Reinforce: *The Rock Cycle*
- Enrich: *The Rock Cycle*

The Rock Cycle and Plate Tectonics

The changes of the rock cycle are closely related to plate tectonics. **Plate movements start the rock cycle by helping to form magma, the source of igneous rocks. Plate movements also cause faulting, folding, and other motions of the crust that help to form sedimentary and metamorphic rocks.**

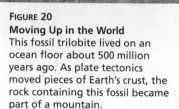

Igneous Rocks Where oceanic plates move apart, magma formed from melted mantle rock moves upward and fills the gap with new igneous rock. Where an oceanic plate is subducted beneath a continental plate, magma forms and rises. The result is a volcano made of igneous rock. A collision of continental plates may push rocks so deep that they melt and form magma. This magma slowly cools and hardens to form igneous rock.

Sedimentary and Metamorphic Rocks The collision of continental plates produces faults, folds, and uplift of the crust. Eventually, the collision could push up a mountain range. Then, erosion begins. The mountains eventually are worn away, leading to the formation of sedimentary rock.

A collision between continental plates can also push rocks down deep into the mantle. There, heat and pressure could change the rocks to metamorphic rock. And so the rock cycle continues, for hundreds of millions of years.

✓ Reading Checkpoint How can plate movements help to form metamorphic rock?

FIGURE 20
Moving Up in the World
This fossil trilobite lived on an ocean floor about 500 million years ago. As plate tectonics moved pieces of Earth's crust, the rock containing this fossil became part of a mountain.

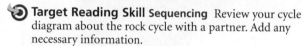

Section 6 Assessment

Target Reading Skill Sequencing Review your cycle diagram about the rock cycle with a partner. Add any necessary information.

Reviewing Key Concepts

1. a. Defining Write a definition of the rock cycle in your own words.
  b. Sequencing Begin with igneous rock and explain how it could change through two more steps in the rock cycle.
2. a. Reviewing How do plate movements help to form igneous rocks?
  b. Relating Cause and Effect How can the collision of plates lead to the formation of sedimentary rock?
  c. Predicting What would be likely to happen to the rock cycle if Earth's interior cooled so much that plate motions stopped?

Writing in Science

Rock Legend Pick one type of rock and write a possible "biography" of the rock as it moves through the rock cycle. Your story should state the type of rock, how the rock formed, and how it might change.

Writing in Science

Writing Skill Explanation

Scoring Rubric

4 includes type of rock, how it formed, how it might change, and an understanding of the cyclic nature of the process
3 includes three types of requested information and a logical path through rock cycle
2 includes three types of requested information but path is incomplete
1 includes one or two types of information, but not a logical path through rock cycle

Lab zone Chapter Project

Keep Students on Track Have students classify their rocks as igneous, sedimentary, or metamorphic. When students have finished classifying their rocks, have them organize their samples into a display.

Testing Rock Flooring

Problem
What kind of building stone makes the best flooring?

Skills Focus
designing experiments, controlling variables, drawing conclusions

Suggested Materials
- steel nail • wire brush • water
- plastic dropper • hand lens
- samples of igneous, sedimentary, and metamorphic rocks with flat surfaces
- greasy materials such as butter and crayons
- materials that form stains, such as ink and paints

Procedure

1. Brainstorm with your partner the qualities of good flooring. For example, good flooring should resist stains, scratches, and grease marks, and be safe to walk on when wet.
2. Predict what you think is the best building stone for a kitchen floor. Why is it the best?
3. Write the steps you plan to follow in answering the problem question. As you design your plan, consider the following factors:
   - What igneous, sedimentary, and metamorphic rocks will you test? (Pick at least one rock from each group.)
   - What materials or equipment will you need to acquire, and in what amounts?
   - What tests will you perform on the samples?
   - How will you control the variables in each test?
   - How will you measure each sample's resistance to staining, grease, and scratches?
   - How will you measure slipperiness?
4. Review your plan. Will it lead to an answer to the problem question?
5. Check your procedure and safety plan with your teacher.

6. Create a data table that includes a column in which you predict how each material will perform in each test.

Analyze and Conclude

1. **Interpreting Data** Which material performed the best on each test? Which performed the worst on each test?
2. **Drawing Conclusions** Which material is best for the kitchen flooring? Which material would you least want to use?
3. **Drawing Conclusions** Do your answers support your initial prediction? Why or why not?
4. **Applying Concepts** The person installing the floor might want stone that is easy to cut to the correct size or shape. What other qualities would matter to the flooring installer?
5. **Communicating** Based on your results, write an advertisement for the building stone that performed best as a flooring material.

Design an Experiment
Suppose you are trying to select flooring material for a laboratory where heavy equipment is frequently moved across the floor. Make a hypothesis predicting which type of stone flooring will be strongest. Then design an experiment to compare how well each type resists breakage.

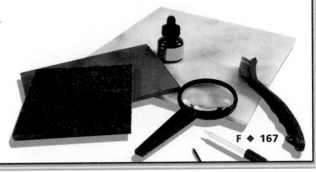

F ◆ 167

Extend Inquiry
Design an Experiment Students might suggest testing pieces of cut stone by applying force. For example, a large metal bar might be dropped from a specified distance or a chisel might be tapped with a hammer.

Testing Rock Flooring **L2**

Prepare for Inquiry

Skills Objectives
After this lab, students will be able to
- design an experiment to determine which building stones are easiest to maintain
- control variables to test only one rock property at a time
- draw conclusions about which building stones would make the best flooring

Prep Time 30 minutes
Class Time 40 minutes

Advance Planning
Provide each group with at least one igneous, sedimentary, and metamorphic rock. If your samples are limited, you can assign different rock samples to each group.

Safety
Caution students to be careful when using nails or wire brushes.

All in One Teaching Resources
- Lab Worksheet: *Testing Rock Flooring*

Guide Inquiry

Introduce the Procedure
- Organize students into small groups and encourage them to brainstorm.
- Encourage students to write a procedure that details how they will perform each type of test on their rock samples.

Expected Outcome
The harder, smoother rocks will be more resistant to scratches, stains, and grease but will be slipperier when wet.

Analyze and Conclude
1. Granite, slate, and marble are hard to stain; limestone and sandstone are easy to stain. All rock samples will scratch; granite will be the hardest to scratch. The smoothest rocks, such as marble, are more slippery than more porous rocks, such as sandstone. During a grease test, porous rocks are harder to clean than smoother rocks.
2. Marble or granite is best for kitchen flooring; sandstone or limestone is least desirable.
3. Answers will vary but should cite results from tests.
4. brittleness and weight
5. Answers should be based on test results.

The BIG Idea

Have students read the answer to the Essential Question. Encourage them to evaluate and revise their own answers as needed.

Help Students Read

Vocabulary Developing

Word Part Analysis Remind students that they can use what they know about word parts to figure out the meanings of words. Point out the words *intrusive* and *extrusive*. Ask students to think of other words that begin with the words parts *-in* and *-ex*. Write the words on the board as the students say them. Then ask what the word parts *-in* and *-ex* mean. (*-in,* "within"; *-ex,* "without") Ask students how close in meaning they think the words *intrude* and *intrusive* are.

Words in Context Provide students with a short, simple sentence that includes a key term from the chapter. For example, *Coral reefs are made of skeletons.* Ask the students to expand and refine the sentence. It might become *Coral reefs, which occur in tropical oceans, are made of calcium carbonate skeletons that were produced by coral animals through thousands of years.*

Connect Concepts

Concept Maps Help students develop one way to show how the information in this chapter is related. Several different processes form all the various rocks that make up Earth's crust. Have students brainstorm to identify the key concepts, key terms, details, and examples, then write each one on a sticky note and attach it at random on chart paper or on the board.

Tell students that this concept map will be organized in hierarchical order and to begin at the top with the key concepts. Ask students these questions to guide them to categorize the information on the stickies: **What are three major groups of rocks and how are they identified? What process in nature forms each type of rock?**

Chapter 5 Study Guide

① Classifying Rocks

Key Concepts

- When studying a rock sample, geologists observe the rock's mineral composition, color, and texture.
- Geologists classify rocks into three major groups: igneous rock, sedimentary rock, and metamorphic rock.

Key Terms

rock-forming mineral	texture
granite	igneous rock
basalt	sedimentary rock
grains	metamorphic rock

② Igneous Rocks

Key Concepts

- Igneous rocks are classified according to their origin, texture, and mineral composition.
- People throughout history have used igneous rock for tools and building materials.

Key Terms

extrusive rock
intrusive rock

③ Sedimentary Rocks

Key Concepts

- Most sedimentary rocks are formed through a series of processes: erosion, deposition, compaction, and cementation.
- There are three major groups of sedimentary rocks: clastic rocks, organic rocks, and chemical rocks.
- People have used sedimentary rocks throughout history for many different purposes, including building materials and tools.

Key Terms

sediment	cementation
erosion	clastic rock
deposition	organic rock
compaction	chemical rock

④ Rocks From Reefs

Key Concepts

- When coral animals die, their skeletons remain. More corals build on top of them, gradually forming a reef.
- Limestone deposits that began as coral reefs provide evidence of how plate motions have changed Earth's surface. These deposits also provide evidence of past environments.

Key Term

coral reef

⑤ Metamorphic Rocks

Key Concepts

- Heat and pressure deep beneath Earth's surface can change any rock into metamorphic rock.
- Geologists classify metamorphic rocks according to the arrangement of the grains that make up the rocks.
- Certain metamorphic rocks are important materials for building and sculpture.

Key Term

foliated

⑥ The Rock Cycle

Key Concepts

- Forces deep inside Earth and at the surface produce a slow cycle that builds, destroys, and changes the rocks in the crust.
- Plate movements start the rock cycle by helping to form magma, the source of igneous rocks. Plate movements also cause the motions of the crust that help to form sedimentary and metamorphic rocks.

Key Term

rock cycle

Prompt students by using connecting words or phrases, such as "formed from," results in, and "measured by," to indicate the basis for the organization of the map. The phrases should form a sentence between or among a set of concepts.

Answer Accept logical presentations by students.

All in One Teaching Resources

- Key Terms Review: *Rocks*
- Connecting Concepts: *Rocks*

Review and Assessment

Organizing Information

Concept Mapping Copy the concept map about classifying rocks onto a separate sheet of paper. Then complete it and give it a title. (For more on concept maps, see the Skills Handbook.)

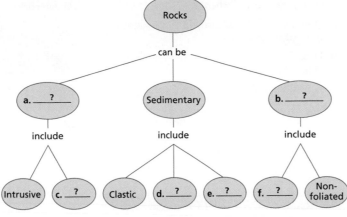

Reviewing Key Terms

Choose the letter of the best answer.

1. A rock formed from fragments of other rocks is a(n)
   a. metamorphic rock.   b. extrusive rock.
   c. sedimentary rock.   d. igneous rock.

2. An igneous rock containing large crystals is most likely a(n)
   a. chemical rock.   b. extrusive rock.
   c. foliated rock.   d. intrusive rock.

3. A sedimentary rock formed from pieces of other rocks is called a(n)
   a. organic rock.   b. chemical rock.
   c. clastic rock.   d. compacted rock.

4. A deposit of organic limestone on land probably formed millions of years ago as a(n)
   a. extrusive rock.   b. coral reef.
   c. chemical rock.   d. metamorphic rock.

5. A metamorphic rock in which the grains line up in parallel bands is a
   a. clastic rock.   b. nonclastic rock.
   c. nonfoliated rock.   d. foliated rock.

6. In the rock cycle, the process by which an igneous rock changes to a sedimentary rock must begin with
   a. cementation.
   b. deposition.
   c. erosion.
   d. compaction.

Writing in Science

Field Guide Research and write a field guide for geologists and visitors to an area such as the Grand Canyon. Describe the types of rocks you might find there, what the rocks look like, and what their properties are. Briefly explain the kinds of forces that shaped the rocks in the area you chose.

Rocks
Video Preview
Video Field Trip
▶ Video Assessment

Chapter 5 F ◆ 169

Review and Assessment

Organizing Information
a. igneous
b. metamorphic
c. extrusive
d. organic
e. chemical
f. foliated

Reviewing Key Terms
1. c   **2.** d   **3.** c   **4.** b   **5.** d   **6.** c

Writing in Science

Writing Skill Research Paragraph

Scoring Rubric
4 includes all information; guide is formatted like an actual guide and includes illustrations
3 includes all criteria
2 includes brief descriptions or omits some criteria
1 includes inaccurate information and omits some criteria

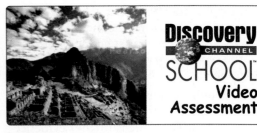

Rocks
Show the Video Assessment to review chapter content and as a prompt for the writing assignment. Discussion questions: **How did the granite in Yosemite National Park form?** *(It formed as magma deep within Earth slowly cooled.)* **Why is granite a good rock for climbers?** *(It has a rough surface and good handholds and footholds.)*

For: Self-Assessment
Visit: PHSchool.com
Web Code: cfa-1050

Students can take a practice test online that is automatically scored.

All in One Teaching Resources
• Transparency F52
• Chapter Test
• Performance Assessment Teacher Notes
• Performance Assessment Student Worksheet
• Performance Assessment Scoring Rubric

ExamView® Computer Test Bank CD-ROM

Checking Concepts

7. An igneous rock with a glassy or fine-grained texture cooled rapidly near or at Earth's surface. An igneous rock with a coarse-grained texture cooled slowly deep underground.

8. Water can pass through sandstone because the cementation process often does not fill all the spaces between sand grains, leaving small connected holes. In shale, the spaces between the clay particles are too small for water to pass through.

9. A rock can form by evaporation when water in a sea or lake evaporates, leaving mineral deposits. These are chemical sedimentary rocks.

10. When a rock changes into metamorphic rock, its appearance, texture, and mineral content change.

11. Forces inside Earth push rock deeper where temperature is higher. Magma rising through the crust also provides heat that can produce metamorphic rock.

12. It might weather and erode to produce sediment, or it might melt to produce magma.

Thinking Critically

13. The pressure and heat that create metamorphic rock reduce space between the rock's grains. Therefore, the metamorphic marble and quartzite resist erosion better than the sedimentary limestone and sandstone.

14. The environment probably was swampy because coal forms from the remains of swamp plants. The shale is further evidence of a wet environment because its clay particles were deposited by water.

15. Clastic rocks and organic rocks are similar because both are sedimentary rocks composed of sediment deposited in layers. These rocks are different because clastic rocks consist of rock fragments that have been compacted and cemented together, whereas organic rocks consist of the remains of plants and animals.

16. Yes; the high temperatures and pressures that occur during metamorphism destroy most fossils.

Applying Skills

17. Rock A is a coarse-grained foliated rock, rock B is a coarse-grained granular rock with rounded clasts, and rock C is a mixture of coarse-grained and fine-grained crystals.

Review and Assessment

Checking Concepts

7. What is the relationship between an igneous rock's texture and where it was formed?

8. Why can water pass easily through sandstone but not through shale?

9. Describe how a rock can form by evaporation. What type of rock is it?

10. How do the properties of a rock change when it becomes a metamorphic rock?

11. What are the sources of the heat that helps metamorphic rocks to form?

12. What are two things that could happen to a metamorphic rock to continue the rock cycle?

Thinking Critically

13. **Developing Hypotheses** The sedimentary rocks limestone and sandstone are used as building materials. However, they wear away more rapidly than marble and quartzite, the metamorphic rocks that are formed from them. Why do you think this is so?

14. **Inferring** A geologist finds an area where the rocks are layers of coal and shale as shown in the diagram below. What kind of environment probably existed in this area millions of years ago when these rocks formed?

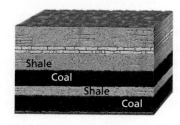

15. **Comparing and Contrasting** How are clastic rocks and organic rocks similar? How are they different?

16. **Predicting** Would you be less likely to find fossils in metamorphic rocks than in sedimentary rocks? Explain your answer.

Applying Skills

Answer Questions 17–20 using the photos of three rocks.

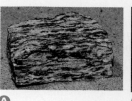

A   **B**

C

17. **Observing** How would you describe the texture of each rock?

18. **Classifying** Which of the three rocks would you classify as a metamorphic rock? Why?

19. **Inferring** A rock's texture gives clues about how the rock formed. What can you infer about the process by which Rock B formed?

20. **Relating Cause and Effect** What conditions led to the formation of the large crystals in Rock C? Explain your answer.

Lab zone Chapter **Project**

Performance Assessment Construct a simple display for your rocks. It should show your classification for each rock sample. In your presentation, describe where you hunted and what kinds of rocks you found. Were any rocks hard to classify? Did you find rocks from each of the three major groups? Can you think of any reason why certain types of rocks would not be found in your area?

Lab zone Chapter **Project**   L3

Project Wrap Up As each student or group presents the rock collection, assess how well the rocks are displayed and how effectively the rocks have been classified and identified. For example, students should give reasons for classifying a rock as igneous or identifying a rock as sandstone. These reasons might be related to observation or to tests performed on the rock.

Reflect and Record Use the questions in the student text as a basis for discussion. Then ask students to write answers to these questions in their journals.

Standardized Test Prep

Choose the letter of the best answer.

1. You find a rock in which the grains are arranged in parallel bands of white and black crystals. The rock is probably a(n)

   A igneous rock.

   B sedimentary rock.

   C metamorphic rock.

   D reef rock.

2. Many sedimentary rocks have visible layers because of the process of

   F eruption.

   G deposition.

   H intrusion.

   J crystallization.

3. Rock salt, made of the mineral halite, is a chemical sedimentary rock. A deposit of rock salt is most likely to be formed when

   A magma cools and hardens inside Earth.

   B hot water solutions form veins of rock salt.

   C the minerals form a solution in magma.

   D a solution of halite and water evaporates.

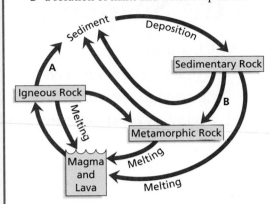

Use the diagram above to answer Questions 4 and 5.

4. If the heat and pressure inside Earth cause a rock to melt, the material that formed would be

   F metamorphic rock.

   G magma.

   H sedimentary rock.

   J igneous rock.

5. How can a metamorphic rock change into a sedimentary rock?

   A erosion and deposition

   B melting and crystallization

   C heat and pressure

   D all of the above

Constructed Response

6. You are studying some moon rocks. Some of the moon rocks are made up of jagged pieces of other rocks. The pieces are cemented together by fine, dust-sized particles called rock powder. How would you classify this type of moon rock? Explain how you used the rock's characteristics to classify it.

Chapter 5 F ◆ 171

18. Rock A is a metamorphic rock because it is foliated.

19. From the texture of rock B, students can infer that it is a sedimentary rock formed from rounded pieces of other rocks that were cemented together.

20. The large crystals cooled slowly in a magma chamber. After the magma was erupted, the small crystals cooled quickly.

Standardized Test Prep

1. C **2.** G **3.** D **4.** G **5.** A
6. It would be classified as breccia. It is made of jagged pieces of other rocks.

Interdisciplinary Exploration

Pompeii: Living in the Shadow of Vesuvius

This interdisciplinary feature presents the central theme of the city of Pompeii and the eruption of Mount Vesuvius in A.D. 79 by connecting four different disciplines: social studies, science, language arts, and math. The four explorations are designed to capture students' interest and help them see how the content they are studying in science relates to other school subjects and to real-world events. Share with others for a team-teaching experience.

All in One Teaching Resources

- Interdisciplinary Exploration: *Social Studies*
- Interdisciplinary Exploration: *Science*
- Interdisciplinary Exploration: *Language Arts*
- Interdisciplinary Exploration: *Mathematics*

Build Background Knowledge

What happens during explosive eruptions

Help students recall what they learned in the chapter *Volcanoes*. Ask: **Why are some volcanic eruptions explosive?** *(Gases can build up pressure in magma that has a high viscosity. This pressure causes the magma to erupt explosively.)* **What happens to the magma during an explosive eruption?** *(Gas rapidly comes out of the magma. This causes the magma to fragment into small pieces.)* **What do these pieces form when they cool?** *(Ash and pumice)* **What is a pyroclastic flow?** *(A flow of hot gas, ash, and rock that comes down the volcano's slope)*

Introduce the Exploration

Ask students to imagine that people 2,000 years in the future have a photograph of your city. Ask: **What could be learned about our civilization from the buildings, the people, and the tools shown in the photo?** *(Responses might include daily activities, religion, culture, and level of technology.)* Tell students that the remains of Pompeii provide this same type of information about the ancient Romans.

Pompeii–
In the Shadow of Vesuvius

Which ancient city . . .
- was destroyed in one day?
- lay buried for centuries?
- is a window on ancient Roman life?

Nearly 2,000 years ago, the city of Pompeii prospered on the fertile slopes near the volcano Vesuvius. About 100 kilometers north of Pompeii was the city of Rome. Rome was the capital of a vast empire that stretched across Europe and around the Mediterranean Sea.

Pompeii was a small but popular trading center and site for luxury Roman villas. When Vesuvius erupted violently in A.D. 79, thousands of Pompeians were caught unawares. Ash, hot gases, and rocks trapped and preserved this ancient city and its inhabitants. Today, excavations at Pompeii reveal the daily life of a bustling city at the height of the Roman Empire.

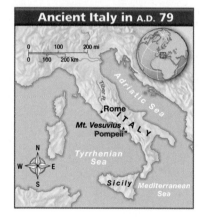

Ancient Italy in A.D. 79

The Forum
Mount Vesuvius looms behind the ruins of the Forum at Pompeii.

Daily Life in Pompeii

Excavations at Pompeii began in the mid-1700s and continue today. The findings have been astounding. Life stopped abruptly that fateful day. Thousands abandoned their meals or left food simmering on the fire. A baker had just placed the day's round loaves of bread in the oven. A jeweler left his work unfinished on a bench. Houses and public buildings that remained intact reveal daily life through frescoes (wall paintings), sculpture, mosaic floors, and expansive indoor courtyards.

At the center of city life was the Forum, a large, rectangular open space where Pompeians conducted business and politics. Here people sold meat and fish as well as fruits, vegetables, grapes, and olives grown on the fertile slopes of Vesuvius. Some merchants sold cloth made from the wool of sheep raised nearby. Others sold copper pots, oil lamps, furniture, and glassware. People of all classes gathered at the Forum to exchange ideas, notices, and gossip. Some even wrote graffiti on the walls!

Fresco From Pompeii
This fresco portrays an educated couple. Here the wife holds a stylus and wax tablet, and the husband holds a scroll.

Bakery and Bread
This fresco, found in Pompeii, shows a man purchasing bread. A carbonized loaf of bread, below, indicates how bread was cut into wedges.

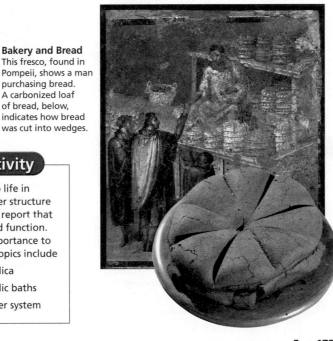

Social Studies Activity

The Forum was central to life in Pompeii. Research another structure in Pompeii. Write a short report that describes its structure and function. Explain the building's importance to Roman society. Possible topics include

- amphitheater
- basilica
- city walls
- public baths
- temples
- water system

F ◆ 173

Explore Social Studies Concepts

Use Maps Vesuvius erupted near the height of the Roman Empire. Use a map to show students how extensive the Roman Empire was at the time. Many maps have been created for this purpose, and some can be downloaded from the Internet. Tell students that the Roman Empire grew in many ways, including both military conquest and the peaceful acquisition of territory. To help students appreciate the size of the Empire, have them identify modern countries partly or wholly within its former borders.

Research Ask students to research Pompeii's importance as a center of agriculture and trade. After they have finished their research, they can create a documentary to communicate what they have learned. (*The region in which Pompeii was located, called Campania, has some of the richest soils in Italy. Pompeii was located along the Gulf of Naples and had easy port access. It was a center of maritime trade in the region.*)

Extend Challenge students to create and perform a play that depicts the daily lives of several citizens in Pompeii. Encourage the use of props, costumes, and settings that were typical of the ancient city.

Social Studies Activity

Focus Help students understand that buildings provide information about how people live. To get the activity started, ask students to describe the purpose of a town hall, a church, and a stadium near your location.

Teach To help students with research, write the following phrases on the board: *What the Building Looked Like, How People Used It, Cultural Importance*. Ask students to address each of these in their reports.

Scoring Rubric
4 Includes identification of structure, description of structure and its function, as well as several detailed examples of how people might have used the structure
3 Includes identification of structure, description of structure and its function, but does not include detailed examples
2 Includes description of structure and its function but does not specifically identify the structure
1 Includes only a few descriptive facts

Background

Facts and Figures

- Before the eruption of Vesuvius, Pompeii was a popular resort community. Many wealthy Romans vacationed there.
- A nearby city called Herculaneum also was buried by ash during the A.D. 79 eruption of Mount Vesuvius. Its ruins were accidentally discovered when a well was being dug in the area in 1709. Subsequent excavations in the region unearthed Pompeii.
- Most citizens of Pompeii gathered water from the public fountain, which can be seen today in the ancient ruins.
- Because Pompeii was originally a Greek settlement, many of the structures and details of the city reflect a Greek influence. Pompeii came under Roman control in about 290 B.C.

Explore Science Concepts

Use Visuals Help students understand the visual illustrating the eruption of Mount Vesuvius. Ask: **What is shown in step 1 of the visual?** *(An eruption column of ash, pumice, and hot gas has formed.)* **In which direction is this eruption column moving? Explain.** *(It is moving upward. The density of the hot eruption column is low enough that the force of the eruption can keep it moving upward.)* **What is happening in step 2?** *(Wind is blowing ash and pumice toward Pompeii. These materials are falling onto the city and accumulating. During this phase, about three meters of ash and pumice covered Pompeii.)* **What is happening in step 3?** *(The eruption column has collapsed, causing a pyroclastic flow. Some of the hot gas and pyroclastic material became too dense to rise and flowed along the ground toward Pompeii.)* **What effect did the pyroclastic flow have?** *(It killed the people who remained in Pompeii.)*

Review To reinforce the identification of ash and pumice, pass out samples or show photos of these materials. Tell students that the average diameter of the pumice pieces that fell on Pompeii was about one centimeter. However, larger blocks of rock hit the city during the pyroclastic flow.

Science Activity

Materials molasses, tablespoon, 3 plastic plates, watch with second hand, sand, hot plate

Focus Review the concept of viscosity with students. Ask: **Which is thicker, a high-viscosity liquid or a low-viscosity liquid?** *(High-viscosity)*

Teach Preview the activity with students. Prompt them to explain what the sand represents *(Silica)* and why the molasses is heated with the hot plate *(To raise its temperature)*. After students have conducted the activity, ask them to summarize the effects of silica content and temperature on magma. *(Magma with a high silica content has a higher viscosity and might erupt explosively; magma that has a high temperature is lower in viscosity—a quieter eruption is likely.)*

Expected Outcome The molasses to which sand has been added will stop spreading in the shortest amount of time. The heated molasses will stop spreading in the longest amount of time.

Vesuvius Erupts!

Most volcanoes and earthquakes occur along plate boundaries where Earth's crust is fractured and weak. Unknown to the people of Pompeii, their city and surrounding areas rested directly over a subduction zone where the Eurasian plate meets the African plate. Although Mount Vesuvius had erupted in the past, the volcano had lain dormant for hundreds of years.

Around noon on August 24, A.D. 79, the volcano suddenly exploded. Volcanic ash and gases shot 27 kilometers into the air. During the rest of the day and into the night, 3 meters of ash blanketed the city. But the destruction wasn't over. Around midnight, a deadly pyroclastic flow poured over the entire area, trapping about 2,000 Pompeians who had not yet escaped. Afterward, an additional 3 meters of volcanic debris rained down on Pompeii. This layer of material sealed the city, preserving it nearly intact for centuries.

The Great Eruption of Mt. Vesuvius This eighteenth-century painting is by Louis-Jean Desprez.

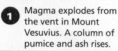

1 Magma explodes from the vent in Mount Vesuvius. A column of pumice and ash rises.

2 Pumice and ash blow southeast and fall on Pompeii.

3 The column of ash collapses and pyroclastic flows cover the region.

Science Activity

Different kinds of lava vary in silica content and temperature and therefore spread at different rates. Use molasses to model lava flow rates.

1. Measure one tablespoon of molasses, and slowly pour it onto a plastic plate. Time and record how long it takes for the molasses to stop spreading.

2. Add one tablespoon of sand to one tablespoon of molasses. Stir the mixture thoroughly. Repeat the pouring and timing of Step 1.

How does the sand affect the viscosity of the molasses? What does the sand represent in your model? How would a volcano with this type of lava be likely to erupt?

3. Heat one tablespoon of molasses over a hot plate. Repeat Step 1. How does the viscosity of the heated molasses compare with the viscosity of the molasses in Step 1? What can you conclude about the effect of temperature on the flow rate of lava?

Background

Facts and Figures During the A.D. 79 eruption of Mount Vesuvius, the volcano exhibited two different eruption styles. During the first several hours, the style of eruption was Plinian. During Plinian eruptions, material is blasted high into the atmosphere and "rains" down onto surrounding regions. This eruption style is named after Pliny the Younger, who described it in his written account of the eruption. Later in the eruption, the style changed to Peléan. Peléan eruptions are characterized by pyroclastic flows. The name comes from Mount Pelée on Martinique, where the town of St. Pierre was destroyed by pyroclastic flows in 1902. More than 25,000 people perished during this eruption.

Eyewitness Account

Pliny the Younger (circa A.D. 62–113) was a nephew of the scholar and historian Pliny the Elder. When he was about 17 years old, he witnessed the eruption of Mount Vesuvius while visiting a city across the bay from Pompeii. Some 25 years later, Pliny the Younger described the terrifying scene in a letter to the historian Tacitus.

▲ Pliny the Younger

Excerpt from Pliny the Younger's letter to Tacitus, circa A.D. 104

"I look back: a dense cloud looms behind us, following us like a flood poured across the land. . . . A darkness came that was not like a moonless or cloudy night, but more like the black of closed and unlighted rooms. You could hear women lamenting, children crying, men shouting. Some were calling for parents, others for children or spouses. . . . There were some so afraid of death that they prayed for death. . . . It grew lighter, though that seemed not a return of day, but a sign that the fire was approaching. The fire itself actually stopped some distance away, but darkness and ashes came again, a great weight of them. We stood up and shook the ash off again and again, otherwise we would have been covered with it and crushed by the weight. . . .

"At last the cloud thinned out and dwindled to no more than smoke or fog. Soon there was real daylight. The sun was even shining, though with the lurid glow it has after an eclipse. The sight that met our still terrified eyes was a changed world, buried in ash like snow."

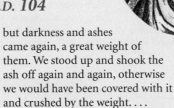

Dog at Pompeii
This is a plaster cast of a dog left chained to a post during the eruption of Vesuvius.

Language Arts Activity

An eyewitness account is a firsthand, factual account of an event or experience. Pliny the Younger filled his letter with vivid sensory details—details that help the reader see, feel, smell, taste, and hear—in order to convey what the Vesuvius eruption was like.

Choose an interesting event that you've witnessed. Write an eyewitness account of it. Provide readers with key facts, such as the time and place of the event, along with interesting and vivid details.

F ◆ 175

Explore Language Arts Concepts

Oral Presentation Ask a volunteer to read the excerpt from Pliny the Younger's letter. Help students understand the meaning of the excerpt. Ask: **What does the first sentence of the excerpt describe?** *(An advancing pyroclastic flow)* **Why does darkness follow?** *(The air is so full of ash and dust that it blocks the sunlight.)* **What do we learn about Pliny the Younger's location?** *(The pyroclastic flow stopped before it reached his location, but then more ash and pumice fell.)* **What is described in the last paragraph?** You might want to have students look up the meaning of *lurid. (The eruption is almost over, and sunlight penetrates the air. The Sun has a pale, orangish glow because of small particles in the atmosphere. A thick layer of white and gray ash and pumice, resembling snow, covers the land.)*

Show Examples Show students examples of other eyewitness accounts of volcanoes. Such accounts can be clipped from newspapers or magazines. Ask students to describe and interpret the accounts.

Language Arts Activity

Focus Ask: **What is an eyewitness?** *(A person who observes an event while it is happening)* **What is an eyewitness account?** *(A description of the event by the eyewitness)*

Teach Invite several students to provide cyewitness accounts of the last 15 minutes of class. Point out important details in their accounts. Work together as a class to add vivid sensory details to the accounts.

Scoring Rubric
4 Includes the key facts and important details using appropriate descriptors, such as lively verbs and colorful adjectives; a picture is created in the reader's mind
3 Includes key facts and significant detail
2 Includes key facts but little detail
1 Includes key facts with no detail

Background

Facts and Figures Born in A.D. 62, Pliny the Younger was an influential and wealthy member of Roman society. He was well educated and an excellent lawyer. He served in Roman government. However, Pliny's letters are quite possibly his most important contribution. In addition to his account of the eruption of Mount Vesuvius, Pliny wrote on a variety of other topics. His letters provide a firsthand account of what life was like in the Roman Empire.

Explore Mathematics Concepts

Use Math Skills Point out to students that the abacus shown in the examples is organized in the same way that whole numbers are written. The column to the far left is the thousands, the next column is the hundreds, the next column is the tens, and to the far right is the ones. Assigning values to the counters on the abacus is another way of writing a whole number.

Discuss Ask: **Why was the abacus a convenient tool for the Roman people?** *(Counts and calculations could be performed quickly and easily.)* **What types of people might need such a device?** *(Merchants and traders)*

Review Help students recall Roman numerals. Write the Roman numerals on the board, and ask the class to identify the value of each. *(M = 1000, D = 500, C = 100, L = 50, X = 10, V = 5, and I = 1.)* Ask: **Which Roman numerals appear on the abacus?** *(M, C, X, and I)* **Why were these values chosen?** *(They are multiples of ten.)*

Math Activity

Materials marker; paper; beans, pennies, or other small objects to use as counters

Focus Refer students to the abacus in the examples. Remind them that they are to model this abacus.

Teach Make a large abacus on a piece of plywood or cardboard. Checkers or other objects can be used as counters. Work as a class to perform some example calculations.

Answers

$801 + 143 = 944$

$8,754 + 241 = 8,995$

$2,788 - 1,517 = 1,271$

$6,487 - 2,382 = 4,105$

Roman Calculators

To calculate business trades in the Forum and elsewhere, Pompeians used an abacus. An abacus is a metal or wood box, with counters that slide along grooves or wires. The Romans made abacuses small enough to be portable, rather like today's pocket calculators.

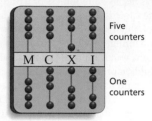

Roman Abacus
This Roman abacus could calculate numbers into the millions. The groove on the right was used to calculate fractions.

Reading the Roman Abacus

A typical Roman abacus could be used to calculate numbers up to 9,999. The ancient Romans used letters to represent numerals. The table below shows the value of the Roman numerals.

Roman Numerals

M	C	X	I
1,000	100	10	1

The Roman numerals divide the abacus into an upper and lower part. Each bead or counter on the upper part stands for five. Each bead on the lower part stands for one.

If you were using a modern calculator, you would start with 0. To set the Roman abacus at 0, move all the counters away from the letters in the middle as shown.

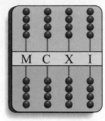

This abacus reads 0.

To read a number, count the beads that are closest to the letters in the middle.

3 hundreds (C) + 5 tens (X) + 1 ten (X) + 2 ones (I) = 362

Five counters

One counters

This abacus reads 362.

Using the Roman Abacus

Adding Clear the abacus to 0. You are now ready to add 25 + 362 on the abacus. Set up the counters to display 362 as shown above. Then add 25 by moving the counters toward the middle.

1. Go to the X (tens) column. Move 2 tens counters up, so that the tens column displays 2 tens + 6 tens = 8 tens.

2. Go to the I (ones) column. Remember that the upper counters are multiples of 5. Move the counter that stands for 5 ones down to the middle, so that the ones column displays 5 ones + 2 ones = 7 ones.

3. The result is 387, as shown.

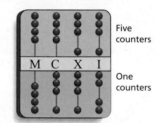

Five counters

One counters

Subtracting You use the same steps to subtract. Clear the abacus to 0. To calculate 387 – 180, first set up the abacus to show 387, as shown above. Subtract by moving the counters away from the middle.

1. Go to the C (hundreds) column. Subtract by moving 1 hundreds counter down.

2. Then go to the X (tens) column. Subtract by moving the counter that stands for 5 tens up and the 3 tens counters down.

After performing the calculation, you should get the number shown below. What number is it?

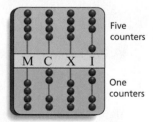

Five counters

One counters

Background

History of Science The first known abacus was the Salamis Tablet. This tablet consisted of a stone plate with horizontal lines on top and bottom, and vertical lines through the center. Numeric symbols were along three of its sides. It dates from about 300 B.C. The Romans used hand abacuses that often could count to the millions place. Such an abacus consisted of a metal or wood plate with beads that could be moved along slots. Four beads were on each of the lower slots, and one bead was on each of the upper slots. Later cultures also used the abacus, although its design varied significantly from one culture to another. The abacus that sometimes is used today was developed in Russia more than 300 years ago.

Math Activity

Create an abacus of your own by drawing heavy lines with a marker or crayon on a sheet of paper. Label each line about halfway up, as shown in the abacus illustrations on these pages. Use beans, pennies, or other small objects as beads. Begin by setting up your abacus to read 0. Perform the following calculations.

801 + 143	2,788 − 1,517
8,754 + 241	6,487 − 2,382

Check your work using Arabic numerals. Now create two of your own problems for a partner to solve.

Products From Pompeii
Colorful glassware and fine jewelry were among the luxury goods traded in ancient Pompeii.

Tie It Together

Press Kit

It's A.D. 80. Your class is a group of Pompeians who escaped the eruption and are living at a safe distance south of Mount Vesuvius. To advertise the businesses in your new location, write a "press kit" to distribute in the Roman Empire. Your kit should include

- a map showing your new location in relation to Vesuvius

- a description of your trade, such as a baker, potter, barber, cloth maker, restaurant owner, mason, or jewelry maker

- the products or services you're selling, such as wool, gold and silver jewelry, oil lamps, glassware, mosaic tiles, and so on

- drawings and photos

Research ancient Pompeii, using the library or the Internet.

Tie It Together

Press Kit

Time 1 week (2 class periods for research and 3 class periods to prepare the press kits)

Tips Organize the students into groups of four or five for this activity. Work can be divided among different members of the groups.

- Encourage students to make large maps. Maps of Italy can be enlarged by using a copying machine.

- Tell students to show trade routes to and from the new location on their maps.

- Remind students that they are trying to sell their products and services. As a class, brainstorm advertising techniques and phrases that students can use in their press kits.

Other Resources Many excellent historical accounts have been written about the Roman Empire. Encyclopedias, both print and online, are also good sources of information. Your school media specialist can help you plan this activity and work with students to help them develop their information literacy skills as they locate resources, conduct research, and write their press kits.

Extend Have students display their press kits and then engage in barter with other student groups. Students can establish trade values and make transactions. Tell them to use an abacus to perform any necessary calculations.

Think Like a Scientist

The Skills Handbook is designed as a reference for students to use whenever they need to review inquiry, reading, or math skills. You can use the activities in this part of the Skills Handbook to teach or reinforce inquiry skills.

Observing

Focus Remind students that an observation is what they can see, hear, smell, taste, or feel.

Teach Invite students to make observations of the classroom. List these observations on the board. Challenge students to identify the senses they used to make each observation. Then, ask: **Which senses will you use to make observations from the photograph on this page?** *(Sight is the only sense that can be used to make observations from the photograph.)*

Activity

Some observations that students might make include that the boy is skateboarding, wearing a white helmet, and flying in the air. Make sure that students' observations are confined to only things that they can actually see in the photograph.

Inferring

Focus Choose one or two of the classroom observations listed on the board, and challenge students to interpret them. Guide students by asking why something appears as it does.

Teach Encourage students to describe their thought processes in making their inferences. Point out where they used their knowledge and experience to interpret the observations. Then invite students to suggest other possible interpretations for the observations. Ask: **How can you find out whether an inference is correct?** *(By further investigation)*

Activity

One possible inference is that the boy just skated off a ramp at a skate park. Invite students to share their experiences that helped them make the inference.

Predicting

Focus Discuss the weather forecast for the next day. Point out that this prediction is an inference about what will happen in the

---

SKILLS
Handbook

Think Like a Scientist

Scientists have a particular way of looking at the world, or scientific habits of mind. Whenever you ask a question and explore possible answers, you use many of the same skills that scientists do. Some of these skills are described on this page.

Observing

When you use one or more of your five senses to gather information about the world, you are **observing.** Hearing a dog bark, counting twelve green seeds, and smelling smoke are all observations. To increase the power of their senses, scientists sometimes use microscopes, telescopes, or other instruments that help them make more detailed observations.

An observation must be an accurate report of what your senses detect. It is important to keep careful records of your observations in science class by writing or drawing in a notebook. The information collected through observations is called evidence, or data.

Inferring

When you interpret an observation, you are **inferring,** or making an inference. For example, if you hear your dog barking, you may infer that someone is at your front door. To make this inference, you combine the evidence— the barking dog—and your experience or knowledge—you know that your dog barks when strangers approach—to reach a logical conclusion.

Notice that an inference is not a fact; it is only one of many possible interpretations for an observation. For example, your dog may be barking because it wants to go for a walk. An inference may turn out to be incorrect even if it is based on accurate observations and logical reasoning. The only way to find out if an inference is correct is to investigate further.

Predicting

When you listen to the weather forecast, you hear many predictions about the next day's weather—what the temperature will be, whether it will rain, and how windy it will be. Weather forecasters use observations and knowledge of weather patterns to predict the weather. The skill of **predicting** involves making an inference about a future event based on current evidence or past experience.

Because a prediction is an inference, it may prove to be false. In science class, you can test some of your predictions by doing experiments. For example, suppose you predict that larger paper airplanes can fly farther than smaller airplanes. How could you test your prediction?

Activity

Use the photograph to answer the questions below.

Observing Look closely at the photograph. List at least three observations.

Inferring Use your observations to make an inference about what has happened. What experience or knowledge did you use to make the inference?

Predicting Predict what will happen next. On what evidence or experience do you base your prediction?

---

future based on observations and experience.

Teach Help students differentiate between a prediction and an inference. You might organize the similarities and differences in a Venn diagram on the board. Both are interpretations of observations using experience and knowledge, and both can be incorrect. Inferences describe current or past events. Predictions describe future events.

Activity

Students might predict that the boy will land and skate to the other side. Others might predict that the boy will fall. Students should also describe the evidence or experience on which they based their predictions.

Classifying

Could you imagine searching for a book in the library if the books were shelved in no particular order? Your trip to the library would be an all-day event! Luckily, librarians group together books on similar topics or by the same author. Grouping together items that are alike in some way is called **classifying.** You can classify items in many ways: by size, by shape, by use, and by other important characteristics.

Like librarians, scientists use the skill of classifying to organize information and objects. When things are sorted into groups, the relationships among them become easier to understand.

Activity

Classify the objects in the photograph into two groups based on any characteristic you choose. Then use another characteristic to classify the objects into three groups.

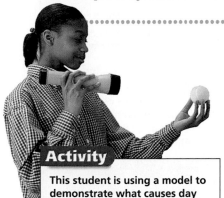

Activity

This student is using a model to demonstrate what causes day and night on Earth. What do the flashlight and the tennis ball in the model represent?

Making Models

Have you ever drawn a picture to help someone understand what you were saying? Such a drawing is one type of model. A model is a picture, diagram, computer image, or other representation of a complex object or process. **Making models** helps people understand things that they cannot observe directly.

Scientists often use models to represent things that are either very large or very small, such as the planets in the solar system, or the parts of a cell. Such models are physical models—drawings or three-dimensional structures that look like the real thing. Other models are mental models—mathematical equations or words that describe how something works.

Communicating

Whenever you talk on the phone, write a report, or listen to your teacher at school, you are communicating. **Communicating** is the process of sharing ideas and information with other people. Communicating effectively requires many skills, including writing, reading, speaking, listening, and making models.

Scientists communicate to share results, information, and opinions. Scientists often communicate about their work in journals, over the telephone, in letters, and on the Internet.

They also attend scientific meetings where they share their ideas with one another in person.

Activity

On a sheet of paper, write out clear, detailed directions for tying your shoe. Then exchange directions with a partner. Follow your partner's directions exactly. How successful were you at tying your shoe? How could your partner have communicated more clearly?

Classifying

Focus Encourage students to think of common things that are classified.

Teach Ask: **What things at home are classified?** (*Clothing might be classified in order to place it in the appropriate dresser drawer; glasses, plates, and silverware are grouped in different parts of the kitchen; screws, nuts, bolts, washers, and nails might be separated into small containers.*) **What are some things that scientists classify?** (*Scientists classify many things they study, including organisms, geological features and processes, and kinds of machines.*)

Activity

Some characteristics students might use include color, pattern of color, use of balls, and size. Students' criteria for classification should clearly divide the balls into two, and then three, distinct groups.

Making Models

Focus Ask: **What are some models you have used to study science?** (*Students might have used human anatomical models, solar system models, maps, or stream tables.*) **How have these models helped you?** (*Models can help you learn about things that are difficult to study because they are very large, very small, or highly complex.*)

Teach Be sure students understand that a model does not have to be three-dimensional. For example, a map is a model, as is a mathematical equation. Have students look at the photograph of the student modeling the causes of day and night on Earth. Ask: **What quality of each item makes this a good model?** (*The flashlight gives off light, and the ball is round and can be rotated by the student.*)

Activity

The flashlight represents the sun and the ball represents Earth.

Communicating

Focus Have students identify the methods of communication they have used today.

Teach Ask: **How is the way you communicate with a friend similar to and different from the way scientists communicate about their work to other scientists?** (*Both may communicate using various methods, but scientists must be very detailed and precise, whereas communication between friends may be less detailed and precise.*) Encourage students to communicate like a scientist as they carry out the activity.

Activity

Students' answers will vary but should identify a step-by-step process for tying a shoe. Help students identify communication errors such as leaving out a step, putting steps in the wrong order, or disregarding the person's handedness.

Making Measurements

Students can refer to this part of the Skills Handbook whenever they need to review how to make measurements with SI units. You can use the activities here to teach or reinforce SI units.

Measuring in SI

Focus Review SI units with students. Begin by providing metric rulers, graduated cylinders, balances, and Celsius thermometers. Use these tools to reinforce that the meter is the unit of length, the liter is the unit of volume, the gram is the unit of mass, and the degree Celsius is the unit of temperature.

Teach Ask: **If you want to measure the length and the width of the classroom, which SI unit would you use?** (*Meter*) **Which unit would you use to measure the amount of mass in your textbook?** (*Gram*) **Which would you use to measure how much water a drinking glass holds?** (*Liter*) **When would you use the Celsius scale?** (*To measure the temperature of something*) Then use the measuring equipment to review SI prefixes. For example, ask: **What are the smallest units on the metric ruler?** (*Millimeters*) **How many millimeters are there in one centimeter?** (*10 millimeters*) **How many in 10 centimeters?** (*100 millimeters*) **How many centimeters are there in one meter?** (*100 centimeters*) **What does 1,000 meters equal?** (*One kilometer*)

Activity

Length The length of the shell is 7.8 centimeters, or 78 millimeters. If students need more practice measuring length, have them use meter sticks and metric rulers to measure various objects in the classroom.

Activity

Liquid Volume The volume of water in the graduated cylinder is 62 milliliters. If students need more practice, have them use a graduated cylinder to measure different volumes of water.

Making Measurements

By measuring, scientists can express their observations more precisely and communicate more information about what they observe.

Measuring in SI

The standard system of measurement used by scientists around the world is known as the International System of Units, which is abbreviated as SI (**Système International d'Unités,** in French). SI units are easy to use because they are based on powers of 10. Each unit is ten times larger than the next smallest unit and one tenth the size of the next largest unit. The table lists the prefixes used to name the most common SI units.

Common SI Prefixes		
Prefix	**Symbol**	**Meaning**
kilo-	k	1,000
hecto-	h	100
deka-	da	10
deci-	d	0.1 (one tenth)
centi-	c	0.01 (one hundredth)
milli-	m	0.001 (one thousandth)

Length To measure length, or the distance between two points, the unit of measure is the **meter (m)**. The distance from the floor to a doorknob is approximately one meter. Long distances, such as the distance between two cities, are measured in kilometers (km). Small lengths are measured in centimeters (cm) or millimeters (mm). Scientists use metric rulers and meter sticks to measure length.

Common Conversions	
1 km	= 1,000 m
1 m	= 100 cm
1 m	= 1,000 mm
1 cm	= 10 mm

Liquid Volume To measure the volume of a liquid, or the amount of space it takes up, you will use a unit of measure known as the **liter (L)**. One liter is the approximate volume of a medium-size carton of milk. Smaller volumes are measured in milliliters (mL). Scientists use graduated cylinders to measure liquid volume.

Activity

The larger lines on the metric ruler in the picture show centimeter divisions, while the smaller, unnumbered lines show millimeter divisions. How many centimeters long is the shell? How many millimeters long is it?

Activity

The graduated cylinder in the picture is marked in milliliter divisions. Notice that the water in the cylinder has a curved surface. This curved surface is called the *meniscus*. To measure the volume, you must read the level at the lowest point of the meniscus. What is the volume of water in this graduated cylinder?

Common Conversion
1 L = 1,000 mL

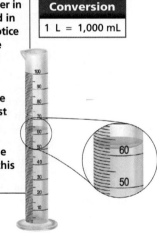

Mass To measure mass, or the amount of matter in an object, you will use a unit of measure known as the **gram (g).** One gram is approximately the mass of a paper clip. Larger masses are measured in kilograms (kg). Scientists use a balance to find the mass of an object.

Common Conversion
1 kg = 1,000 g

Activity

The mass of the potato in the picture is measured in kilograms. What is the mass of the potato? Suppose a recipe for potato salad called for one kilogram of potatoes. About how many potatoes would you need?

Temperature To measure the temperature of a substance, you will use the **Celsius scale.** Temperature is measured in degrees Celsius (°C) using a Celsius thermometer. Water freezes at 0°C and boils at 100°C.

Time The unit scientists use to measure time is the **second (s).**

Activity

What is the temperature of the liquid in degrees Celsius?

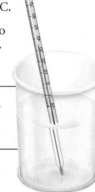

Converting SI Units

To use the SI system, you must know how to convert between units. Converting from one unit to another involves the skill of **calculating,** or using mathematical operations. Converting between SI units is similar to converting between dollars and dimes because both systems are based on powers of ten.

Suppose you want to convert a length of 80 centimeters to meters. Follow these steps to convert between units.

1. Begin by writing down the measurement you want to convert—in this example, 80 centimeters.

2. Write a conversion factor that represents the relationship between the two units you are converting. In this example, the relationship is 1 meter = 100 centimeters. Write this conversion factor as a fraction, making sure to place the units you are converting from (centimeters, in this example) in the denominator.

3. Multiply the measurement you want to convert by the fraction. When you do this, the units in the first measurement will cancel out with the units in the denominator. Your answer will be in the units you are converting to (meters, in this example).

Example

80 centimeters = ■ meters

$$80 \text{ centimeters} \times \frac{1 \text{ meter}}{100 \text{ centimeters}} = \frac{80 \text{ meters}}{100}$$

$$= 0.8 \text{ meters}$$

Activity

Convert between the following units.

1. 600 millimeters = ■ meters
2. 0.35 liters = ■ milliliters
3. 1,050 grams = ■ kilograms

Skills Handbook ◆ 181

Activity

Mass The mass of the potato is 0.25 kilograms. You would need 4 potatoes to make one kilogram. If students need more practice, give them various objects, such as coins, paper clips, and books, to measure mass.

Activity

Temperature The temperature of the liquid is 35°C. Students who need more practice can measure the temperatures of various water samples.

Converting SI Units

Focus Review the steps for converting SI units, and work through the example with students.

Teach Ask: **How many millimeters are in 80 centimeters?** *(With the relationship 10 millimeters = 1 centimeter, students should follow the steps to calculate that 80 centimeters is equal to 800 millimeters.)* Have students do the conversion problems in the activity.

Activity

1. 600 millimeters = 0.6 meters
2. 0.35 liters = 350 milliliters
3. 1,050 grams = 1.05 kilograms
If students need more practice converting SI units, have them make up conversion problems to trade with partners.

Conducting a Scientific Investigation

Students can refer to this part of the Skills Handbook whenever they need to review the steps of a scientific investigation. You can use the activities here to teach or reinforce these steps.

Posing Questions

Focus Ask: **What do you do when you want to learn about something?** (*Answers might include asking questions about it or looking for information in books or on the Internet.*) Explain that scientists go through the same process to learn about something.

Teach Tell students that the questions scientists ask may have no answers or many different answers. To answer their questions, scientists often conduct experiments. Ask: **Why is a scientific question important to a scientific investigation?** (*It helps the scientist decide if an experiment is necessary; the answer might already be known. It also helps focus the idea so that the scientist can form a hypothesis.*) **What is the scientific question in the activity on the next page?** (*Is a ball's bounce affected by the height from which it is dropped?*)

Developing a Hypothesis

Focus Emphasize that a hypothesis is one possible explanation for a set of observations. It is *not* a guess. It is often based on an inference.

Teach Ask: **On what information do scientists base their hypotheses?** (*Their observations and previous knowledge or experience*) Point out that a hypothesis does not always turn out to be correct. Ask: **When a hypothesis turns out to be incorrect, do you think the scientist wasted his or her time? Explain.** (*No. The scientist learned from the investigation and will develop another hypothesis that could prove to be correct.*)

Designing an Experiment

Focus Have a volunteer read the Experimental Procedure in the box. Invite students to identify the manipulated variable (*amount of table salt*), the variables kept constant (*amount and starting temperature of water, location of containers*), the control (*Container 3*), and the responding variable (*the temperature at which water freezes*).

Conducting a Scientific Investigation

In some ways, scientists are like detectives, piecing together clues to learn about a process or event. One way that scientists gather clues is by carrying out experiments. An experiment tests an idea in a careful, orderly manner. Although experiments do not all follow the same steps in the same order, many follow a pattern similar to the one described here.

Posing Questions

Experiments begin by asking a scientific question. A scientific question is one that can be answered by gathering evidence. For example, the question "Which freezes faster—fresh water or salt water?" is a scientific question because you can carry out an investigation and gather information to answer the question.

Developing a Hypothesis

The next step is to form a hypothesis. A **hypothesis** is a possible explanation for a set of observations or answer to a scientific question. In science, a hypothesis must be something that can be tested. A hypothesis can be worded as an *If . . . then . . .* statement. For example, a hypothesis might be *"If I add table salt to fresh water, then the water will freeze at a lower temperature."* A hypothesis worded this way serves as a rough outline of the experiment you should perform.

Teach Ask: **How might the experiment be affected if Container 1 had only 100 milliliters of water?** (*It wouldn't be an accurate comparison with the containers that have more water.*) Also make sure that students understand the importance of the control. Then, ask: **What operational definition is used in this experiment?** (*"Frozen" means the condition when the wooden stick can no longer move in a container.*)

Designing an Experiment

Next you need to plan a way to test your hypothesis. Your plan should be written out as a step-by-step procedure and should describe the observations or measurements you will make.

Two important steps involved in designing an experiment are controlling variables and forming operational definitions.

Controlling Variables In a well-designed experiment, you need to keep all variables the same except for one. A **variable** is any factor that can change in an experiment. The factor that you change is called the **manipulated variable**. In this experiment, the manipulated variable is the amount of table salt added to the water. Other factors, such as the amount of water or the starting temperature, are kept constant.

The factor that changes as a result of the manipulated variable is called the **responding variable**. The responding variable is what you measure or observe to obtain your results. In this experiment, the responding variable is the temperature at which the water freezes.

An experiment in which all factors except one are kept constant is called a **controlled experiment**. Most controlled experiments include a test called the control. In this experiment, Container 3 is the control. Because no salt is added to Container 3, you can compare the results from the other containers to it. Any difference in results must be due to the addition of salt alone.

Forming Operational Definitions Another important aspect of a well-designed experiment is having clear operational definitions. An **operational definition** is a statement that describes how a particular variable is to be measured or how a term is to be defined. For example, in this experiment, how will you determine if the water has frozen? You might decide to insert a stick in each container at the start of the experiment. Your operational definition of "frozen" would be the time at which the stick can no longer move.

Experimental Procedure

1. Fill 3 containers with 300 milliliters of cold tap water.

2. Add 10 grams of salt to Container 1; stir. Add 20 grams of salt to Container 2; stir. Add no salt to Container 3.

3. Place the 3 containers in a freezer.

4. Check the containers every 15 minutes. Record your observations.

Interpreting Data

The observations and measurements you make in an experiment are called **data**. At the end of an experiment, you need to analyze the data to look for any patterns or trends. Patterns often become clear if you organize your data in a data table or graph. Then think through what the data reveal. Do they support your hypothesis? Do they point out a flaw in your experiment? Do you need to collect more data?

Drawing Conclusions

A **conclusion** is a statement that sums up what you have learned from an experiment. When you draw a conclusion, you need to decide whether the data you collected support your hypothesis or not. You may need to repeat an experiment several times before you can draw any conclusions from it. Conclusions often lead you to pose new questions and plan new experiments to answer them.

Activity

Is a ball's bounce affected by the height from which it is dropped? Using the steps just described, plan a controlled experiment to investigate this problem.

Skills Handbook ◆ 183

Interpreting Data

Focus Ask: **What kind of data would you collect from the experiment with freezing salt water?** (*Amount of salt and temperature when the water freezes*)

Teach Ask: **What if you forgot to record some data during an investigation?** (*You wouldn't be able to draw valid conclusions because some data are missing.*) Then, ask: **Why are data tables and graphs a good way to organize data?** (*They make it easier to record data accurately, as well as compare and analyze data.*) **What kind of data table and graph might you use for this experiment?** (*A table would have a row for each container and a column in which the freezing temperature of the water is recorded. A bar graph would show the temperature at which the water froze in each container.*)

Drawing Conclusions

Focus Help students understand that a conclusion is not necessarily the end of a scientific investigation. A conclusion about one experiment may lead right into another experiment.

Teach Point out that in scientific investigations, a conclusion is a summary and explanation of the results of an experiment. For the Experimental Procedure described on this page, tell students to suppose that they obtained the following results: Container 3 froze at about 0°C, Container 1 froze at a slightly lower temperature, and Container 2 froze at the lowest temperature. Ask: **What conclusions can you draw from this experiment?** (*Students might conclude that the more table salt there is in the water, the lower the temperature at which the water freezes. The hypothesis is supported, and the question of which freezes at a lower temperature is answered—salt water.*)

Activity

You might wish to have students work in pairs to plan the controlled experiment. Students should develop a hypothesis, such as, "If I increase the height from which a ball is dropped, then the height of its bounce will increase." They can test the hypothesis by dropping a ball from varying heights (the manipulated variable). All trials should be done with the same kind of ball and on the same surface (constants). For each trial, they should measure the height of the bounce (responding variable). After students have designed the experiment, provide rubber balls, and invite them to carry out the experiment so they can collect and interpret data and draw conclusions.

Technology Design Skills

Students can refer to this part of the Skills Handbook whenever they need to review the process of designing new technologies. You can use the activities here to teach or reinforce the steps in this process.

Identify a Need

Focus Solicit from students any situations in which they have thought that a tool, machine, or other object would be really helpful to them or others. Explain that this is the first step in the design of new products.

Teach Point out that identifying specific needs is very important to the design process. Ask: **If it was specified that the toy boat be wind-powered, how might that affect the design?** *(The boat would likely be designed with sails.)*

Research the Problem

Focus Explain that research focuses the problem so that the design is more specific.

Teach Ask: **What might happen if you didn't research the problem before designing the solution?** *(Answers include developing a design that has already been found to fail, using materials that aren't the best, or designing a solution that already exists.)* **What would you research before designing your toy boat?** *(Students might research designs and materials.)*

Design a Solution

Focus Emphasize the importance of a design team. Ask: **Why are brainstorming sessions important in product design?** *(A group will propose more new ideas than one person.)*

Teach Divide the class into teams to design the toy boat. Instruct them to brainstorm design ideas. Then, ask: **Why do you think engineers evaluate constraints after brainstorming?** *(Evaluating constraints while brainstorming often stops the flow of new ideas.)* **What design constraints do you have for your toy boat?** *(Materials must be readily available and teacher-approved. The boat must be 15 centimeters or less in length and must travel 2 meters in a straight line carrying a load of 20 pennies.)*

Technology Design Skills

Engineers are people who use scientific and technological knowledge to solve practical problems. To design new products, engineers usually follow the process described here, even though they may not follow these steps in the exact order. As you read the steps, think about how you might apply them in technology labs.

Identify a Need

Before engineers begin designing a new product, they must first identify the need they are trying to meet. For example, suppose you are a member of a design team in a company that makes toys. Your team has identified a need: a toy boat that is inexpensive and easy to assemble.

Research the Problem

Engineers often begin by gathering information that will help them with their new design. This research may include finding articles in books, magazines, or on the Internet. It may also include talking to other engineers who have solved similar problems. Engineers often perform experiments related to the product they want to design.

For your toy boat, you could look at toys that are similar to the one you want to design. You might do research on the Internet. You could also test some materials to see whether they will work well in a toy boat.

Drawing for a boat design ▼

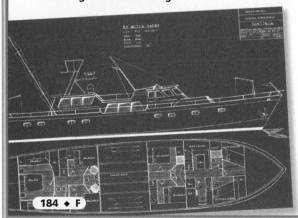

184 ◆ F

Design a Solution

Research gives engineers information that helps them design a product. When engineers design new products, they usually work in teams.

Generating Ideas Often design teams hold brainstorming meetings in which any team member can contribute ideas. **Brainstorming** is a creative process in which one team member's suggestions often spark ideas in other group members. Brainstorming can lead to new approaches to solving a design problem.

Evaluating Constraints During brainstorming, a design team will often come up with several possible designs. The team must then evaluate each one.

As part of their evaluation, engineers consider constraints. **Constraints** are factors that limit or restrict a product design. Physical characteristics, such as the properties of materials used to make your toy boat, are constraints. Money and time are also constraints. If the materials in a product cost a lot, or if the product takes a long time to make, the design may be impractical.

Making Trade-offs Design teams usually need to make trade-offs. In a **trade-off,** engineers give up one benefit of a proposed design in order to obtain another. In designing your toy boat, you will have to make trade-offs. For example, suppose one material is sturdy but not fully waterproof. Another material is more waterproof, but breakable. You may decide to give up the benefit of sturdiness in order to obtain the benefit of waterproofing.

Build and Evaluate a Prototype

Once the team has chosen a design plan, the engineers build a prototype of the product. A **prototype** is a working model used to test a design. Engineers evaluate the prototype to see whether it works well, is easy to operate, is safe to use, and holds up to repeated use.

Think of your toy boat. What would the prototype be like? Of what materials would it be made? How would you test it?

Troubleshoot and Redesign

Few prototypes work perfectly, which is why they need to be tested. Once a design team has tested a prototype, the members analyze the results and identify any problems. The team then tries to **troubleshoot,** or fix the design problems. For example, if your toy boat leaks or wobbles, the boat should be redesigned to eliminate those problems.

Communicate the Solution

A team needs to communicate the final design to the people who will manufacture and use the product. To do this, teams may use sketches, detailed drawings, computer simulations, and word descriptions.

Activity

You can use the technology design process to design and build a toy boat.

Research and Investigate

1. Visit the library or go online to research toy boats.

2. Investigate how a toy boat can be powered, including wind, rubber bands, or baking soda and vinegar.

3. Brainstorm materials, shapes, and steering for your boat.

Design and Build

4. Based on your research, design a toy boat that
   • is made of readily available materials
   • is no larger than 15 cm long and 10 cm wide

   • includes a power system, a rudder, and an area for cargo
   • travels 2 meters in a straight line carrying a load of 20 pennies

5. Sketch your design and write a step-by-step plan for building your boat. After your teacher approves your plan, build your boat.

Evaluate and Redesign

6. Test your boat, evaluate the results, and troubleshoot any problems.

7. Based on your evaluation, redesign your toy boat so it performs better.

Skills Handbook ♦ 185

Build and Evaluate a Prototype

Focus Explain that building a prototype enables engineers to test design ideas.

Teach Relate building and testing a prototype to conducting an experiment. Explain that engineers set up controlled experiments to test the prototype. Ask: **Why do you think engineers set up controlled experiments?** *(From the data, they can determine which component of the design is working and which is failing.)* **How would you test your prototype of the toy boat**? *(Answers will vary depending on the toy boat's propulsion system.)*

Troubleshoot and Redesign

Focus Make sure students know what it means to troubleshoot. If necessary, give an example. One example is a stapler that isn't working. In that case, you would check to see if it is out of staples or if the staples are jammed. Then you would fix the problem and try stapling again. If it still didn't work, you might check the position of staples and try again.

Teach Explain that engineers often are not surprised if the prototype doesn't work. Ask: **Why isn't it a failure if the prototype doesn't work?** *(Engineers learn from the problems and make changes to address the problems. This process makes the design better.)* Emphasize that prototypes are completely tested before the product is made in the factory.

Communicate the Solution

Focus Inquire whether students have ever read the instruction manual that comes with a new toy or electronic device.

Teach Emphasize the importance of good communication in the design process. Ask: **What might happen if engineers did not communicate their design ideas clearly?** *(The product might not be manufactured correctly or used properly.)*

Activity

The design possibilities are endless. Students might use small plastic containers, wood, foil, or plastic drinking cups for the boat. Materials may also include toothpicks, straws, or small wooden dowels. Brainstorm with students the different ways in which a toy boat can be propelled. The boats may be any shape, but must be no longer than 15 centimeters.

As student groups follow the steps in the design process, have them record their sources, brainstorming ideas, and prototype design in a logbook. Also give them time to troubleshoot and redesign their boats. When students turn in their boats, they should include assembly directions with a diagram, as well as instructions for use.

Creating Data Tables and Graphs

Students can refer to this part of the Skills Handbook whenever they need to review the skills required to create data tables and graphs. You can use the activities provided here to teach or reinforce these skills.

Data Tables

Focus Emphasize the importance of organizing data. Ask: **What might happen if you didn't use a data table for an experiment?** *(Possible answers include that data might not be collected or they might be forgotten.)*

Teach Have students create a data table to show how much time they spend on different activities during one week. Suggest that students first list the main activities they do every week. Then they should determine the amount of time they spend on each activity each day. Remind students to give the data table a title. A sample data table is shown below.

Bar Graphs

Focus Have students compare and contrast the data table and the bar graph on this page. Ask: **Why would you make a bar graph if the data are already organized in a table?** *(The bar graph organizes the data in a visual way that makes them easier to interpret.)*

Teach Students can use the data from the data table they created to make a bar graph that shows the amount of time they spend on different activities during a week. The vertical axis should be divided into units of time, such as hours. Remind students to label both axes and give their graph a title. A sample bar graph is shown below.

Creating Data Tables and Graphs

How can you make sense of the data in a science experiment? The first step is to organize the data to help you understand them. Data tables and graphs are helpful tools for organizing data.

Data Tables

You have gathered your materials and set up your experiment. But before you start, you need to plan a way to record what happens during the experiment. By creating a data table, you can record your observations and measurements in an orderly way.

Suppose, for example, that a scientist conducted an experiment to find out how many Calories people of different body masses burn while doing various activities. The data table shows the results.

Notice in this data table that the manipulated variable (body mass) is the heading of one column. The responding variable (for

Calories Burned in 30 Minutes			
Body Mass	Experiment 1: Bicycling	Experiment 2: Playing Basketball	Experiment 3: Watching Television
30 kg	60 Calories	120 Calories	21 Calories
40 kg	77 Calories	164 Calories	27 Calories
50 kg	95 Calories	206 Calories	33 Calories
60 kg	114 Calories	248 Calories	38 Calories

Experiment 1, the number of Calories burned while bicycling) is the heading of the next column. Additional columns were added for related experiments.

Bar Graphs

To compare how many Calories a person burns doing various activities, you could create a bar graph. A bar graph is used to display data in a number of separate, or distinct, categories. In this example, bicycling, playing basketball, and watching television are the three categories.

To create a bar graph, follow these steps.

1. On graph paper, draw a horizontal, or *x*-, axis and a vertical, or *y*-, axis.

2. Write the names of the categories to be graphed along the horizontal axis. Include an overall label for the axis as well.

3. Label the vertical axis with the name of the responding variable. Include units of measurement. Then create a scale along the axis by marking off equally spaced numbers that cover the range of the data collected.

4. For each category, draw a solid bar using the scale on the vertical axis to determine the height. Make all the bars the same width.

5. Add a title that describes the graph.

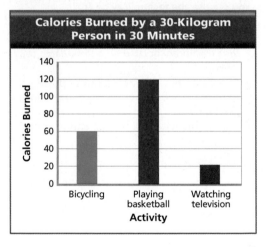

Time Spent on Different Activities in a Week				
	Going to Classes	Eating Meals	Playing Soccer	Watching Television
Monday	6	2	2	0.5
Tuesday	6	1.5	1.5	1.5
Wednesday	6	2	1	2
Thursday	6	2	2	1.5
Friday	6	2	2	0.5
Saturday	0	2.5	2.5	1
Sunday	0	3	1	2

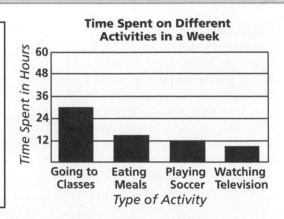

Line Graphs

To see whether a relationship exists between body mass and the number of Calories burned while bicycling, you could create a line graph. A line graph is used to display data that show how one variable (the responding variable) changes in response to another variable (the manipulated variable). You can use a line graph when your manipulated variable is **continuous,** that is, when there are other points between the ones that you tested. In this example, body mass is a continuous variable because there are other body masses between 30 and 40 kilograms (for example, 31 kilograms). Time is another example of a continuous variable.

Line graphs are powerful tools because they allow you to estimate values for conditions that you did not test in the experiment. For example, you can use the line graph to estimate that a 35-kilogram person would burn 68 Calories while bicycling.

To create a line graph, follow these steps.

1. On graph paper, draw a horizontal, or *x*-, axis and a vertical, or *y*-, axis.

2. Label the horizontal axis with the name of the manipulated variable. Label the vertical axis with the name of the responding variable. Include units of measurement.

3. Create a scale on each axis by marking off equally spaced numbers that cover the range of the data collected.

4. Plot a point on the graph for each piece of data. In the line graph above, the dotted lines show how to plot the first data point (30 kilograms and 60 Calories). Follow an imaginary vertical line extending up from the horizontal axis at the 30-kilogram mark. Then follow an imaginary horizontal line extending across from the vertical axis at the 60-Calorie mark. Plot the point where the two lines intersect.

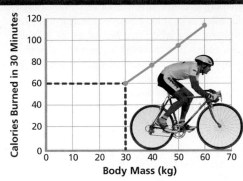

Effect of Body Mass on Calories Burned While Bicycling

5. Connect the plotted points with a solid line. (In some cases, it may be more appropriate to draw a line that shows the general trend of the plotted points. In those cases, some of the points may fall above or below the line. Also, not all graphs are linear. It may be more appropriate to draw a curve to connect the points.)

6. Add a title that identifies the variables or relationship in the graph.

Activity

Create line graphs to display the data from Experiment 2 and Experiment 3 in the data table.

Activity

You read in the newspaper that a total of 4 centimeters of rain fell in your area in June, 2.5 centimeters fell in July, and 1.5 centimeters fell in August. What type of graph would you use to display these data? Use graph paper to create the graph.

Skills Handbook ◆ 187

Line Graphs

Focus Ask: **Would a bar graph show the relationship between body mass and the number of Calories burned in 30 minutes?** *(No. Bar graphs can only show data in distinct categories.)* Explain that line graphs are used to show how one variable changes in response to another variable.

Teach Walk students through the steps involved in creating a line graph using the example illustrated on the page. For example, ask: **What is the label on the horizontal axis? On the vertical axis?** *(Body Mass (kg); Calories Burned in 30 Minutes)* **What scale is used on each axis?** *(10 kg on the x-axis and 20 Calories on the y-axis)* **What does the second data point represent?** *(77 Calories burned for a body mass of 40 kg)* **What trend or pattern does the graph show?** *(The number of Calories burned in 30 minutes of cycling increases with body mass.)*

Activity

Students should make a different graph for each experiment. Each graph should have a different *x*-axis scale that is appropriate for the data. See sample graphs below.

Activity

Students should conclude that a bar graph would be best for displaying the data.

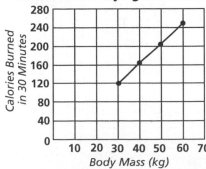

Effect of Body Mass on Calories Burned While Playing Basketball

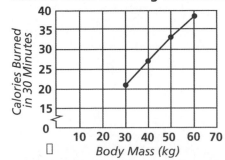

Effect of Body Mass on Calories Burned While Watching Television

Circle Graphs

Focus Emphasize that a circle graph must include 100 percent of the categories for the topic being graphed. For example, ask: **Could the data in the bar graph titled "Calories Burned by a 30-kilogram Person in Various Activities" (on the previous page) be shown in a circle graph? Why or why not?** (*No. It does not include all the possible ways a 30-kilogram person can burn Calories.*)

Teach Walk students through the steps for making a circle graph. If necessary, help them with the compass and the protractor. Use the protractor to illustrate that a circle has 360 degrees. Make sure students understand the mathematical calculations involved in making a circle graph.

Activity

You might have students work in pairs to complete the activity. Students' circle graphs should look like the graph below.

Ways Students Get to School

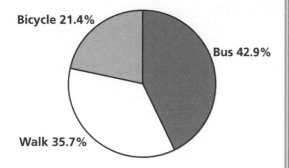

Bicycle 21.4%

Bus 42.9%

Walk 35.7%

Circle Graphs

Like bar graphs, circle graphs can be used to display data in a number of separate categories. Unlike bar graphs, however, circle graphs can only be used when you have data for *all* the categories that make up a given topic. A circle graph is sometimes called a pie chart. The pie represents the entire topic, while the slices represent the individual categories. The size of a slice indicates what percentage of the whole a particular category makes up.

The data table below shows the results of a survey in which 24 teenagers were asked to identify their favorite sport. The data were then used to create the circle graph at the right.

Favorite Sports	
Sport	Students
Soccer	8
Basketball	6
Bicycling	6
Swimming	4

To create a circle graph, follow these steps.

1. Use a compass to draw a circle. Mark the center with a point. Then draw a line from the center point to the top of the circle.

2. Determine the size of each "slice" by setting up a proportion where x equals the number of degrees in a slice. (*Note:* A circle contains 360 degrees.) For example, to find the number of degrees in the "soccer" slice, set up the following proportion:

$$\frac{\text{Students who prefer soccer}}{\text{Total number of students}} = \frac{x}{\text{Total number of degrees in a circle}}$$

$$\frac{8}{24} = \frac{x}{360}$$

Cross-multiply and solve for x.

$$24x = 8 \times 360$$
$$x = 120$$

The "soccer" slice should contain 120 degrees.

Sports That Teens Prefer

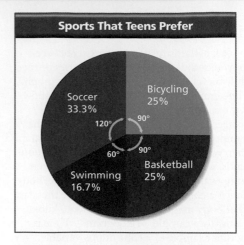

3. Use a protractor to measure the angle of the first slice, using the line you drew to the top of the circle as the 0° line. Draw a line from the center of the circle to the edge for the angle you measured.

4. Continue around the circle by measuring the size of each slice with the protractor. Start measuring from the edge of the previous slice so the wedges do not overlap. When you are done, the entire circle should be filled in.

5. Determine the percentage of the whole circle that each slice represents. To do this, divide the number of degrees in a slice by the total number of degrees in a circle (360), and multiply by 100%. For the "soccer" slice, you can find the percentage as follows:

$$\frac{120}{360} \times 100\% = 33.3\%$$

6. Use a different color for each slice. Label each slice with the category and with the percentage of the whole it represents.

7. Add a title to the circle graph.

Activity

In a class of 28 students, 12 students take the bus to school, 10 students walk, and 6 students ride their bicycles. Create a circle graph to display these data.

Math Review

Scientists use math to organize, analyze, and present data.
This appendix will help you review some basic math skills.

Mean, Median, and Mode

The **mean** is the average, or the sum of the data divided by the number of data items. The middle number in a set of ordered data is called the **median**. The **mode** is the number that appears most often in a set of data.

Example

A scientist counted the number of distinct songs sung by seven different male birds and collected the data shown below.

Male Bird Songs							
Bird	A	B	C	D	E	F	G
Number of Songs	36	29	40	35	28	36	27

To determine the mean number of songs, add the total number of songs and divide by the number of data items—in this case, the number of male birds.

$$\text{Mean} = \frac{231}{7} = 33 \text{ songs}$$

To find the median number of songs, arrange the data in numerical order and find the number in the middle of the series.

27 28 29 35 36 36 40

The number in the middle is 35, so the median number of songs is 35.

The mode is the value that appears most frequently. In the data, 36 appears twice, while each other item appears only once. Therefore, 36 songs is the mode.

Practice

Find out how many minutes it takes each student in your class to get to school. Then find the mean, median, and mode for the data.

Probability

Probability is the chance that an event will occur. Probability can be expressed as a ratio, a fraction, or a percentage. For example, when you flip a coin, the probability that the coin will land heads up is 1 in 2, or $\frac{1}{2}$, or 50 percent.

The probability that an event will happen can be expressed in the following formula.

$$P(\text{event}) = \frac{\text{Number of times the event can occur}}{\text{Total number of possible events}}$$

Example

A paper bag contains 25 blue marbles, 5 green marbles, 5 orange marbles, and 15 yellow marbles. If you close your eyes and pick a marble from the bag, what is the probability that it will be yellow?

$$P(\text{yellow marbles}) = \frac{15 \text{ yellow marbles}}{50 \text{ marbles total}}$$

$$P = \frac{15}{50}, \text{ or } \frac{3}{10}, \text{ or } 30\%$$

Practice

Each side of a cube has a letter on it. Two sides have *A*, three sides have *B*, and one side has *C*. If you roll the cube, what is the probability that *A* will land on top?

Math Review

Students can refer to this part of the Skills Handbook whenever they need to review some basic math skills. You can use the activities provided here to teach or reinforce these skills.

Mean, Median, and Mode

Focus Remind students that data from an experiment might consist of hundreds or thousands of numbers. Unless analyzed, the numbers likely will not be helpful.

Teach Work through the process of determining mean, median, and mode using the example in the book. Make sure students realize that these three numbers do not always equal each other. Point out that taken together, these three numbers give more information about the data than just one of the numbers alone.

Practice

Answers will vary based on class data. The mean should equal the total number of minutes divided by the number of students. The median should equal the number in the middle after arranging the data in numerical order. The mode should equal the number of minutes that is given most frequently.

Probability

Focus Show students a coin and ask: **What is the chance that I will get tails when I flip the coin?** *(Some students might know that there is a 1 in 2, or 50 percent, chance of getting tails.)*

Teach Set up a bag of marbles like the one in the example. Allow students to practice determining the probabilities of picking marbles of different colors. Then, encourage them to actually pick marbles and compare their actual results with those results predicted by probability.

Practice

$P(A) = 2 \text{ sides with } \frac{A}{6} \text{ sides total}$

$P = \frac{2}{6}, \text{ or } \frac{1}{3}, \text{ or } 33\%$

Area

Focus Ask: **Who knows what area is?** (*Area is equal to the number of square units needed to cover a certain shape or object.*) On the board, write the formulas for the area of a rectangle and a circle.

Teach Give students various objects of different shapes. Have them measure each object and determine its area based on the measurements. Point out that the units of the answer are squared because they are multiplied together. If students are interested, you might also explain that π is equal to the ratio of the circumference of a circle to its diameter. For circles of all sizes, π is approximately equal to the number 3.14, or $\frac{22}{7}$.

Practice

The area of the circle is equal to $21 \text{ m} \times 21 \text{ m} \times \frac{22}{7}$, or $1,386 \text{ m}^2$.

Circumference

Focus Draw a circle on the board. Then trace the outline with your finger and explain that this is the circumference of the circle, or the distance around it.

Teach Show students that the radius is equal to the distance from the center of the circle to any point on it. Point out that the diameter of a circle is equal to two times the radius. Give students paper circles of various sizes, and have them calculate the circumference of each.

Practice

The circumference is equal to $2 \times 28 \text{ m} \times \frac{22}{7}$, or 176 m.

Volume

Focus Fill a beaker with 100 milliliters of water. Ask: **What is the volume of water?** (*100 milliliters*) Explain that volume is the amount of space that something takes up. Then point out that one milliliter is equal to one cubic centimeter (cm^3).

Teach Write on the board the formulas for calculating the volumes of a rectangle and a cylinder. Point out that volume is equal to the area of an object multiplied by its height. Then measure the beaker to show students the relationship between liquid volume (100 milliliters) and the number of cubic units it contains (100 cubic centimeters).

Area

The **area** of a surface is the number of square units that cover it. The front cover of your textbook has an area of about 600 cm^2.

Area of a Rectangle and a Square To find the area of a rectangle, multiply its length times its width. The formula for the area of a rectangle is

$$A = \ell \times w, \text{ or } A = \ell w$$

Since all four sides of a square have the same length, the area of a square is the length of one side multiplied by itself, or squared.

$$A = s \times s, \text{ or } A = s^2$$

Example
A scientist is studying the plants in a field that measures 75 m × 45 m. What is the area of the field?

$$A = \ell \times w$$
$$A = 75 \text{ m} \times 45 \text{ m}$$
$$A = 3,375 \text{ m}^2$$

Area of a Circle The formula for the area of a circle is

$$A = \pi \times r \times r, \text{ or } A = \pi r^2$$

The length of the radius is represented by r, and the value of π is approximately $\frac{22}{7}$.

Example
Find the area of a circle with a radius of 14 cm.

$$A = \pi r^2$$
$$A = 14 \times 14 \times \frac{22}{7}$$
$$A = 616 \text{ cm}^2$$

Practice
Find the area of a circle that has a radius of 21 m.

190 ♦ F

Circumference

The distance around a circle is called the circumference. The formula for finding the circumference of a circle is

$$C = 2 \times \pi \times r, \text{ or } C = 2\pi r$$

Example
The radius of a circle is 35 cm. What is its circumference?

$$C = 2\pi r$$
$$C = 2 \times 35 \times \frac{22}{7}$$
$$C = 220 \text{ cm}$$

Practice
What is the circumference of a circle with a radius of 28 m?

Volume

The volume of an object is the number of cubic units it contains. The volume of a wastebasket, for example, might be about $26,000 \text{ cm}^3$.

Volume of a Rectangular Object To find the volume of a rectangular object, multiply the object's length times its width times its height.

$$V = \ell \times w \times h, \text{ or } V = \ell w h$$

Example
Find the volume of a box with length 24 cm, width 12 cm, and height 9 cm.

$$V = \ell w h$$
$$V = 24 \text{ cm} \times 12 \text{ cm} \times 9 \text{ cm}$$
$$V = 2,592 \text{ cm}^3$$

Practice
What is the volume of a rectangular object with length 17 cm, width 11 cm, and height 6 cm?

Practice

The volume of the rectangular object is equal to $17 \text{ cm} \times 11 \text{ cm} \times 6 \text{ cm}$, or $1,122 \text{ cm}^3$.

Fractions

A **fraction** is a way to express a part of a whole. In the fraction $\frac{4}{7}$, 4 is the numerator and 7 is the denominator.

Adding and Subtracting Fractions To add or subtract two or more fractions that have a common denominator, first add or subtract the numerators. Then write the sum or difference over the common denominator.

To find the sum or difference of fractions with different denominators, first find the least common multiple of the denominators. This is known as the least common denominator. Then convert each fraction to equivalent fractions with the least common denominator. Add or subtract the numerators. Then write the sum or difference over the common denominator.

> **Example**
>
> $$\frac{5}{6} - \frac{3}{4} = \frac{10}{12} - \frac{9}{12} = \frac{10-9}{12} = \frac{1}{12}$$

Multiplying Fractions To multiply two fractions, first multiply the two numerators, then multiply the two denominators.

> **Example**
>
> $$\frac{5}{6} \times \frac{2}{3} = \frac{5 \times 2}{6 \times 3} = \frac{10}{18} = \frac{5}{9}$$

Dividing Fractions Dividing by a fraction is the same as multiplying by its reciprocal. Reciprocals are numbers whose numerators and denominators have been switched. To divide one fraction by another, first invert the fraction you are dividing by—in other words, turn it upside down. Then multiply the two fractions.

> **Example**
>
> $$\frac{2}{5} \div \frac{7}{8} = \frac{2}{5} \times \frac{8}{7} = \frac{2 \times 8}{5 \times 7} = \frac{16}{35}$$

> **Practice**
>
> Solve the following: $\frac{3}{7} \div \frac{4}{5}$.

Decimals

Fractions whose denominators are 10, 100, or some other power of 10 are often expressed as decimals. For example, the fraction $\frac{9}{10}$ can be expressed as the decimal 0.9, and the fraction $\frac{7}{100}$ can be written as 0.07.

Adding and Subtracting With Decimals To add or subtract decimals, line up the decimal points before you carry out the operation.

> **Example**
>
> $$\begin{array}{r} 27.4 \\ +\ 6.19 \\ \hline 33.59 \end{array} \qquad \begin{array}{r} 278.635 \\ -\ 191.4 \\ \hline 87.235 \end{array}$$

Multiplying With Decimals When you multiply two numbers with decimals, the number of decimal places in the product is equal to the total number of decimal places in each number being multiplied.

> **Example**
>
> $$\begin{array}{r} 46.2 \ \text{(one decimal place)} \\ \times\ 2.37 \ \text{(two decimal places)} \\ \hline 109.494 \ \text{(three decimal places)} \end{array}$$

Dividing With Decimals To divide a decimal by a whole number, put the decimal point in the quotient above the decimal point in the dividend.

> **Example**
>
> $$15.5 \div 5$$
> $$\begin{array}{r} 3.1 \\ 5\overline{)15.5} \end{array}$$

To divide a decimal by a decimal, you need to rewrite the divisor as a whole number. Do this by multiplying both the divisor and dividend by the same multiple of 10.

> **Example**
>
> $$1.68 \div 4.2 = 16.8 \div 42$$
> $$\begin{array}{r} 0.4 \\ 42\overline{)16.8} \end{array}$$

> **Practice**
>
> Multiply 6.21 by 8.5.

Fractions

Focus Draw a circle on the board, and divide it into eight equal sections. Shade in one of the sections, and explain that one out of eight, or one eighth, of the sections is shaded. Also use the circle to show that four eighths is the same as one half.

Teach Write the fraction $\frac{3}{4}$ on the board. Ask: **What is the numerator?** (*Three*) **What is the denominator?** (*Four*) Emphasize that when adding and subtracting fractions, the denominators of the two fractions must be the same. If necessary, review how to find the least common denominator. Remind students that when multiplying and dividing, the denominators do not have to be the same.

> **Practice**
>
> $$\frac{3}{7} \div \frac{4}{5} = \frac{3}{7} \times \frac{5}{4} = \frac{15}{28}$$

Decimals

Focus Write the number *129.835* on the board. Ask: **What number is in the ones position?** (*9*) **The tenths position?** (*8*) **The hundredths position?** (*3*) Make sure students know that 0.8 is equal to $\frac{8}{10}$ and 0.03 is equal to $\frac{3}{100}$.

Teach Use the examples in the book to review addition, subtraction, multiplication, and division with decimals. Make up a worksheet of similar problems to give students additional practice. Also show students how a fraction is converted to a decimal by dividing the numerator by the denominator. For example, $\frac{1}{2}$ is equal to 0.5.

> **Practice**
>
> $6.21 \times 8.5 = 52.785$

Ratio and Proportion

Focus Differentiate a ratio from a fraction. Remind students that a fraction tells how many parts of the whole. In contrast, a ratio compares two different numbers. For example, $\frac{12}{22}$, or $\frac{6}{11}$, of a class are girls. But the ratio of boys to girls in the class is 10 to 12, or $\frac{5}{6}$.

Teach Use the example in the book to explain how to use a proportion to find an unknown quantity. Provide students with additional practice problems, if needed.

Practice

$6 \times 49 = 7x$
$294 = 7x$
$294 \div 7 = x$
$x = 42$

Percentage

Focus On the board, write $50\% = \frac{50}{100}$. Explain that a percentage is a ratio that compares a number to 100.

Teach Point out that when calculating percentages, you are usually using numbers other than 100. In this case, you set up a proportion. Go over the example in the book. Emphasize that the number representing the total goes on the bottom of the ratio, as does the 100%.

Practice

Students should set up the proportion

$\frac{42 \text{ marbles}}{300 \text{ marbles}} = \frac{x\%}{100\%}$

$42 \times 100 = 300x$

$4200 = 300x$

$4200 \div 300 = 14\%$

Ratio and Proportion

A **ratio** compares two numbers by division. For example, suppose a scientist counts 800 wolves and 1,200 moose on an island. The ratio of wolves to moose can be written as a fraction, $\frac{800}{1,200}$, which can be reduced to $\frac{2}{3}$. The same ratio can also be expressed as 2 to 3 or 2 : 3.

A **proportion** is a mathematical sentence saying that two ratios are equivalent. For example, a proportion could state that $\frac{800 \text{ wolves}}{1,200 \text{ moose}} = \frac{2 \text{ wolves}}{3 \text{ moose}}$. You can sometimes set up a proportion to determine or estimate an unknown quantity. For example, suppose a scientist counts 25 beetles in an area of 10 square meters. The scientist wants to estimate the number of beetles in 100 square meters.

Example

1. Express the relationship between beetles and area as a ratio: $\frac{25}{10}$, simplified to $\frac{5}{2}$.

2. Set up a proportion, with x representing the number of beetles. The proportion can be stated as $\frac{5}{2} = \frac{x}{100}$.

3. Begin by cross-multiplying. In other words, multiply each fraction's numerator by the other fraction's denominator.

   $5 \times 100 = 2 \times x$, or $500 = 2x$

4. To find the value of x, divide both sides by 2. The result is 250, or 250 beetles in 100 square meters.

Practice

Find the value of x in the following proportion: $\frac{6}{7} = \frac{x}{49}$.

Percentage

A **percentage** is a ratio that compares a number to 100. For example, there are 37 granite rocks in a collection that consists of 100 rocks. The ratio $\frac{37}{100}$ can be written as 37%. Granite rocks make up 37% of the rock collection.

You can calculate percentages of numbers other than 100 by setting up a proportion.

Example

Rain falls on 9 days out of 30 in June. What percentage of the days in June were rainy?

$$\frac{9 \text{ days}}{30 \text{ days}} = \frac{d\%}{100\%}$$

To find the value of d, begin by cross-multiplying, as for any proportion:

$9 \times 100 = 30 \times d$ $d = \frac{900}{30}$ $d = 30$

Practice

There are 300 marbles in a jar, and 42 of those marbles are blue. What percentage of the marbles are blue?

Significant Figures

The **precision** of a measurement depends on the instrument you use to take the measurement. For example, if the smallest unit on the ruler is millimeters, then the most precise measurement you can make will be in millimeters.

The sum or difference of measurements can only be as precise as the least precise measurement being added or subtracted. Round your answer so that it has the same number of digits after the decimal as the least precise measurement. Round up if the last digit is 5 or more, and round down if the last digit is 4 or less.

Example

Subtract a temperature of 5.2°C from the temperature 75.46°C.

75.46 − 5.2 = 70.26

5.2 has the fewest digits after the decimal, so it is the least precise measurement. Since the last digit of the answer is 6, round up to 3. The most precise difference between the measurements is 70.3°C.

Practice

Add 26.4 m to 8.37 m. Round your answer according to the precision of the measurements.

Significant figures are the number of nonzero digits in a measurement. Zeroes between nonzero digits are also significant. For example, the measurements 12,500 L, 0.125 cm, and 2.05 kg all have three significant figures. When you multiply and divide measurements, the one with the fewest significant figures determines the number of significant figures in your answer.

Example

Multiply 110 g by 5.75 g.

110 × 5.75 = 632.5

Because 110 has only two significant figures, round the answer to 630 g.

Scientific Notation

A **factor** is a number that divides into another number with no remainder. In the example, the number 3 is used as a factor four times.

An **exponent** tells how many times a number is used as a factor. For example, $3 \times 3 \times 3 \times 3$ can be written as 3^4. The exponent 4 indicates that the number 3 is used as a factor four times. Another way of expressing this is to say that 81 is equal to 3 to the fourth power.

Example

$$3^4 = 3 \times 3 \times 3 \times 3 = 81$$

Scientific notation uses exponents and powers of ten to write very large or very small numbers in shorter form. When you write a number in scientific notation, you write the number as two factors. The first factor is any number between 1 and 10. The second factor is a power of 10, such as 10^3 or 10^6.

Example

The average distance between the planet Mercury and the sun is 58,000,000 km. To write the first factor in scientific notation, insert a decimal point in the original number so that you have a number between 1 and 10. In the case of 58,000,000, the number is 5.8.

To determine the power of 10, count the number of places that the decimal point moved. In this case, it moved 7 places.

58,000,000 km = 5.8×10^7 km

Practice

Express 6,590,000 in scientific notation.

Significant Figures

Focus Measure the length of a paper clip using two different rulers. Use one ruler that is less precise than the other. Compare the two measurements. Ask: **Which measurement is more precise?** *(The ruler with the smallest units will give the more precise measurement.)*

Teach Give students the opportunity to take measurements of an object using tools with different precision. Encourage students to add and subtract their measurements, making sure that they round the answers to reflect the precision of the instruments. Go over the example for significant digits. Check for understanding by asking: **How many significant digits are in the number 324,000?** *(Three)* **In the number 5,901?** *(Four)* **In the number 0.706?** *(Three)* If students need additional practice, create a worksheet with problems in multiplying and dividing numbers with various significant digits.

Practice

26.4 m + 8.37 m = 34.77 m
This answer should be rounded to 34.8 m because the least precise measurement has only one digit after the decimal. This number is rounded up to 8 because the last digit is more than 5.

Scientific Notation

Focus Write a very large number on the board, such as 100 million, using all the zeros. Then, write the number using scientific notation. Ask: **Why do you think scientists prefer to write very large numbers using scientific notation?** *(Possible answers include that it is easier to do calculations, convert units, and make comparisons with other numbers.)*

Teach Go over the examples, and ask: **In the second example, which numbers are the factors?** *(5.8 and 10^7)* **Which number is the exponent?** *(7)* Explain that very small numbers have a negative exponent because the decimal point is moved to the right to produce the first factor. For example, 0.00000628 is equal to 6.28×10^{-6}.

Practice

$6,590,000 = 6.59 \times 10^6$

Reading Comprehension Skills

Students can refer to this part of the Skills Handbook whenever they need to review a reading skill. You can use the activities provided here to teach or reinforce these skills.

All in One Teaching Resources
- Target Reading Skills Handbook

Using Prior Knowledge

Focus Explain to students that using prior knowledge helps connect what they already know to what they are about to read.

Teach Point out that prior knowledge might not be accurate because memories have faded or perspectives have changed. Encourage students to ask questions to resolve discrepancies between their prior knowledge and what they have learned.

Asking Questions

Focus Demonstrate to students how to change a text heading into a question to help them anticipate the concepts, facts, and events they will read about.

Teach Encourage students to use this reading skill for the next section they read. Instruct them to turn the text headings into questions. Also challenge students to write at least four *what, how, why, who, when,* or *where* questions. Then, have students evaluate the skill. Ask: **Did asking questions about the text help you focus on the reading and remember what you read?** *(Answers will vary, but encourage honesty.)* If this reading skill didn't help, challenge them to assess why not.

Previewing Visuals

Focus Explain to students that looking at the visuals before reading will help them activate prior knowledge and predict what they are about to read.

Teach Assign a section for students to preview the visuals. First, instruct them to write a sentence describing what the section will be about. Then, encourage them to write one or two questions for each visual to give purpose to their reading. Also have them list any prior knowledge about the subject.

Reading Comprehension Skills

Each section in your textbook introduces a Target Reading Skill. You will improve your reading comprehension by using the Target Reading Skills described below.

Using Prior Knowledge

Your prior knowledge is what you already know before you begin to read about a topic. Building on what you already know gives you a head start on learning new information. Before you begin a new assignment, think about what you know. You might look at the headings and the visuals to spark your memory. You can list what you know. Then, as you read, consider questions like these.

- How does what you learn relate to what you know?
- How did something you already know help you learn something new?
- Did your original ideas agree with what you have just learned?

Asking Questions

Asking yourself questions is an excellent way to focus on and remember new information in your textbook. For example, you can turn the text headings into questions. Then your questions can guide you to identify the important information as you read. Look at these examples:

Heading: Using Seismographic Data
Question: How are seismographic data used?
Heading: Kinds of Faults
Question: What are the kinds of faults?

You do not have to limit your questions to text headings. Ask questions about anything that you need to clarify or that will help you understand the content. *What* and *how* are probably the most common question words, but you may also ask *why, who, when,* or *where* questions.

Previewing Visuals

Visuals are photographs, graphs, tables, diagrams, and illustrations. Visuals contain important information. Before you read, look at visuals and their labels and captions. This preview will help you prepare for what you will be reading.

Often you will be asked what you want to learn about a visual. For example, after you look at the normal fault diagram below, you might ask: What is the movement along a normal fault? Questions about visuals give you a purpose for reading—to answer your questions.

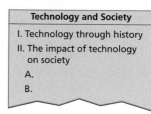
Footwall   Hanging wall
Normal Fault

Outlining

An outline shows the relationship between main ideas and supporting ideas. An outline has a formal structure. You write the main ideas, called topics, next to Roman numerals. The supporting ideas, called subtopics, are written under the main ideas and labeled A, B, C, and so on. An outline looks like this:

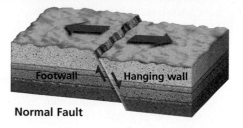

Technology and Society
I. Technology through history
II. The impact of technology on society
A.
B.

Outlining

Focus Explain that using an outline format helps organize information by main topic, subtopic, and details.

Teach Choose a section in the book, and demonstrate how to make an outline for it. Make sure students understand the structure of the outline by asking: **Is this a topic or a subtopic? Where does this information go in the outline? Would I write this heading next to a Roman numeral or a capital letter?** *(Answers depend on the section being outlined.)* Also show them how to indent and add details to the outline using numerals and lowercase letters.

Identifying Main Ideas

When you are reading science material, it is important to try to understand the ideas and concepts that are in a passage. Each paragraph has a lot of information and detail. Good readers try to identify the most important—or biggest—idea in every paragraph or section. That's the main idea. The other information in the paragraph supports or further explains the main idea.

Sometimes main ideas are stated directly. In this book, some main ideas are identified for you as key concepts. These are printed in bold-face type. However, you must identify other main ideas yourself. In order to do this, you must identify all the ideas within a paragraph or section. Then ask yourself which idea is big enough to include all the other ideas.

Comparing and Contrasting

When you compare and contrast, you examine the similarities and differences between things. You can compare and contrast in a Venn diagram or in a table.

Venn Diagram A Venn diagram consists of two overlapping circles. In the space where the circles overlap, you write the characteristics that the two items have in common. In one of the circles outside the area of overlap, you write the differing features or characteristics of one of the items. In the other circle outside the area of overlap, you write the differing characteristics of the other item.

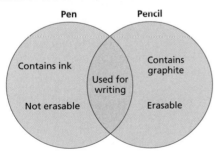

Table In a compare/contrast table, you list the characteristics or features to be compared across the top of the table. Then list the items to be compared in the left column. Complete the table by filling in information about each characteristic or feature.

Blood Vessel	Function	Structure of Wall
Artery	Carries blood away from heart	
Capillary		
Vein		

Identifying Supporting Evidence

A hypothesis is a possible explanation for observations made by scientists or an answer to a scientific question. Scientists must carry out investigations and gather evidence that either supports or disproves the hypothesis.

Identifying the supporting evidence for a hypothesis or theory can help you understand the hypothesis or theory. Evidence consists of facts—information whose accuracy can be confirmed by testing or observation.

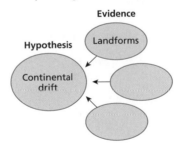

Identifying Main Ideas

Focus Explain that identifying main ideas and details helps sort the facts from the information into groups. Each group can have a main topic, subtopics, and details.

Teach Tell students that paragraphs are often written so that the main idea is in the first or second sentence, or in the last sentence. Assign students a page in the book. Instruct them to write the main idea for each paragraph on that page. If students have difficulty finding the main idea, suggest that they list all of the ideas given in the paragraph, and then choose the idea that is big enough to include all the others.

Comparing and Contrasting

Focus Explain that comparing and contrasting information shows how concepts, facts, and events are similar or different. The results of the comparison can have importance.

Teach Point out that Venn diagrams work best when comparing two things. To compare more than two things, students should use a compare/contrast table. Have students make a Venn diagram or compare/contrast table using two or more different sports or other activities, such as playing musical instruments. Emphasize that students should select characteristics that highlight the similarities and differences in the activities.

Identifying Supporting Evidence

Focus Explain to students that identifying the supporting evidence will help them to understand the relationship between the facts and the hypothesis.

Teach Remind students that a hypothesis is neither right nor wrong, but it is either supported or not supported by the evidence from testing or observation. If evidence is found that does not support a hypothesis, the hypothesis can be changed to accommodate the new evidence, or it can be dropped.

Sequencing

Focus Tell students that organizing information from beginning to end will help them understand a step-by-step process.

Teach Encourage students to create a flowchart to show the things they did this morning to get ready for school. Remind students that a flowchart should show the correct order in which events occur. *(A typical flowchart might include: got up → took a shower → got dressed → ate breakfast → brushed teeth → gathered books and homework → put on jacket.)*

Then explain that a cycle diagram shows a sequence of events that is continuous. Point out the cycle diagram that shows how the weather changes with the seasons of the year. Ask: **Why is a cycle diagram used instead of a flowchart to show the sequence of the seasons?** *(A cycle diagram shows that the sequence is continuous, not just a series of events.)* Challenge students to make a sequence diagram for a section of the text. Have them explain why they chose either a cycle diagram or a flowchart. Remind them to include at least four steps in the sequence.

Relating Cause and Effect

Focus Explain to students that cause is the reason for what happens. The effect is what happens in response to the cause. Relating cause and effect helps students relate the reason for what happens to what happens as a result.

Teach Emphasize that not all events that occur together have a cause-and-effect relationship. For example, tell students that you went to the grocery store and your car stalled. Ask: **Is there a cause-and-effect relationship in this situation? Explain.** *(No. Going to the grocery store could not cause a car to stall. There must be another cause to make the car stall.)*

Sequencing

A sequence is the order in which a series of events occurs. A flowchart or a cycle diagram can help you visualize a sequence.

Flowchart To make a flowchart, write a brief description of each step or event in a box. Place the boxes in order, with the first event at the top of the chart. Then draw an arrow to connect each step or event to the next.

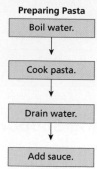

Preparing Pasta

Boil water.

↓

Cook pasta.

↓

Drain water.

↓

Add sauce.

Cycle Diagram A cycle diagram shows a sequence that is continuous, or cyclical. A continuous sequence does not have an end because when the final event is over, the first event begins again. To create a cycle diagram, write the starting event in a box placed at the top of a page in the center. Then, moving in a clockwise direction, write each event in a box in its proper sequence. Draw arrows that connect each event to the one that occurs next.

Seasons of the Year

Winter · Spring · Summer · Fall

Concept Mapping

Focus Elicit from students how a map shows the relationship of one geographic area to another. Connect this idea to how a concept map shows the relationship between terms and concepts.

Relating Cause and Effect

Science involves many cause-and-effect relationships. A cause makes something happen. An effect is what happens. When you recognize that one event causes another, you are relating cause and effect.

Words like *cause, because, effect, affect,* and *result* often signal a cause or an effect. Sometimes an effect can have more than one cause, or a cause can produce several effects.

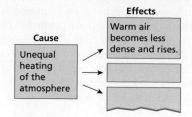

Cause — Unequal heating of the atmosphere

Effects — Warm air becomes less dense and rises.

Concept Mapping

Concept maps are useful tools for organizing information on any topic. A concept map begins with a main idea or core concept and shows how the idea can be subdivided into related subconcepts or smaller ideas.

You construct a concept map by placing concepts (usually nouns) in ovals and connecting them with linking words (usually verbs). The biggest concept or idea is placed in an oval at the top of the map. Related concepts are arranged in ovals below the big idea. The linking words connect the ovals.

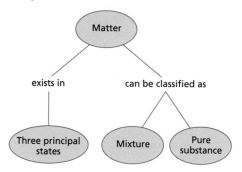

Matter — exists in — Three principal states; can be classified as — Mixture, Pure substance

Teach Challenge students to make a concept map with at least three levels of concepts to organize information about types of transportation. All students should start with the phrase *Types of transportation* at the top of the concept map. After that point, their concepts may vary. *(For example, some students might place* private transportation *and* public transportation *at the next level, while other students might choose* human-powered *and* gas-powered.)* Make sure students connect the concepts with linking words.

Building Vocabulary

Knowing the meaning of these prefixes, suffixes, and roots will help you understand the meaning of words you do not recognize.

Word Origins Many science words come to English from other languages, such as Greek and Latin. By learning the meaning of a few common Greek and Latin roots, you can determine the meaning of unfamiliar science words.

Prefixes A prefix is a word part that is added at the beginning of a root or base word to change its meaning.

Suffixes A suffix is a word part that is added at the end of a root word to change the meaning.

Greek and Latin Roots		
Greek Roots	**Meaning**	**Example**
ast-	star	astronaut
geo-	Earth	geology
metron-	measure	kilometer
opt-	eye	optician
photo-	light	photograph
scop-	see	microscope
therm-	heat	thermostat
Latin Roots	**Meaning**	**Example**
aqua-	water	aquarium
aud-	hear	auditorium
duc-, duct-	lead	conduct
flect-	bend	reflect
fract-, frag-	break	fracture
ject-	throw	reject
luc-	light	lucid
spec-	see	inspect

Prefixes and Suffixes		
Prefix	**Meaning**	**Example**
com-, con-	with	communicate, concert
de-	from; down	decay
di-	two	divide
ex-, exo-	out	exhaust
in-, im-	in, into; not	inject, impossible
re-	again; back	reflect, recall
trans-	across	transfer
Suffix	**Meaning**	**Example**
-al	relating to	natural
-er, -or	one who	teacher, doctor
-ist	one who practices	scientist
-ity	state of	equality
-ology	study of	biology
-tion, -sion	state or quality of	reaction, tension

Building Vocabulary

Reading in a content area presents challenges different from those encountered when reading fiction. Science texts often have more new vocabulary and more unfamiliar concepts that place greater emphasis on inferential reasoning. Students who can apply vocabulary strategies will be more successful in reading and understanding a science textbook. Challenge students to use Greek and Latin word origins and the meanings of prefixes and suffixes to learn the Key Terms in each section.

Word Origins

Focus Explain that word origins describe the older, foreign words that many modern English words have come from. Many science words come from Greek and Latin.

Teach Tell students that most dictionaries give the word origin just before the definition. Choose a section that has a Key Term with a Greek or Latin word origin. Encourage students to learn the meaning of the root word. Ask: **How does knowing the word origin help you remember the meaning of the Key Term?** (*Answers will vary, but the meaning of the Latin or Greek root should provide a clue to the definition of the Key Term.*) Ask: **What other words do you know that come from the same word origin?** (*Students may mention other words related to the Key Term.*) Challenge students to use word origins to figure out the meanings of unfamiliar words as they read. Students should confirm their definitions as necessary by checking a dictionary.

Prefixes

Focus Tell students that learning the meaning of common prefixes can help them determine the meaning of words they don't recognize. They will also increase their vocabulary.

Teach Remind students that a prefix is a word part that is added at the beginning of a root word to change its meaning. List some of the familiar prefixes and meanings, such as *de-* and *re-*, on the chalkboard. Ask: **What words do you know that use these same prefixes?** (*Students should list at least two words for each prefix.*) Ask: **How does the prefix affect the meaning of the root word?** (*Students should explain how it changes the meaning.*) Challenge students to learn the meaning of common prefixes and to use the skill to increase their vocabulary.

Suffixes

Focus Explain to students that learning the meanings of common suffixes and recognizing them in words are two effective strategies for learning word meanings and building vocabulary.

Teach Remind students that a suffix is added to the end of a word to change its meaning. In addition, students can use suffixes to discover the part of speech of an unfamiliar word. On the chalkboard, draw a four-column chart. Label the columns Noun, Verb, Adjective, and Adverb. Choose a Key Term that has a familiar base word, such as *tension*. Ask: **What are the noun, verb, adjective, and adverb forms of this word?** (*Students should give all possible answers, which may include only two forms of the word.*) Ask: **What endings signal that the word is a noun, adjective, or adverb?** (*Students should list the suffixes.*) Challenge students to learn meanings of suffixes and to use them to decode new words.

F ● 197

- Complete student edition
- Video and audio
- Simulations and activities
- Section and chapter activities

Laboratory Safety

Laboratory safety is an essential element of a successful science class. Students need to understand exactly what is safe and unsafe behavior and what the rationale is behind each safety rule.

All in One Teaching Resources

- Laboratory Safety Teacher Notes
- Laboratory Safety Rules
- Laboratory Safety Symbols
- Laboratory Safety Contract

General Precautions

- Post safety rules in the classroom, and review them regularly with students before beginning every science activity.
- Familiarize yourself with the safety procedures for each activity before introducing it to your students.
- For open-ended activities like Chapter Projects, have students submit their procedures or design plans in writing and check them for safety considerations.
- Always act as an exemplary role model by displaying safe behavior.
- Know how to use safety equipment, such as fire extinguishers and fire blankets, and always have it accessible.
- Have students practice leaving the classroom quickly and orderly to prepare them for emergencies.
- Explain to students how to use the intercom or other available means of communication to get help during an emergency.
- Never leave students unattended while they are engaged in science activities.
- Provide enough space for students to safely carry out science activities.
- Instruct students to report all accidents and injuries to you immediately.

Safety Symbols

These symbols warn of possible dangers in the laboratory and remind you to work carefully.

 Safety Goggles Wear safety goggles to protect your eyes in any activity involving chemicals, flames or heating, or glassware.

 Lab Apron Wear a laboratory apron to protect your skin and clothing from damage.

 Breakage Handle breakable materials, such as glassware, with care. Do not touch broken glassware.

 Heat-Resistant Gloves Use an oven mitt or other hand protection when handling hot materials such as hot plates or hot glassware.

 Plastic Gloves Wear disposable plastic gloves when working with harmful chemicals and organisms. Keep your hands away from your face, and dispose of the gloves according to your teacher's instructions.

 Heating Use a clamp or tongs to pick up hot glassware. Do not touch hot objects with your bare hands.

 Flames Before you work with flames, tie back loose hair and clothing. Follow instructions from your teacher about lighting and extinguishing flames.

 No Flames When using flammable materials, make sure there are no flames, sparks, or other exposed heat sources present.

 Corrosive Chemical Avoid getting acid or other corrosive chemicals on your skin or clothing or in your eyes. Do not inhale the vapors. Wash your hands after the activity.

 Poison Do not let any poisonous chemical come into contact with your skin, and do not inhale its vapors. Wash your hands when you are finished with the activity.

 Fumes Work in a ventilated area when harmful vapors may be involved. Avoid inhaling vapors directly. Only test an odor when directed to do so by your teacher, and use a wafting motion to direct the vapor toward your nose.

 Sharp Object Scissors, scalpels, knives, needles, pins, and tacks can cut your skin. Always direct a sharp edge or point away from yourself and others.

 Animal Safety Treat live or preserved animals or animal parts with care to avoid harming the animals or yourself. Wash your hands when you are finished with the activity.

 Plant Safety Handle plants only as directed by your teacher. If you are allergic to certain plants, tell your teacher; do not do an activity involving those plants. Avoid touching harmful plants such as poison ivy. Wash your hands when you are finished with the activity.

 Electric Shock To avoid electric shock, never use electrical equipment around water, or when the equipment is wet or your hands are wet. Be sure cords are untangled and cannot trip anyone. Unplug equipment not in use.

 Physical Safety When an experiment involves physical activity, avoid injuring yourself or others. Alert your teacher if there is any reason you should not participate.

 Disposal Dispose of chemicals and other laboratory materials safely. Follow the instructions from your teacher.

 Hand Washing Wash your hands thoroughly when finished with the activity. Use soap and warm water. Rinse well.

 General Safety Awareness When this symbol appears, follow the instructions provided. When you are asked to develop your own procedure in a lab, have your teacher approve your plan before you go further.

End-of-Experiment Rules

- Always have students use warm water and soap for washing their hands.

Heating and Fire Safety

- No flammable substances should be in use around hot plates, light bulbs, or open flames.
- Test tubes should be heated only in water baths.

- Students should be permitted to strike matches to light candles or burners *only* with strict supervision. When possible, you should light the flames, especially when working with younger students.
- Be sure to have proper ventilation when fumes are produced during a procedure.
- All electrical equipment used in the lab should have GFI (Ground Fault Interrupter) switches.

Science Safety Rules

General Precautions
Follow all instructions. Never perform activities without the approval and supervision of your teacher. Do not engage in horseplay. Never eat or drink in the laboratory. Keep work areas clean and uncluttered.

Dress Code
Wear safety goggles whenever you work with chemicals, glassware, heat sources such as burners, or any substance that might get into your eyes. If you wear contact lenses, notify your teacher.

Wear a lab apron or coat whenever you work with corrosive chemicals or substances that can stain. Wear disposable plastic gloves when working with organisms and harmful chemicals. Tie back long hair. Remove or tie back any article of clothing or jewelry that can hang down and touch chemicals, flames, or equipment. Roll up long sleeves. Never wear open shoes or sandals.

First Aid
Report all accidents, injuries, or fires to your teacher, no matter how minor. Be aware of the location of the first-aid kit, emergency equipment such as the fire extinguisher and fire blanket, and the nearest telephone. Know whom to contact in an emergency.

Heating and Fire Safety
Keep all combustible materials away from flames. When heating a substance in a test tube, make sure that the mouth of the tube is not pointed at you or anyone else. Never heat a liquid in a closed container. Use an oven mitt to pick up a container that has been heated.

Using Chemicals Safely
Never put your face near the mouth of a container that holds chemicals. Never touch, taste, or smell a chemical unless your teacher tells you to.

Use only those chemicals needed in the activity. Keep all containers closed when chemicals are not being used. Pour all chemicals over the sink or a container, not over your work surface. Dispose of excess chemicals as instructed by your teacher.

Be extra careful when working with acids or bases. When mixing an acid and water, always pour the water into the container first and then add the acid to the water. Never pour water into an acid. Wash chemical spills and splashes immediately with plenty of water.

Using Glassware Safely
If glassware is broken or chipped, notify your teacher immediately. Never handle broken or chipped glass with your bare hands.

Never force glass tubing or thermometers into a rubber stopper or rubber tubing. Have your teacher insert the glass tubing or thermometer if required for an activity.

Using Sharp Instruments
Handle sharp instruments with extreme care. Never cut material toward you; cut away from you.

Animal and Plant Safety
Never perform experiments that cause pain, discomfort, or harm to animals. Only handle animals if absolutely necessary. If you know that you are allergic to certain plants, molds, or animals, tell your teacher before doing an activity in which these are used. Wash your hands thoroughly after any activity involving animals, animal parts, plants, plant parts, or soil.

During field work, wear long pants, long sleeves, socks, and closed shoes. Avoid poisonous plants and fungi as well as plants with thorns.

End-of-Experiment Rules
Unplug all electrical equipment. Clean up your work area. Dispose of waste materials as instructed by your teacher. Wash your hands after every experiment.

Handling Organisms Safely
- In an activity where students are directed to taste something, be sure to store the material in clean, *nonscience* containers. Distribute the material to students in *new* plastic or paper dispensables, which should be discarded after the tasting. Tasting or eating should never be done in a lab classroom.
- When growing bacterial cultures, use only disposable petri dishes. After streaking, the dishes should be sealed and not opened again by students. After the lab, students should return the unopened dishes to you.
- Two methods are recommended for the safe disposal of bacterial cultures. *First method:* Autoclave the petri dishes and discard them without opening. *Second method:* If no autoclave is available, carefully open the dishes (never have a student do this), pour full-strength bleach into the dishes, and let them stand for a day. Then pour the bleach from the petri dishes down a drain, and flush the drain with lots of water. Tape the petri dishes back together, and place them in a sealed plastic bag. Wrap the plastic bag with a brown paper bag or newspaper, and tape securely. Throw the sealed package in the trash. Thoroughly disinfect the work area with bleach.
- To grow mold, use a new, sealable plastic bag that is two to three times larger than the material to be placed inside. Seal the bag and tape it shut. After the bag is sealed, students should not open it. To dispose of the bag and mold culture, make a small cut near an edge of the bag, and cook the bag in a microwave oven on a high setting for at least one minute. Discard the bag according to local ordinance, usually in the trash.
- Students should wear disposable nitrile, latex, or food-handling gloves when handling live animals or nonliving specimens.

Using Glassware Safely
- Use plastic containers, graduated cylinders, and beakers whenever possible. If using glass, students should wear safety goggles.
- Use only nonmercury thermometers with anti-roll protectors.

Using Chemicals Safely
- When students use both chemicals and microscopes in one activity, microscopes should be in a separate part of the room from the chemicals so that when students remove their goggles to use the microscopes, their eyes are not at risk.

Group 1: Metallic Luster, Mostly Dark-Colored

Mineral/ Formula	Hardness	Density (g/cm³)	Luster	Streak	Color	Other Properties/Remarks
Pyrite FeS_2	6–6.5	5.0	Metallic	Greenish, brownish black	Light yellow	Called "fool's gold," but harder than gold and very brittle
Magnetite Fe_3O_4	6	5.2	Metallic	Black	Iron black	Very magnetic; important iron ore; some varieties known as "lodestone"
Hematite Fe_2O_3	5.5–6.5	4.9–5.3	Metallic or earthy	Red or red brown	Reddish brown to black	Most important ore of iron; used as red pigment in paint
Pyrrhotite FeS	4	4.6	Metallic	Gray black	Brownish bronze	Less hard than pyrite; slightly magnetic
Sphalerite ZnS	3.5–4	3.9–4.1	Resinous	Brown to light yellow	Brown to yellow	Most important zinc ore
Chalcopyrite $CuFeS_2$	3.5–4	4.1–4.3	Metallic	Greenish black	Golden yellow, often tarnished	Most important copper ore; softer than pyrite and more yellow
Copper Cu	2.5–3	8.9	Metallic	Copper red	Copper red to black	Used in making electrical wires, coins, pipes
Gold Au	2.5–3	19.3	Metallic	Yellow	Rich yellow	High density; does not tarnish; used in jewelry, coins, dental fillings
Silver Ag	2.5–3	10.0–11.0	Metallic	Silver to light gray	Silver white (tarnishes)	Used in jewelry, coins, electrical wire, photography
Galena PbS	2.5	7.4–7.6	Metallic	Lead gray	Lead gray	Main ore of lead; used in shields against radiation
Graphite C	1–2	2.3	Metallic to dull	Black	Black	Feels greasy; very soft; used as pencil "lead" and as a lubricant

Group 2: Nonmetallic Luster, Mostly Dark-Colored

Mineral/ Formula	Hardness	Density (g/cm³)	Luster	Streak	Color	Other Properties/Remarks
Corundum Al_2O_3	9	3.9–4.1	Brilliant to glassy	White	Usually brown	Very hard; used as an abrasive; transparent crystals used as "ruby" (red) and "sapphire" (blue) gems
Garnet $(Ca,Mg,Fe)_3$ $(Al,Fe,Cr)_2$ $(SiO_4)_3$	7–7.5	3.5–4.3	Glassy to resinous	White, light brown	Red, brown, black, green	A group of minerals used in jewelry, as a birthstone, and as an abrasive
Olivine $(Mg,Fe)_2SiO_4$	6.5–7	3.3–3.4	Glassy	White or gray	Olive green	Found in igneous rocks; sometimes used as a gem
Augite $Ca(Mg,Fe,Al)$ $(Al,Si)_2O_6$	5–6	3.2–3.4	Glassy	Greenish gray	Dark green to black	Found in igneous rocks
Hornblende $NaCa_2$ $(Mg,Fe,Al)_5$ $(Si,Al)_8O_{22}(OH)_2$	5–6	3.0–3.4	Glassy, silky	White to gray	Dark green, brown, black	Found in igneous and metamorphic rocks

Group 2: Nonmetallic Luster, Mostly Dark-Colored

Mineral/ Formula	Hardness	Density (g/cm³)	Luster	Streak	Color	Other Properties/Remarks
Apatite $Ca_5(PO_4)_3F$	5	3.1–3.2	Glassy	White	Green, brown, red, blue	Sometimes used as a gem; source of the phosphorus needed by plants
Azurite $Cu_3(CO_3)_2(OH)_2$	3.5–4	3.8	Glassy to dull	Pale blue	Intense blue	Ore of copper; used as a gem
Biotite $K(Mg,Fe)_3$ $AlSiO_{10}(OH)_2$	2.5–3	2.8–3.4	Glassy or pearly	White to gray	Dark green, brown, or black	A type of mica; sometimes used as a lubricant
Serpentine $Mg_6Si_4O_{10}(OH)_8$	2–5	2.2–2.6	Greasy, waxy, silky	White	Usually green	Once used in insulation but found to cause cancer; used in fireproofing; can be in the form of asbestos
Bauxite aluminum oxides	1–3	2.0–2.5	Dull to earthy	Colorless to gray	Brown, yellow, gray, white	Ore of aluminum, smells like clay when wet; a mixture, not strictly a mineral

Group 3: Nonmetallic Luster, Mostly Light-Colored

Mineral/ Formula	Hardness	Density (g/cm³)	Luster	Streak	Color	Other Properties/Remarks
Diamond C	10	3.5	Brilliant	White	Colorless and varied	Hardest substance; used in jewelry, abrasives, cutting tools
Topaz $Al_2SiO_4(F,OH)_2$	8	3.5–3.6	Glassy	White	Straw yellow, pink, bluish	Valuable gem
Quartz SiO_2	7	2.6	Glassy, greasy	White	Colorless, white; any color when not pure	The second most abundant mineral; many varieties are gems (amethyst, jasper); used in making glass
Feldspar (K,Na,Ca) $(AlSi_3O_8)$	6	2.6	Glassy	Colorless, white	Colorless, white; various colors	As a family, the most abundant of all minerals; the feldspars make up over 60 percent of Earth's crust
Fluorite CaF_2	4	3.0–3.3	Glassy	Colorless	Purple, light green, yellow, bluish green	Some types are fluorescent (glow in ultraviolet light); used in making steel
Calcite $CaCO_3$	3	2.7	Glassy	White to grayish	Colorless, white	Easily scratched; bubbles in dilute hydrochloric acid; frequently fluorescent
Halite $NaCl$	2.5	2.1–2.6	Glassy	White	Colorless	Perfect cubic crystals; has salty taste
Gypsum $CaSO_4 \cdot 2H_2O$	2	2.3	Glassy, pearly	White	Colorless, white	Very soft; used in plaster of Paris; form known as alabaster used for statues
Sulfur S	2	2.0–2.1	Resinous to greasy	White	Yellow to brown	Used in medicines, in production of sulfuric acid, and in vulcanizing rubber
Talc $Mg_3Si_4O_{10}(OH)_2$	1	2.7–2.8	Pearly to greasy	White	Gray, white, greenish	Very soft; used in talcum powder; also called "soapstone"

English and Spanish Glossary

A

aa A slow-moving type of lava that hardens to form rough chunks; cooler than pahoehoe. (p. 90)
malpaís Tipo de lava de movimiento lento que al endurecerse forma aglutinaciones ásperas; es más fría que la lava cordada.

aftershock An earthquake that occurs after a larger earthquake in the same area. (p. 70)
réplica Sismo que ocurre después de un terremoto mayor en la misma área.

alloy A solid mixture of two or more elements, at least one of which is a metal. (p. 135)
aleación Mezcla sólida de dos o más elementos, de los cuales por lo menos uno es un metal.

anticline An upward fold in rock formed by compression of Earth's crust. (p. 48)
anticlinal Pliegue de la roca hacia arriba ocasionado por compresión de la corteza terrestre.

asthenosphere The soft layer of the mantle on which the lithosphere floats. (p. 11)
astenosfera Capa suave del manto en la que flota la litosfera.

B

basalt A dark, dense, igneous rock with a fine texture, found in oceanic crust. (p. 10)
basalto Roca ígnea, oscura y densa, de textura fina, que se encuentra en la corteza oceánica.

base-isolated building A building mounted on bearings designed to absorb the energy of an earthquake. (p. 73)
edificio de base aislada Edificio montado sobre soportes diseñados para absorber la energía liberada por los terremotos.

batholith A mass of rock formed when a large body of magma cools inside the crust. (p. 104)
batolito Masa de roca formada cuando una gran masa de magma se enfría dentro de la corteza.

C

caldera The large hole at the top of a volcano formed when the roof of a volcano's magma chamber collapses. (p. 102)
caldera Gran agujero en la parte superior de un volcán que se forma cuando la tapa de la cámara magmática del volcán se desploma.

cementation The process by which dissolved minerals crystallize and glue particles of sediment together into one mass. (p. 153)
cementación Proceso mediante el cual minerales disueltos se cristalizan y adhieren partículas de sedimento para formar una masa.

chemical property Any property of a substance that produces a change in the composition of matter. (p. 88)
propiedad química Cualquier propiedad de una sustancia que produce cambios en la composición de la materia.

chemical rock Sedimentary rock that forms when minerals crystallize from a solution. (p. 155)
roca química Roca sedimentaria que se forma cuando los minerales en una solución se cristalizan.

cinder cone A steep, cone-shaped hill or small mountain made of volcanic ash, cinders, and bombs piled up around a volcano's opening. (p. 100)
cono de escoria Colina o pequeña montaña escarpada en forma de cono que se forma cuando ceniza volcánica, escoria y bombas se acumulan alrededor de la boca de un volcán.

clastic rock Sedimentary rock that forms when rock fragments are squeezed together under high pressure. (p. 154)
roca clástica Roca sedimentaria que se forma cuando fragmentos de roca se unen bajo una gran presión.

cleavage A mineral's ability to split easily along flat surfaces. (p. 120)
exfoliación La facilidad con la que un mineral se divide en capas planas.

compaction The process by which sediments are pressed together under their own weight. (p. 153)
compactación Proceso mediante el cual los sedimentos se unen por la presión de su propio peso.

composite volcano A tall, cone-shaped mountain in which layers of lava alternate with layers of ash and other volcanic materials. (p. 101)
volcán compuesto Montaña alta con forma de cono en la que las capas de lava se alternan con capas de ceniza y otros materiales volcánicos.

compound A substance in which two or more elements are chemically joined. (p. 87)
compuesto Sustancia en la que dos o más elementos están unidos químicamente.

compression Stress that squeezes rock until it folds or breaks. (p. 45)
compresión Esfuerzo que oprime una roca hasta que se pliega o rompe.

conduction The transfer of heat within a material or between materials that are touching. (p. 15)
conducción Transferencia de calor dentro de un material o entre materiales que están en contacto.

continental drift The hypothesis that the continents slowly move across Earth's surface. (p. 19)
deriva continental Hipótesis según la cual los continentes se desplazan lentamente en la superficie de la Tierra.

convection The transfer of heat by movement of a fluid. (p. 16)
convección Transferencia de calor mediante el movimiento de un líquido.

convection current The movement of a fluid, caused by differences in temperature, that transfers heat from one part of the fluid to another. (p. 16)
corriente de convección Movimiento de un líquido ocasionado por diferencias en la temperatura, que transfiere calor de un punto del líquido a otro.

convergent boundary A plate boundary where two plates move toward each other. (p. 35)
borde convergente Borde de placa donde dos placas se deslizan una hacia la otra.

coral reef A structure of calcite skeletons built up by coral animals in warm, shallow ocean water. (p. 158)
arrecife de coral Estructura de esqueletos calcáreos formada por corales en aguas oceánicas templadas y poco profundas.

crater A bowl-shaped area that forms around a volcano's central opening. (p. 92)
cráter Área en forma de tazón que se forma alrededor de la abertura central de un volcán.

crust The layer of rock that forms Earth's outer surface. (p. 10)
corteza Capa de rocas que forma la superficie externa de la Tierra.

crystal A solid in which the atoms are arranged in a pattern that repeats again and again. (p. 115)
cristal Sólido en el que los átomos están dispuestos en un patrón que se repite una y otra vez.

crystallization The process by which atoms are arranged to form a material with a crystal structure. (p. 124)
cristalización Proceso mediante el cual los átomos se organizan para formar materiales con estructura cristalina.

D

deep-ocean trench A deep valley along the ocean floor beneath which oceanic crust slowly sinks toward the mantle. (p. 28)
fosa oceánica profunda Valle profundo a lo largo del suelo oceánico debajo del cual la corteza oceánica se hunde lentamente hacia el manto.

density The amount of mass in a given space; mass per unit volume. (p. 16)
densidad Cantidad de masa en un espacio dado; masa por unidad de volumen.

deposition The process by which sediment settles out of the water or wind that is carrying it. (p. 153)
sedimentación Proceso mediante el cual el sedimento es depositado por el agua o el viento que lo transporta.

dike A slab of volcanic rock formed when magma forces itself across rock layers. (p. 103)
dique discordante Placa de roca volcánica formada cuando el magma se abre paso a través de las capas de roca.

divergent boundary A plate boundary where two plates move away from each other. (p. 34)
borde divergente Borde de placa donde dos placas se separan.

dormant Describes a volcano that is not currently active, but that may become active in the future. (p. 97)
atenuado Volcán que en la actualidad no está activo, pero que puede volver a ser activo en el futuro.

E

earthquake The shaking that results from the movement of rock beneath Earth's surface. (p. 51)
terremoto Temblor que resulta del movimiento de la roca debajo de la superficie de la Tierra.

element A substance that cannot be broken down into other substances. (p. 87)
elemento Sustancia que no puede descomponerse en otras sustancias.

epicenter The point on Earth's surface directly above an earthquake's focus. (p. 51)
epicentro Punto en la superficie de la Tierra directamente sobre el foco de un terremoto.

erosion The destructive process in which water or wind loosens and carries away fragments of rock. (p. 153)
erosión Proceso destructivo en el que el agua o el viento desprenden fragmentos de roca y los transportan.

extinct Describes a volcano that is no longer active and is unlikely to erupt again. (p. 97)
extinto Describe un volcán que ya no es activo y es poco probable que haga erupción otra vez.

extrusive rock Igneous rock that forms from lava on Earth's surface. (p. 148)
roca extrusiva Roca ígnea que se forma de la lava en la superficie de la Tierra.

F

fault A break in Earth's crust where masses of rock slip past each other. (p. 34)
falla Fractura en la corteza de la Tierra que ocurre cuando grandes placas de roca se deslizan una con respecto a la otra.

focus The point beneath Earth's surface where rock breaks under stress and causes an earthquake. (p. 51)
foco Punto debajo de la superficie de la Tierra en el que la roca se rompe a raíz del esfuerzo, y causa un terremoto.

foliated Term used to describe metamorphic rocks that have grains arranged in parallel layers or bands. (p. 161)
esquistocidad Término usado para describir las rocas metamórficas que tienen granos dispuestos en capas paralelas o bandas.

footwall The block of rock that forms the lower half of a fault. (p. 46)
labio inferior Bloque de roca que constituye la mitad inferior de una falla.

fossil A trace of an ancient organism that has been preserved in rock. (p. 20)
fósil Vestigio de un organismo de la antigüedad que se ha preservado en la roca.

fracture The way a mineral looks when it breaks apart in an irregular way. (p. 121)
fractura Apariencia de un mineral cuando se rompe irregularmente.

friction The force that opposes the motion of one surface as it moves across another surface. (p. 64)
fricción Fuerza que se opone al movimiento de una superficie a medida que se mueve a través de otra superficie.

G

gemstone A hard, colorful mineral that has a brilliant or glassy luster and is valued for its appearance. (p. 131)
gema Mineral duro y colorido, con lustre brillante o vidrioso.

geode A hollow rock inside which mineral crystals have grown. (p. 124)
geoda Roca hueca dentro de la que se forman cristales minerales.

geothermal activity The heating of underground water by magma. (p. 104)
actividad geotérmica Calentamiento del agua subterránea por el magma.

geyser A fountain of water and steam that builds up pressure underground and erupts at regular intervals. (p. 105)
géiser Fuente de agua y vapor que acumula presión subterránea y hace erupción a intervalos regulares.

grains The particles of minerals or other rocks that give a rock its texture. (p. 146)
granos Partículas de minerales o de otras rocas que dan la textura a una roca.

granite A usually light-colored igneous rock that is found in continental crust. (p. 10, 145)
granito Roca usualmente de color claro que se encuentra en la corteza continental.

 H

hanging wall The block of rock that forms the upper half of a fault. (p. 46)
labio superior Bloque de roca que constituye la mitad superior de una falla.

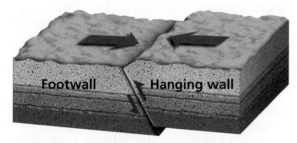

Footwall   Hanging wall

hot spot An area where magma from deep within the mantle melts through the crust above it. (p. 85)
punto caliente Área por donde el magma de las profundidades del manto atraviesa la corteza.

I

igneous rock A type of rock that forms from the cooling of molten rock at or below the surface. (p. 147)
roca ígnea Tipo de roca que se forma cuando se enfrían las rocas fundidas en la superficie o debajo de la superficie.

inner core A dense sphere of solid iron and nickel at the center of Earth. (p. 12)
núcleo interno Densa esfera de hierro y níquel situada en el centro de la Tierra.

inorganic Not formed from living things or the remains of living things. (p. 115)
inorgánico Que no está formado de seres vivos o de los restos de seres vivos.

intrusive rock Igneous rock that forms when magma hardens beneath Earth's surface. (p. 149)
roca intrusiva Roca ígnea que se forma cuando el magma se endurece bajo la superficie de la Tierra.

island arc A string of islands formed by the volcanoes along a deep-ocean trench. (p. 84)
arco de islas Cadena de islas formadas por los volcanes que se encuentran a lo largo de una fosa oceánica profunda.

 L

lava Liquid magma that reaches the surface; also the rock formed when liquid lava hardens. (p. 82)
lava Magma líquida que sale a la superficie; también, la roca que se forma cuando la lava líquida se solidifica.

lava flow The area covered by lava as it pours out of a volcano's vent. (p. 92)
colada de lava Área cubierta de lava a medida que ésta sale por la boca del volcán.

liquefaction The process by which an earthquake's violent movement suddenly turns loose soil into liquid mud. (p. 70)
licuefacción Proceso mediante el que las violentas sacudidas de un terremoto de pronto convierten la tierra suelta en lodo líquido.

lithosphere A rigid layer made up of the uppermost part of the mantle and the crust. (p. 11)
litosfera Capa rígida constituida por la parte superior del manto y la corteza.

luster The way a mineral reflects light from its surface. (p. 117)
brillo La manera en la que un mineral refleja la luz en su superficie.

 M

magma The molten mixture of rock-forming substances, gases, and water from the mantle. (p. 82)
magma Mezcla fundida de las sustancias que forman las rocas, gases y agua, proveniente del manto.

magma chamber The pocket beneath a volcano where magma collects. (p. 92)
cámara magmática Bolsa debajo de un volcán en la que se acumula el magma.

magnitude The measurement of an earthquake's strength based on seismic waves and movement along faults. (p. 54)
magnitud Medida de la fuerza de un sismo basada en las ondas sísmicas y en el movimiento que ocurre a lo largo de las fallas.

mantle The layer of hot, solid material between Earth's crust and core. (p. 11)
manto Capa de material caliente y sólido entre la corteza terrestre y el núcleo.

Mercalli scale A scale that rates earthquakes according to their intensity and how much damage they cause at a particular place. (p. 54)
escala de Mercalli Escala con la que se miden los sismos basándose en la intensidad y el daño que ocasionan.

metamorphic rock A type of rock that forms from an existing rock that is changed by heat, pressure, or chemical reactions. (p. 147)
roca metamórfica Tipo de roca que se forma cuando una roca es transformada por el calor, presión o reacciones químicas.

mid-ocean ridge An undersea mountain chain where new ocean floor is produced; a divergent plate boundary. (p. 24)
dorsal oceánica Cadena montañosa submarina donde se produce el nuevo suelo oceánico; borde de placa divergente.

mineral A naturally occurring, inorganic solid that has a crystal structure and a definite chemical composition. (p. 114)
mineral Sólido inorgánico que ocurre en la naturaleza, de estructura cristalina y composición química definida.

Mohs hardness scale A scale ranking ten minerals from softest to hardest; used in testing the hardness of minerals. (p. 118)
escala de dureza de Mohs Escala en la que se clasifican diez minerales del más blando al más duro; se usa para probar la dureza de los minerales.

moment magnitude scale A scale that rates earthquakes by estimating the total energy released by an earthquake. (p. 55)
escala de magnitud del momento Escala con la que se miden los sismos estimando la cantidad total de energía liberada por un terremoto.

normal fault A type of fault where the hanging wall slides downward; caused by tension in the crust. (p. 46)
falla normal Tipo de falla en la cual el labio superior se desliza hacia abajo como resultado de la tensión en la corteza.

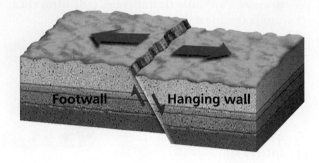

Footwall   Hanging wall

ore Rock that contains a metal or other economically useful mineral. (p. 132)
mena Roca que contiene un metal u otro mineral de importancia económica.

organic rock Sedimentary rock that forms from remains of organisms deposited in thick layers. (p. 154)
roca orgánica Roca sedimentaria que se forma cuando los restos de organismos se depositan en capas gruesas.

outer core A layer of molten iron and nickel that surrounds the inner core of Earth. (p. 12)
núcleo externo Capa de hierro y níquel fundidos que rodea el núcleo interno de la Tierra.

pahoehoe A hot, fast-moving type of lava that hardens to form smooth, ropelike coils. (p. 90)
cordada Tipo de lava caliente de movimiento muy veloz que al endurecerse forma espirales lisas en forma de cuerda.

Pangaea The name of the single landmass that broke apart 200 million years ago and gave rise to today's continents. (p. 19)
Pangea Nombre de la masa terrestre única que se dividió hace 200 millones de años, dando origen a los continentes actuales.

physical property Any characteristic of a substance that can be observed or measured without changing the composition of the substance. (p. 88)
propiedad física Cualquier característica de una sustancia que se puede observar o medir sin que cambie la composición de la misma.

pipe A long tube through which magma moves from the magma chamber to Earth's surface. (p. 92)
chimenea Largo tubo por el que el magma sube desde la cámara magmática hasta la superficie de la Tierra.

plate A section of the lithosphere that slowly moves over the asthenosphere, carrying pieces of continental and oceanic crust. (p. 32)
placa Sección de la litosfera que se desplaza lentamente sobre la astenosfera, llevando consigo trozos de la corteza continental y de la oceánica.

plateau A large area of flat land elevated high above sea level. (p. 50)
meseta Zona extensa de tierra plana elevada por encima del nivel del mar.

plate tectonics The theory that pieces of Earth's lithosphere are in constant motion, driven by convection currents in the mantle. (p. 33)
tectónica de placas Teoría según la cual las partes de la litosfera de la Tierra están en continuo movimiento, impulsadas por las corrientes de convección del manto.

pressure The force exerted on a surface divided by the area over which the force is exerted. (p. 9)
presión Fuerza que actúa sobre una superficie, dividida por el área sobre la que la fuerza actúa.

P wave A type of seismic wave that compresses and expands the ground. (p. 53)
onda P Tipo de onda sísmica que comprime y expande el suelo.

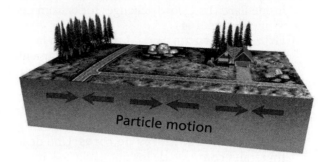

pyroclastic flow The expulsion of ash, cinders, bombs, and gases during an explosive volcanic eruption. (p. 95)
flujo piroclástico Emisión de ceniza, escoria, bombas y gases durante una erupción volcánica explosiva.

R

radiation The transfer of energy through space. (p. 15)
radiación Transferencia de energía a través del espacio.

reverse fault A type of fault where the hanging wall slides upward; caused by compression in the crust. (p. 47)
falla inversa Tipo de falla en la cual el labio superior se desliza hacia arriba como resultado de compresión cn la corteza.

Richter scale A scale that rates an earthquake's magnitude based on the size of its seismic waves. (p. 54)
escala de Richter Escala con la que se mide la magnitud de un terremoto basándose en el tamaño de sus ondas sísmicas.

rift valley A deep valley that forms where two plates move apart. (p. 34)
valle de fisura Valle profundo que se forma cuando dos placas se separan.

Ring of Fire A major belt of volcanoes that rims the Pacific Ocean. (p. 83)
Cinturón de Fuego Gran cadena de volcanes que rodea el océano Pacífico.

rock A solid mixture of minerals and other materials. (p. 145)
roca Mezcla sólida de minerales y otros materiales.

rock cycle A series of processes on the surface and inside Earth that slowly changes rocks from one kind to another. (p. 164)
ciclo de las rocas Serie de procesos en la superficie y dentro de la Tierra que lentamente transforman las rocas de un tipo de roca a otro.

rock-forming minerals One of the common minerals that make up most of the rocks of Earth's crust. (p. 145)
minerales formadores de rocas Uno de los minerales comunes de los que están compuestas la mayoría de las rocas de la corteza de la Tierra.

scientific theory A well-tested concept that explains a wide range of observations. (p. 32)
teoría científica Concepto bien comprobado que explica una amplia gama de observaciones.

sea-floor spreading The process by which molten material adds new oceanic crust to the ocean floor. (p. 25)
expansión del suelo oceánico Proceso mediante el cual la materia fundida añade nueva corteza oceánica al suelo oceánico.

sediment Small, solid pieces of material that come from rocks or organisms. (p. 152)
sedimento Partículas sólidas de materiales que provienen de rocas u organismos.

sedimentary rock A type of rock that forms when particles from other rocks or the remains of plants and animals are pressed and cemented together. (p. 147)
roca sedimentaria Tipo de roca que se forma cuando las partículas de otras rocas o los restos de plantas y animales son presionados y cementados.

seismic waves Vibrations that travel through Earth carrying the energy released during an earthquake. (p. 8)
ondas sísmicas Vibraciones que se desplazan por la Tierra, llevando la energía liberada durante un terremoto.

seismogram The record of an earthquake's seismic waves produced by a seismograph. (p. 61)
sismograma Registro producido por un sismógrafo de las ondas sísmicas de un terremoto.

seismograph A device that records ground movements caused by seismic waves as they move through Earth. (p. 54)
sismógrafo Aparato con el que se registran los movimientos del suelo ocasionados por las ondas sísmicas a medida que éstas se desplazan por la Tierra.

shearing Stress that pushes masses of rock in opposite directions, in a sideways movement. (p. 45)
cizallamiento Esfuerzo que presiona masas de roca en sentidos opuestos.

shield volcano A wide, gently sloping mountain made of layers of lava and formed by quiet eruptions. (p. 100)
volcán en escudo Montaña ancha de pendientes suaves, compuesta por capas de lava y formada durante erupciones no violentas.

silica A material found in magma that is formed from the elements oxygen and silicon. (p. 89)
sílice Material presente en el magma, compuesto por los elementos oxígeno y silicio.

sill A slab of volcanic rock formed when magma squeezes between layers of rock. (p. 103)
dique concordante Placa de roca volcánica formada cuando el magma se mete entre las capas de roca.

smelting The process by which ore is melted to separate the useful metal from other elements. (p. 134)
fundición Proceso mediante el que una mena se funde para separar el mineral útil de otros elementos.

solution A mixture in which one substance is dissolved in another. (p. 125)
solución Mezcla en la que una sustancia se halla disuelta en otra.

sonar A device that determines the distance of an object under water by recording echoes of sound waves. (p. 24)
sonar Aparato con el cual se determina la distancia de un objeto sumergido en el agua mediante el registro del eco de las ondas sonoras.

streak The color of a mineral's powder. (p. 117)
raya El color del polvo de un mineral.

stress A force that acts on rock to change its shape or volume. (p. 44)
esfuerzo Fuerza que al actuar sobre una roca cambia su forma o volumen.

strike-slip fault A type of fault in which rocks on either side move past each other sideways with little up or down motion. (p. 47)
falla transcurrente Tipo de falla en la cual las rocas a ambos lados se deslizan horizontalmente en sentidos opuestos, con poco desplazamiento hacia arriba o abajo.

subduction The process by which oceanic crust sinks beneath a deep-ocean trench and back into the mantle at a convergent plate boundary. (p. 28)
subducción Proceso mediante el cual la corteza oceánica se hunde debajo de una fosa oceánica profunda y vuelve al manto por el borde de una placa convergente.

surface wave A type of seismic wave that forms when P waves and S waves reach Earth's surface. (p. 53)
onda superficial Tipo de onda sísmica que se forma cuando las ondas P y las ondas S llegan a la superficie de la Tierra.

S wave A type of seismic wave that moves the ground up and down or side to side. (p. 53)
onda S Tipo de onda sísmica que hace que el suelo se mueva de arriba abajo o de lado a lado.

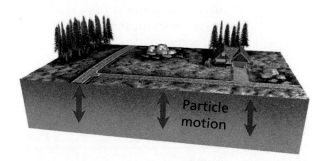
Particle motion

syncline A downward fold in rock formed by compression in Earth's crust. (p. 48)
sinclinal Pliegue de la roca hacia abajo ocasionado por la compresión de la corteza terrestre.

T

tension Stress that stretches rock so that it becomes thinner in the middle. (p. 45)
tensión Esfuerzo que estira una roca, haciéndola más delgada en el centro.

texture The look and feel of a rock's surface, determined by the size, shape, and pattern of a rock's grains. (p. 146)
textura Apariencia y sensación producida por la superficie de una roca, determinadas por el tamaño, forma y patrón de los granos de la roca.

transform boundary A plate boundary where two plates move past each other in opposite directions. (p. 35)
borde de transformación Borde de placa donde dos placas se deslizan una respecto a la otra, pero en sentidos opuestos.

tsunami A large wave produced by an earthquake on the ocean floor. (p. 71)
tsunami Gran ola producida cuando un terremoto sacude el suelo oceánico.

V

vein A narrow deposit of a mineral that is sharply different from the surrounding rock. (p. 126)
vena Acumulación delgada de un mineral que es marcadamente distinta de la roca que la rodea.

vent The opening through which molten rock and gas leave a volcano. (p. 92)
boca Abertura a través de la que la roca en fusión y los gases salen de un volcán.

viscosity The resistance of a liquid to flowing. (p. 88)
viscosidad La resistencia que presenta un líquido al fluir.

volcanic neck A deposit of hardened magma in a volcano's pipe. (p. 103)
cuello volcánico Depósito de magma solidificada en la chimenea de un volcán.

volcano A weak spot in the crust where magma has come to the surface. (p. 82)
volcán Punto débil en la corteza por donde el magma escapa hacia la superficie.

Index

Page numbers for key terms are printed in **boldface** type.
Page numbers for illustrations, maps, and charts are printed in *italics*.

Index

Page numbers for key terms are printed in **boldface** type.
Page numbers for illustrations, maps, and charts are printed in *italics*.

Index

Page numbers for key terms are printed in **boldface** type.
Page numbers for illustrations, maps, and charts are printed in *italics*.